SELENIUM

GEOBOTANY, BIOCHEMISTRY, TOXICITY, and NUTRITION

SELENIUM

GEOBOTANY, BIOCHEMISTRY, TOXICITY, and NUTRITION

IRENE ROSENFELD

Division of Biochemistry
University of Wyoming
Laramie, Wyoming

and

ORVILLE A. BEATH

Professor Emeritus of Research Chemistry
University of Wyoming
Laramie, Wyoming

1964

ACADEMIC PRESS New York and London

ACADEMIC PRESS INC.
111 Fifth Avenue, New York, New York 10003

United Kingdom Edition published by
ACADEMIC PRESS INC. (LONDON) LTD.
Berkeley Square House, London W.1

Library of Congress Catalog Card Number: 64-21674

For their unfailing interest and perseverance in the study of selenium, this book is dedicated to past and present research workers and to those who will follow.

Wherever (the reader) finds that I have ventur'd at any small conjectures, at the causes of the things that I have observed, I beseech him to look upon them only as doubtful Problems, and uncertain ghesses, and not as unquestionable Conclusions, or matters of unconfutable Science; I have produced nothing here, with intent to bind his understanding to an implicit consent. . . .

ROBERT HOOKE: *Micrographia* (1665)

PREFACE

In this volume, the authors' intent has been to give a comprehensive review on the element selenium. The challenge to summarize and review the published information dealing with selenium culminated in the publication in 1949 of a book, also entitled "Selenium," by Professor S. F. Trelease of Columbia University and Professor O. A. Beath of the University of Wyoming. In many respects the present volume has kept that challenge in mind, but has also aimed to reflect the added importance of selenium in biological studies as well as to retain and revise the highly specialized and descriptive botanical and geological aspects.

Selenium as subject matter can and may appeal to scientists who are interested in the interdisciplinary aspects of physical and biological sciences. The interrelation of knowledge in many fields of science cannot be better exemplified than by following selenium from its geological origin to its effect on living systems as a natural sequence of events. Our aim was to retain this continuity and present each discipline in such a manner that a specialist in the field may find it rewarding to read and at the same time a non-specialist may gain information on the interrelated disciplines. The book, therefore, is written for specialists or graduate students in geology, soil science, botany, biology, veterinary science, industrial and human medicine, nutrition, and, last but not least, research workers in biochemistry. Numerous books have discussed to a limited extent the chemistry and toxic and nutritional effects of selenium, but this is the only book which is primarily designed to give a broad and detailed discussion of the element, selenium.

The present review is aimed to include research publications not only from the United States but from other countries and continents.

To write on such diversified disciplines, the authors received assistance from colleagues to whom they wish to express their appreciation. Thanks are due to those who have contributed immeasurably to the writing of the book. Dr. David Love, U. S. Geological Survey, revised our geological tables (Chapter II) and critically read the chapter, thereby saving us from the many pitfalls of non-specialists in a highly specialized field. Appreciation is also extended to Professor R. J. McColloch and Associate Professor W. W. Ellis for their critical comments and suggestions on the whole book; to Professor G. J. Miller for invaluable comments on the chapters on nutrition, chemistry, and biochemistry; and to Professor C. S. Gilbert and Associate Professor H. F. Eppson for suggestions and comments on the chapters dealing with their earlier work on selenium.

Special thanks are due to all research workers who so generously supplied us with their earlier as well as present publications and pictures, and to many colleagues who encouraged us and inquired about the progress of the book.

In a book of such magnitude as this, there may be omissions, simplifications, or errors in the interpretation of or in the presentation of the various disciplines. The authors assume the responsibility for any or all of these shortcomings of the book and give credit for its merits to the invaluable comments, criticisms, and assistance of all who toiled to make this book possible.

The authors wish to acknowledge their indebtedness for financial assistance received from the National Science Foundation and the National Institutes of Health in preparing the manuscript. We are deeply indebted to Mrs. H. M. Trelease for relinquishing the copyright of the book by Professors Trelease and Beath and transferring it to us.

Laramie, Wyoming
June 1964

IRENE ROSENFELD
ORVILLE A. BEATH

CONTENTS

CHAPTER I

HISTORY

There are few elements in the periodic table which merit a historical consideration in order to evaluate the uniqueness of biological effects of the element. The element selenium can be traced in an orderly sequence from its origin in the earth's crust to specific geological formation, to distribution of specific genera and groups of plants which require the element for their growth, to the accumulation in vegetation, and to its subsequent toxicity to birds or mammals that consume the seleniferous foods.

The disease syndrome produced by selenium is a disease of antiquity and has been described in widely separated areas of the world. Marco Polo (*12*) circa 1295 may have been referring to alkali disease when he wrote of his travels in western China near the borders of Turkestan and Tibet:

> Throughout all the mountainous parts of it the most excellent kind of rhubarb is produced, in large quantities, and the merchants who come to buy it convey it to all parts of the world. It is a fact that when they take that road, they cannot venture amongst the mountains with any beasts of burden excepting those accustomed to the country, on account of a poisonous plant growing there, which, if eaten by them, has the effect of causing the hoofs of the animal to drop off. Those of the country, however, being aware of its dangerous quality, take care to avoid it.

Stein (*17*), who traveled in Turkestan and western China in 1906 to 1908 as a representative of the British Government, suspected that his ponies had eaten some of the poisonous plants about which Marco Polo had written. Stein recounts the following incident:

> I was just gleefully reflecting how our ponies would revel in their alpine pasture when Sahib Bai . . . came up with alarmed mien to report that five of the animals were standing about benumbed and refusing to touch grass or fodder. I at once suspected that they had eaten of the poisonous grass which infests certain parts of the Non-Shan and about which old Marco has much to tell in his chapter on "Sukchur" or Su-chou. The Vene-

tian's account had proved quite true, for while my own ponies showed all the effects of this inebriating plant, the local animals had evidently been wary of it. . . .

In the Americas, chronic selenosis resembling alkali disease in livestock, malformations in chicks and children, and loss of hair and nails of the people were first described in Colombia by Father Pedro Simon in 1560 (*16*). For more details, see Chapter VIII.

In Mexico, a disease in the neighborhood of Irapuato was described over 200 years ago; it appeared at the time when patio processing of ores from mines was instituted in or about the city of Guanajuato (*20*). It was called Soliman disease from the Spanish name of corrosive sublimate ($HgCl_2$). The disease described in the early records was similar to alkali disease in livestock; among the people, loss of hair and teeth and a form of paralysis were noted.

The earliest account of the form of poisoning known as alkali disease in the United States is contained in a report written in 1857 by T. C. Madison, an army surgeon. Dr. Madison (*8*) described the symptoms of a fatal disease that afflicted the cavalry horses at Fort Randall, situated on the right bank of the Missouri River in the territory of Nebraska, but now included in South Dakota close to the Nebraska state line (Fig. 1). His accurate and interesting report follows:

> Four companies of the second dragoons arrived at this post about the 10th of August, 1856, one squadron from Fort Lookout and one from Big Sioux River. . . . The four companies encamped on the east or lower side of the dry ravine, separating the dragoon and infantry camps. About the 20th of August the disease commenced simultaneously in all four companies, and many horses died, not however, until after the lapse of weeks and months. The following symptoms were observed: first, that, among the remount horses from below, there was a sort of catarrh, or distemper, with running at the nose, and among all the horses a swelling of the skin of the throat and jaw; also inflammation, swelling and suppuration of the sheath, tenderness and inflammation of the feet, followed by suppuration at the point where the hoof joins the skin, the hoof, in a measure, detaching itself, and a new one forming in its place. These were also accompanied by loss of the manes and tails. The appetite was uniformly good, but, from extreme tenderness of the feet, they were unable to move about in search of food, and it appears that at the time they were entirely dependent upon grazing, there being no forage at the post for issue. . . . A few mules and Indian ponies were similarly affected. The acclimated suffered equally

with the unacclimated. No treatment was effectual, or afforded permanent relief.

In the third annual report in 1893 of the Wyoming Agriculture Experiment Station (*20a*) reference was made to a peculiar ailment in horses in the Shirley Basin, Carbon County, Wyoming. The horses developed symptoms of an unusual nature after feeding on hay that had been grown on a newly irrigated grass range. In the early stages of the disease the horses lost their hoofs, mane, and switch of the tail, and severe losses were recorded.

FIG. 1. Ruins of the chapel at Fort Randall, South Dakota, where selenium afflicted cavalry horses in 1856. The chapel was built of seleniferous Niobrara limestone.

Peters (*11*) of the Nebraska Agricultural Experiment Station conducted a field investigation of Boyd County, Nebraska, after the receipt of a letter from a resident describing a very peculiar disease among the domestic animals. The disease had been prevalent among all kinds of livestock since the settlement of Boyd County in 1891. The residents named it alkali disease because they thought it was due to alkali or mineral salt.

Farmers in affected areas early learned to associate the disease with particular and often rather restricted tracts of land. Many of them believed that the disease was caused by something in the vegetation.

Throughout the vast grazing areas in fifteen of the western states, acute and chronic poisoning of obscure origin, frequently attributed to poisonous forage plants, have taken a heavy toll of cattle and sheep on the ranges. During the summers of 1907 and 1908 more than 15,000 sheep died in a region north of Medicine Bow, Wyoming. These statistics illustrate the magnitude of the losses from acute poisoning. The deaths were attributed to grazing in an area of profuse growth of woody aster and Gray's vetch (*22*).

Extensive losses from acute poisoning in livestock were reported not only in Wyoming but in Utah and Nebraska as well. Chronic poisoning also was responsible for very serious losses, but the extent of these losses was not easily evaluated owing to the delayed death of the animals.

In a brief account of alkali disease in South Dakota, Lipp (*7*) stated that farmers living in the affected areas were firmly convinced that the growing forage plants store a sufficient quantity of the alkalies to cause the disease. Dealers in grain and hay refused to purchase products raised in certain restricted areas. The only means of prevention was to use feeds grown where the disease was unknown.

Since 1919 acute and chronic livestock poisoning was described and recognized in Wyoming. Mainly cattle were affected (*21*). While some associated the losses with a form of forage poisoning, yet the consistency of the symptoms led to the general use of the term blind staggers. The occurrence of the disease was spotty, and occasional seasonal variations were observed. It was recognized by Beath and co-workers that a number of factors could be responsible for the losses of livestock. Much attention was given to chemical analyses of some widely distributed native vegetations—common saltwort, *Glaux maritima*, arrow grass, *Triglochin maritima*, and *Arenaria hookeri*—and to feeding tests. None of the plants used produced a type of poisoning that was in any way comparable to that which causes blind staggers (*21*).

In 1932, some native species of *Astragalus* were used for studies of the chemical properties and physiological effects of these plants (*1*). Animals that survived the extended feeding period showed lesions which suggested the action of an irritant poison, presumably of mineral origin. It became evident that certain native milk vetches growing on restricted soils may have been responsible for many acute and chronic poisonings of livestock.

In 1931 at a meeting of an interbureau committee in Washington, D.C., H. G. Knight is said to have suggested that the toxic agent in the grain may be selenium (*5*). Toxic wheat from South Dakota was analyzed by Robinson (*13*). In 1933 he published a report stating that one sample contained 10–12 ppm selenium, and another, 5–6 ppm, whereas nontoxic wheat yielded none (*13*). The gluten of the toxic wheat contained 90 ppm. A sample of soil had about 0.3 ppm. Poisonous wheat and corn grown on fertile soil were virtually unknown until that year. A connection between selenium and livestock poisoning was established.

In 1929, Franke and co-workers at the South Dakota Experiment Station, began a series of investigations of the toxic foodstuffs. His first publication on the subject, withheld until 1934, demonstrated that grain raised on certain soil was highly toxic to animals, and that selenium present in grain and grasses produced alkali disease in livestock (*6*).

In 1932 Taboury (*18*) published results on the occurrence of selenium in vegetation. His work established that different species of plants differ in their selenium content. The work of Taboury led Beath and his co-workers to analyze all types of vegetation in Wyoming for selenium.

In early 1934, Beath *et al.* (*2*) reported that selenium was present in several species of native plants (*Astragalus*). In the same year Beath *et al.* (*3*) reported the occurrence of selenium in certain geological formations. The findings of Beath and co-workers were substantiated by Byers (*5*), Williams *et al.* (*20*) and their co-workers from the U.S. Department of Agriculture. The ability of widely distributed native plants of *Astragalus* to accumulate several thousand parts per million selenium explained the losses of livestock and the hitherto unknown cause of blind staggers.

Later studies by Beath *et al.* (*4*) indicated that a number of species of *Astragalus, Stanleya,* and sections *Xylorhiza* of *Machaeranthera* and *Oonopsis* of *Haplopappus* had the ability to convert the selenium from soils or geological deposits to an available form. The distribution of these plants was restricted to seleniferous formations and soils. These plants are called selenium indicator plants or "Beath's selenium indicators."

The administration of selenium compounds to livestock or laboratory animals produces toxic symptoms in the animals, but does not produce typical alkali disease or blind staggers. The syndrome alkali disease is produced by seleniferous grains and grasses. Blind staggers is produced by seleniferous indicator plants. The selenium compounds in the plants that can produce different disease syndromes in livestock are not known. Only limited data are available on the compounds which are present in indicator plants and those present in grains and grasses.

Trelease and Trelease (*19*) in 1938 presented experimental evidence that selenium indicator plants require selenium for their growth and development. They suggested that selenium may be an essential element for these groups of plants.

Evidence is accumulating that selenium is not only an essential element for indicator plants but has important dietary functions in mammals as well as birds.

Schwarz and Foltz in 1957 (*14*) reported that a dietary agent isolated from natural source materials, which they named Factor 3, contained selenium. Factor 3-selenium prevented liver necrosis in rats on selenium-deficient diet.

The effectiveness of selenium compounds or of Factor 3-selenium against exudative diathesis in chicks was reported in 1957 simultaneously by Schwarz *et al.* (*15*) and Patterson *et al.* (*10*).

Muth *et al.* (*9*) in 1958 demonstrated the protective effect of selenium against white muscle disease in livestock when the diet was deficient in selenium.

The prevention by selenium compounds or Factor 3-selenium of some mammalian and some avian disease syndromes, considered to be vitamin E deficiency, stimulated further studies on the intimately related biological functions of vitamin E and selenium.

It is challenging to speculate on the mode of action of selenium by excess or trace amounts in the organism. The apparent interaction of selenium and sulfur compounds and structurally unrelated vitamin E promises some interesting developments in basic studies.

The rapid applications of basic information on selenium were indicated by the rate at which correlations of geology, of indicator plants, and of livestock poisoning were made (within a few years) after it was recognized that the toxic agent was selenium. In the same manner, basic studies on the role of selenium in nutrition found almost immediate practical application.

References

1. Beath, O. A., J. H. Draize and H. F. Eppson. 1932. Three poisonous vetches. *Wyoming Agr. Expt. Sta. Bull. No.* **189**:1–23.
2. Beath, O. A., J. H. Draize, H. F. Eppson, C. S. Gilbert and O. C. McCreary. 1934. Certain poisonous plants of Wyoming activated by selenium and their association with respect to soil types. *J. Am. Pharm. Assoc. Sci. Ed.* **23**:94–97.
3. Beath, O. A., J. H. Draize and C. S. Gilbert. 1934. Plants poisonous to livestock. *Wyoming Agr. Expt. Sta. Bull. No.* **200**:1–84.
4. Beath, O. A., H. F. Eppson and C. S. Gilbert. 1935. Selenium and other toxic minerals in soils and vegetation. *Wyoming Agr. Expt. Sta. Bull. No.* **206**:1–55.
5. Byers, H. G. 1935. Selenium occurrence in certain soils in the United States, with a discussion of related topics. *U. S. Dept. Agr. Tech. Bull. No.* **482**:1–47.
6. Franke, K. W. 1934. A new toxicant occurring naturally in certain samples of

plant foodstuffs. I. Results obtained in preliminary feeding trials. *J. Nutrition* **8**:597–608.

7. Lipp, C. C. 1922. Alkali disease. *Vet. Alumni Quart.* (*Ohio State Univ.*) **10**: 54–55.
8. Madison, T. C. 1860. Sanitary report–Fort Randall. Written Sept., 1857. *In* Coolidge, R. H., Statistical report on the sickness and mortality in the Army of the United States. Jan. 1855 to Jan. 1860. (*U. S.*) *Congr. 36th, 1st Session, Senate Exch. Doc.* **52**:37–41.
9. Muth, O. H., J. E. Oldfield, L. F. Remmert and J. R. Schubert. 1958. Effects of selenium and vitamin E on white muscle disease. *Science* **128**:1090.
10. Patterson, E. L., R. Milstrey and E. L. R. Stokstad. 1957. Effect of selenium in preventing exudative diathesis in chicks. *Proc. Soc. Exptl. Biol. Med.* **95**: 617–620.
11. Peters, A. T. 1904. A fungus disease in corn. *Nebraska Agr. Expt. Sta. Ann. Rept.* **17**:13–22.
12. Polo, Marco. (1926). "The Travels of Marco Polo," Revised from Marsden's translation and edited with introduction by Manual Komroff. Chapter 43, p. 81. Liveright, New York.
13. Robinson, W. O. 1933. Determination of selenium in wheat and soils. *J. Assoc. Offic. Agr. Chem.* **16**:423–424.
14. Schwarz, K. and C. M. Foltz. 1957. Selenium as an integral part of Factor 3 against dietary necrotic liver degeneration. *J. Am. Chem. Soc.* **79**:3293.
15. Schwarz, K., J. G. Bieri, G. M. Briggs and M. L. Scott. 1957. Prevention of exudative diathesis in chicks by Factor 3 and selenium. *Proc. Soc. Exptl. Biol. Med.* **95**:621–625.
16. Simon, P. F. (1560). Noticias Historiales de las conquistas de tierre firme en las Indias occidentales. *Biblioteca Autores Colombianos.* **4**:226–254. Kelly Publ. Co., Bogotá. 1953.
17. Stein, M. A. 1912. Through the Richtohofen Range of the Nan-Shan. "Ruins of Desert Cathay," Chapter 77, p. 202. Macmillan, London.
18. Taboury, F. 1932. Sur la présence accidentelle du sélénium dans certains végétaux. *Compt. Rend. Acad. Sci.* **195**:171.
19. Trelease, S. F. and H. M. Trelease. 1938. Selenium as a stimulating and possibly essential element for indicator plants. *Science* **87**:70–71.
20. Williams, K. T., H. W. Lakin and H. G. Byers. 1940. Selenium occurrence in certain soils in the United States with a discussion of related topics: Fourth report. *U. S. Dept. Agr. Tech. Bull. No.* **702**:1–59.

20a. Wyoming Agriculture Experiment Station. 1893. *3rd Annual Report.*

21. Wyoming Agriculture Experiment Station. 1919. *30th Annual Report.*
22. Wyoming State Board of Sheep Commissioners. 1908. 10th Annual Report, Cheyenne, Wyoming.

CHAPTER II

GEOLOGICAL DISTRIBUTION OF SELENIUM

Selenium has been found in toxic amounts in wheat and plants in areas in North and South America, Australia, New Zealand, South Africa, Algeria, Morocco, Spain, Bulgaria, France, and Germany (*89*). The distribution of selenium has been discussed by Strock (*97*), Goldschmidt and Strock (*48*), and Goldschmidt (*49*). An annotated bibliography of the geology of selenium was published by Luttrell (*70*).

Seleniferous soils and vegetation are known in many regions in the western part of the United States—from North Dakota to Texas and west to the Pacific Ocean. They extend north into the Canadian provinces of Alberta, Saskatchewan, and Manitoba and south into Mexico. Although distribution of selenium is not uniform in these regions, relatively large areas contain this element.

That certain species of indicator plants grow on seleniferous formations has been recognized by Beath *et al.* (*2*). These species, "Beath's selenium indicators," have been useful in locating and mapping seleniferous areas in the western United States and Canada. Figure 2 indicates distribution of seleniferous vegetation.

ORIGIN OF SELENIUM

Hypotheses regarding the origin of selenium in rocks and soils have been offered (*4, 23, 26, 38*) to explain differences in selenium content of formations, variations within a single formation, and differences in availability of selenium to plants.

Various processes have been postulated for the anomalous concentration of selenium in geological strata. Preceding and during Cretaceous time, there was extensive volcanic activity throughout the land mass from which sediments were derived. According to Beath *et al.* (*4*), it is probable that selenium present in Cretaceous rocks was a primary constituent of magmas.

The presence of selenium in volcanic emanations in Hawaii led Byers *et al.* (*23, 26*) to conclude that Cretaceous shales might have derived their selenium wholly from volcanic dust and gases brought down directly by rain into the Cretaceous sea. In Hawaii, no selenium was found in parent material in sufficient quantities to account for its presence in the soil.

Recent studies on the selenium content of 81 volcanic rocks from the western United States, including Hawaii, indicated no particular relation between selenium content of samples and rock type (38). The authors (38) agreed with Byers' concept that deposition of selenium in sediments

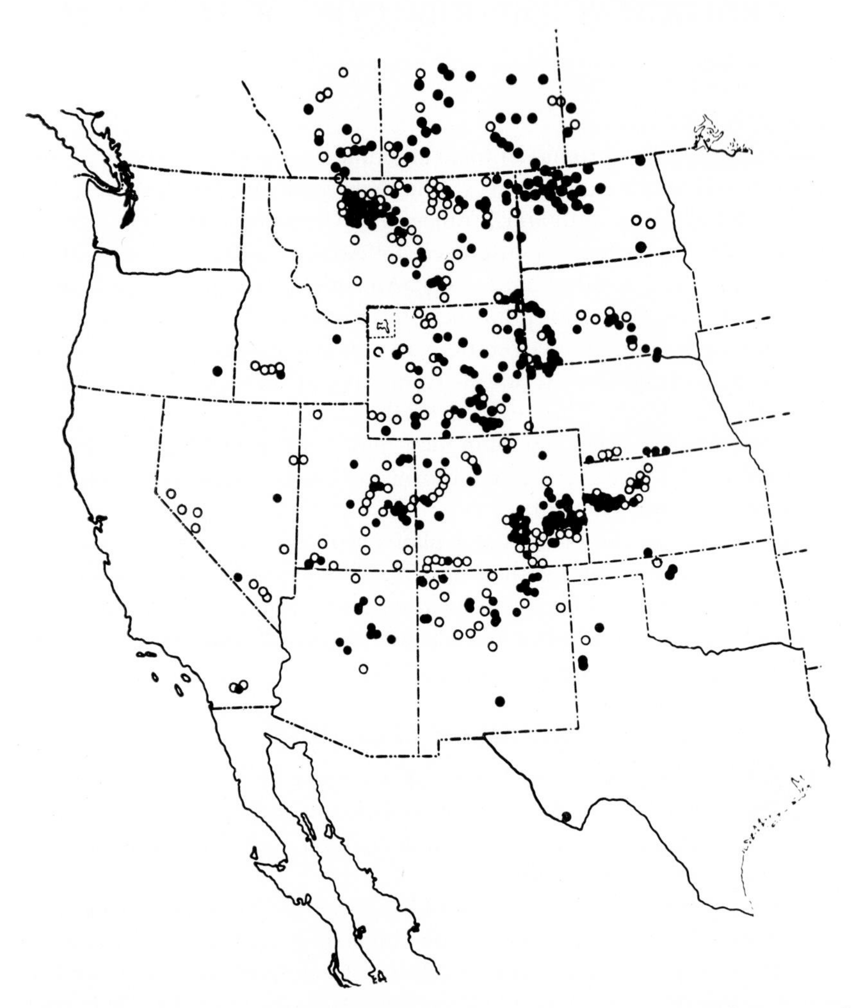

FIG. 2. Distribution of seleniferous vegetation in the western United States and Canada. Each open dot represents the place of collection of a plant specimen containing 50–500 ppm selenium; each solid dot, specimens containing more than 500 ppm. (Base map copyright, American Map Co., Inc., New York.)

was from volcanic emanations. The selenium content of these rocks was less than 1 or 2 ppm regardless of the area of collection, with the exception of one volcanic rock from "Lysite tuffs" which contained 40 ppm selenium.

The "Lysite tuffs" (Eocene age) in central Wyoming contain a high concentration of selenium probably owing to the localization of selenium by ground water. The erratic distribution of selenium in "Lysite tuffs" has been indicated by a recent survey of the area (*43*).

Although volcanic emanations seem to have contributed debris to many seleniferous areas, some geological formations rich in selenium do not appear to have a direct connection with volcanic activity. The Manning Canyon Shale of late Mississippian or early Pennsylvanian age in Utah contains beds that are among the most seleniferous in the western United States (*10*), yet there is no evidence that volcanoes were active in Utah during or immediately preceding the time that these beds were laid down. The selenium is concentrated primarily in carbonaceous shale, whereas little is present in limestone or carbonate.

The primary origin of selenium in beds of this formation may have been due to erosion of igneous or seleniferous sedimentary rocks or there may have been considerable absorption of selenium from brackish waters by marine organisms with subsequent accumulation of these organisms on the floor of the sea. Perhaps selenium accumulator plants growing in shallow basins and on adjacent flood plains became incorporated in sediments. In these sediments, decaying organic matter may have served as a sponge for selenium leached from nearby rocks.

Present evidence suggests that all of these processes have had a part in deposition of trace elements in sediments. Thus, factors other than volcanic activity probably have contributed during past geological periods to the selenium enrichment of marine carbonaceous shales of Pennsylvanian age and a number of other ages. The present vegetation on these areas is seleniferous, and selenium is available for absorption by indicator and other plants.

The biogeochemical relationship of plants to uranium-vanadium-selenium deposits is indicated by recent studies by Cannon (*28*), and the association of selenium, arsenic, molybdenum, and uranium with organic matter has been recently described by Tourtelot (*101*). The manner of association of arsenic, selenium, molybdenum, and uranium with organic matter is not certain at the present time. Carbon-selenium-vanadium association at least suggests the possibility that occurrences of selenium in geological deposits may have been the results of accumulation or adsorption and deposition of these elements in sediments during past geological times.

Association of selenium with vanadium in some deposits is of interest. The presence of vanadium in blood of certain marine organisms, such as echinoderms and ascidians, was used by Phillips (*84*) in 1918 as a basis for a hypothesis concerning the presence of vanadium in sedimentary rocks. He suggested that marine animals capable of accumulating vanadium in high concentrations lived in shallow waters and during deposition of sediments their vanadium content may have been fixed in sedimentary rocks. It appears that at least selenium and vanadium might have accumulated in geological formations by decomposition of organic matter in past ages.

Until more conclusive scientific evidence is presented concerning the origin of high concentrations of selenium in localized areas, the concepts of Beath *et al.* (*4*) and Byers *et al.* (*23, 26*) are at present the only explanations for the distribution of selenium in different geological formations.

STRATIGRAPHIC PRINCIPLES

A few essential terms used in geology as related to the discussion in this chapter are presented.

The geological column, or stratigraphic succession, comprising all of the rocks of the earth is described in time terms and rock terms. The division of the geological time scale and the corresponding rock terms are given in the following tabulation.

Time term	Rock term
Era	–
Period	System
Epoch	Series
	Group
	Formation

The *era* is the largest practical division of geological time for use in this type of study. Geological eras are subdivided into a number of *periods* of time and each period is represented by a *system* of rocks. The major subdivisions of the geological column as used in this chapter are shown in Table 1.

Periods are subdivided into *epochs* and corresponding systems into *series*. Series are, in turn, subdivided into *groups* and groups into *formations*. The formation is the fundamental unit in the local classification of rocks; it may range in thickness from a few feet to many thousand feet and may be composed of a succession of various rock types such as sandstones and shales. Formations are generally named for geographical features or localities where they were first described. For example, the Sundance Formation is named for the town of Sundance, Wyoming.

Members, lentils, tongues, and lenses are subdivisions of a formation. Specially developed parts of a formation composed of various rock types are called *members* if they are of considerable geographical extent; *lentils* if they are of slight geographical extent; *tongues* if they wedge out laterally in one direction between sediments of a different character; and

TABLE 1
Subdivisions of the Geological Column[a]

Era	Periods (of time) or systems (of rocks)	Epochs (of time) or series (of rocks)	Age (in million years)	Relative lengths of major time divisions, to actual scale
Cenozoic	Quaternary	Recent		Cenozoic
		Pleistocene	1	
	Tertiary	Pliocene		Mesozoic
		Miocene		
		Oligocene		
		Eocene		
		Paleocene	63	
Mesozoic	Cretaceous Upper Lower		135	Paleozoic
	Jurassic Upper Middle Lower		181	
	Triassic Upper Middle Lower		230	
Paleozoic	Permian Upper Middle Lower		280	Precambrian (approximately 4,000 million years)
	Carboniferous Pennsylvanian Mississippian		345	
	Devonian		405	
	Silurian		425	
	Ordovician		500	
	Cambrian		600	
Precambrian				

[a] Kulp (63).

lenses if they wedge out laterally in all directions. *Beds, strata, laminae,* and *layers* are terms applied to the smallest units recognized in classification.

The present discussion of the geological distribution of selenium is mainly designed to correlate the presence of selenium in soils derived from formations with distribution of selenium as related to toxic vegetation that produces livestock poisoning and may produce public health problems.

Tables 2 to 7 show the stratigraphic succession of rocks in selected important seleniferous areas. The designation of seleniferous formations or members is based on the occurrence of selenium in the formation (as found by analysis) or deduced from occurrence of seleniferous vegetation on these outcrops. Descriptions of formations or members in all periods are limited mainly to those that are known to support growth of indicator plants. The sequence of the discussion begins with the geologically oldest rocks and ends with the geologically youngest rocks.

Precambrian and Pre-Carboniferous Paleozoic Rocks

Some Precambrian rocks contain selenium but no seleniferous vegetation has been found in the areas where these rocks occur. The relationship of these rock types and their selenium content has not been studied.

Rocks of the Cambrian, Ordovician, Silurian, and Devonian ages were not investigated as to the presence of selenium. There are no reports which would suggest that selenium indicators grow on these rocks.

Carboniferous (Pennsylvanian, Some Mississippian)

Rocks of Pennsylvanian age in the western interior of the United States consist mostly of marine limestones, sandstones, and shales. They contain some nonmarine red beds and sandstones, but little or no coal west of the Great Plains.

The Paradox Formation in southwestern Colorado and southern Utah is exposed in broad areas (Table 2). In some localities thinly laminated black shale is interbedded with gray sandstone and, locally, with macerated lignitic fragments. Outcrops of these rocks have a number of species of indicator plants with fairly high selenium content but the distribution of plants suggests sporadic occurrences of selenium.

In Provo Canyon, central Utah, the seleniferous Manning Canyon Shale is exposed. It is, in part at least, early Pennsylvanian and equivalent to some portion of the Paradox Formation. One bed, 24 feet thick, is composed of black and brown shale and contained 96 ppm of selenium. Because of limited outcrops and steep slopes, little vegetation grows on this formation.

TABLE 2
Pennsylvanian Formations

	SOUTHERN UTAH AND SOUTHWESTERN COLORADO	WESTERN WYOMING	EASTERN WYOMING	
PENNSYLVANIAN SYSTEM	Hermosa Fm.--upper part is a complex of shs. with occasional lss; middle part is many bands of massive dark-gray ls., often highly fossiliferous, alter. with sss. and cgls.; lower part is greenish-gray sss. and shs., the latter being sometimes nearly black, 1800', marine, seleniferous.	Wells Fm.--(uppermost part is Permian) calc. ss., non-fossiliferous sandy ls. with occasional thin beds of qtzite. and sss., weathering white, red or yellow, cherty ls., 2000-5000', marine in part, non-seleniferous.	Casper Fm.--(uppermost part is Permian) ss., tan to pink, cross-bedded, marine ls. in lower part, 0-350', non-seleniferous.	
	Paradox Fm.--salt, gyp. and anhydrite, with interbedded black and brown sh. and some ls., 0-1700', (?) dead sea deposits, marine, seleniferous.	"Amsden" Fm.--red shs., white lss. and cherty and sandy lss., 150-350', marine, seleniferous.	Casper and Fountain Fms. intertongue	Fountain Fm.--ark. grits and sss., 0-500', non-marine non-seleniferous.

ABBREVIATIONS USED IN TABLES 2-7

Fm(s). = formation (s); cgl (s). = conglomerate (s); ark. = arkose;

ls (s). = limestone (s); dol (s). = dolomite (s); gyp. = gypsum

ss (s). = sandstone (s); qtzite (s). = quartzite (s); [zigzag symbol] = possible but undefined boundaries.

On the seleniferous formations of the "Amsden" in western Wyoming and the Hermosa in southwestern Colorado (Table 2), growth of indicator plants with low selenium content has been noted.

Permian

Formations of the Permian age were deposited during the last period of the Paleozoic Era. In many parts of North America, Permian rocks are characterized by continental red sandstones and red shales. Marine deposits include limestone, black shale, phosphatic shale, sandstone, and evaporites. Exposed Permian rocks cover an area of about 80,000 square miles in the western United States; the most extensive outcrops are in Kansas, Oklahoma, Texas, New Mexico, Utah, and Arizona. The Permian formations in northern Arizona, southwestern Colorado, western and southeastern Wyoming are indicated in Table 3.

The Rico and Cutler formations in southwestern Colorado and southern Utah are seleniferous (Table 3). The Cutler Formation (Table 3) is a complex sequence of bright-red sandstones and conglomerates which supports abundant growth of *Stanleya pinnata* and some species of seleniferous *Astragalus*. The selenium content of plants on the Rico Formation is low.

The Phosphoria Formation is exposed in the Wyoming and Salt River Ranges, in broad slopes along the northeast side of the Wind River Range, and along both flanks of the Owl Creek Range in central Wyoming (Table 3). Several species of selenium indicator plants grow on shales and on soils derived from the shales in western Wyoming. The Phosphoria equivalent in northeastern Utah supports a variety of highly seleniferous indicator plants.

The Freezeout tongue of the Chugwater Formation in southeastern Wyoming (Table 3) supports the growth of a number of selenium indicator plants.

The few field studies of exposed areas of Permian rocks in northern New Mexico, western Texas, Oklahoma, and Kansas indicate that seleniferous plants are rare.

Large areas of soil in Oklahoma are derived wholly or in part from rocks of Permian age and have been tentatively identified as the upper part of the Enid Formation (lower or middle Permian). Indicator plants growing on this formation contained moderate amounts of selenium.

Triassic

Rocks of Triassic age in most parts of the western United States are characterized by brilliant red and brown colors. The rocks are mainly of continental origin and consist of sandy shales, sandstones, conglomerates, evaporites, limestones, and volcanic or pyroclastic rocks.

Triassic strata crop out chiefly in Texas, New Mexico, Arizona, Utah,

TABLE 3
Permian Formations

	NORTHERN ARIZONA	SOUTHWESTERN COLORADO	WESTERN WYOMING	SOUTHEASTERN WYOMING
OCHOAN SERIES	Absent	Absent	Absent	Goose Egg Fm.--(lower part) red sh. purple and gray dol. and ls.,some gyp., marine in part, 250-400', seleniferous.
GUADALUPIAN SERIES	Absent	Absent	Phosphoria Fm.--phosphatic shs., some thin lss., sss., and dols., 150-500', marine, seleniferous.	Freezeout Tongue of Chugwater Fm.--(lower part) 0-108', seleniferous. Forelle Ls.--blue gray compact ls., much gyp., 0-30', marine, non-seleniferous. ? Satanka Sh.--sandy red sh., thin lss., and sss., some gyp., 0-240', marine, non-seleniferous.
LEONARDIAN SERIES	Kaibab Ls.--ls. with chert, 820', marine, non-seleniferous. Coconino Ss.--cross-bedded, gray to white ss., 50-610', non-marine, non-selenif. Hermit Sh.--deep brick-red sandy shs., fine-grained friable sss., thin platy lamination, "red bed," 75', non-marine, seleniferous?	Cutler Fm.--"red beds" complex of bright red sss. and lighter red or pinkish grits and cgls. alter. with sandy sh., and earthy or sandy lss. of varying shades of red, 1000', non-marine, seleniferous.	Absent	
WOLFCAMPIAN SERIES	Supai Fm.--red sss. and shs., 1400', non-marine, seleniferous.	Cutler and Rico Fms. intertongue Rico Fm.--"red beds", sss. and cgls. with intercal. sh. and sandy fossilif. lss., 300', marine in part, seleniferous.	? ? Wells Fm.--(uppermost part) calc. ss., non-fossiliferous sandy ls. with occasional thin beds of qtzite. and sss., weathering white, red or yellow cherty ls., 2000'-5000', marine in part non-seleniferous.	Casper Fm.--(uppermost part) ss., tan to pink, cross-bedded, marine ls. in lower part, 0-350', non-seleniferous.

NOTE: For explanation of abbreviations, see Table 2.

southeastern Idaho, Nevada, Wyoming, Montana, and Colorado. The thickness of the system ranges from a few hundred feet on the eastern edge of the area to four thousand feet or more in parts of Arizona, Utah, and Wyoming. The Triassic formations in southern Utah and southwestern Colorado and eastern and western Wyoming are indicated in Table 4.

TABLE 4
Triassic Formations

Series	SOUTHERN UTAH AND SOUTHWESTERN COLORADO	WESTERN WYOMING	EASTERN WYOMING
UPPER TRIASSIC SERIES	Navajo Ss.--(lower part) red ss. massive, exceedingly cross-bedded, locally thin-bedded and greatly reduced in thickness, 50-2000', non-marine, non-seleniferous.	Nugget Ss.--(lower part) group of yellow, pink & red sss., bounded below by brown to dark red sss. and sh. of Ankareh Sh. & above by dark-colored fossiliferous sh. and lss. of Twin Creek Fm., 1900', non-marine, non-selenif.	Jelm Fm.--red beds including ls. cgl. with wood fragments and Triassic vertebrates, 250', non-marine, non-seleniferous.
	Kayenta Fm. irregularly bedded, gray to red ss. with subor. sh., 0-320', non-marine, seleniferous.	Ankareh Sh.--brown to dark-red ss. and sh., 500-1000', non-marine, seleniferous? (intertongues with units shown at right.)	
	Wingate Ss.--bright-red sss., 450', non-marine, seleniferous.	Wood Sh. / Deadman Ls. / Higham Grit / Timothy Ss. non-marine, non-selenif.	
	Chinle Fm.--purple, lavender, green and light-colored var. shs. with ls. cgl. lenses, chocolate-colored arenaceous shs. at base, 400-1000', non-marine, seleniferous.		
	Shinarump Mbr.--yellow cgl. with silicified wood, badland ss. with gyp. often argil., sometimes indur. sss., 0-200', non-marine, seleniferous.		Alcova Ls. Mbr. of Chugwater Fm.--8' bed of marine ls. lying 335' below top of Chugwater Fm., seleniferous.
		? ?	? ?
MIDDLE TRIASSIC SERIES	Absent	Absent	Absent
		? ?	? ?
LOWER TRIASSIC SERIES	Moenkopi Fm.--consists of (descending) 200' of dark chocolate-brown argil. and saliferous sh.; 100' of soft dark-brown argil. sss.; 200' of dark-brown argil. sh.; and 100' of saliferous argil. sh., marine in part, seleniferous.	Thaynes Ls.--yellow, gray, blue, cherty lss., some yellow sss., 1000-2600', marine, seleniferous?	Chugwater Fm.--red sh., soft sss., thin lss., gyp., "red beds," 550-1250', non-marine, seleniferous in part. (Alcova Ls. Mbr. of central Wyoming, marine, selenif.
		Woodside Sh.--red and brown shaly sss., and sh., 400-500', marine, non-seleniferous.	
		Dinwoody Fm.--greenish-gray shs. with many thin plates of dense calc. ss. or argil dol. which weathers brown, tawny and even black, 50-350', mostly marine, seleniferous.	Goose Egg Fm.--(upper part) red sh., purple and gray dol. and ls., some gyp., marine in part, 250-400', seleniferous.

NOTE: For explanation of abbreviations, see Table 2.

The Moenkopi Formation (Table 4) is exposed in southern Utah, northern Arizona, southeastern Nevada, and southwestern Colorado. In Utah and Arizona, the Moenkopi supports the growth of a variety of seleniferous plants. High concentrations of selenium are present in plants in the vicinity of Holbrook, Leupp, and Cameron in northern Arizona. Seleniferous plants collected in the middle part of the formation (near Cameron) have the highest concentrations of selenium. Figure 3 shows the growth of *A. beathii* on the raw shale of the Moenkopi. Due to the profuse growth and variety of selenium indicator plants, all vegetation on the Moenkopi is potentially hazardous to livestock.

FIG. 3. A single clump of *A. beathii* rooted in raw Moenkopi shale near Cameron, Arizona.

The Dinwoody Formation (Table 3) is exposed in the Wind River Range in central and western Wyoming and supports an abundant growth of indicator plants of low selenium content.

The Little Medicine tongue of the Dinwoody Formation is a widespread unit of varicolored limy sandstone separated from the older Ervay tongue of the Phosphoria Formation by a tongue of red siltstone and is overlain by the upper part of the Chugwater Formation. Selenium indicator plants of low selenium content grow in abundance wherever exposures in eastern and central Wyoming have been examined.

The Alcova Member of the Chugwater (Table 4) is a marine limestone overlain by variegated claystones, siltstones, and conglomerates. The Alcova Member in central Wyoming usually supports a dense growth of selenium indicator plants. These indicator plants also grow on some lenticular red siltstones in the Chugwater Formation in eastern and central Wyoming. The occurrence of these seleniferous lenses is unpredictable because of their random distribution within the formation.

The Chinle Formation in southern Utah, northern Arizona, southeastern Nevada, southwestern Colorado, and northern New Mexico is in the upper Triassic series (Table 4). Extensive and varied species of selenium indicator plants are rooted in this formation. Although these plants contain less selenium than those on the Moenkopi, their prevalence and wide distribution make them a serious hazard to livestock. Sulfides from the Chinle and Shinarump contain less than 3 ppm selenium (*34*).

Jurassic

Rocks of Jurassic age are chiefly continental in origin but also include marine shales, limestones, and sandstones. They display a spectacular array of colors—red, brown, green, cream, gray, and white—and form the impressive walls of Zion Canyon, Vermillion Cliffs, White Cliffs, and Rainbow Natural Bridge.

Seleniferous vegetation on Jurassic formations is found on the Colorado Plateau. The Jurassic formations in southwestern Colorado, southern Utah, and eastern and western Wyoming are indicated in Table 5.

The Curtis Formation (Table 5), near Jensen, in northeastern Utah, is covered with dense growths of *Astragalus toanus* and *Stanleya integrifolia;* both plants have a fairly high selenium content. The Summerville Formation in southern Utah and southwestern Colorado (Table 5) supports the growth of seleniferous indicator plants.

The Sundance Formation and its equivalents are widespread in Wyoming, (Table 5) central and southern Montana, southwestern South Dakota, northwestern Nebraska, and central northern Colorado. In southeastern and central Wyoming, the Sundance Formation consists of marine shales and sandstones. There are scattered growths of moderately seleniferous plants in these areas. In southwestern South Dakota, the basal portion of the Sundance Formation (Stockade Beaver Shale Member) has a dense growth of moderately seleniferous *Astragalus bisulcatus.*

The Morrison Formation supports the growth of selenium indicator plants wherever it crops out (Table 5). It is exposed in large areas of southern Utah, southwestern Colorado, Arizona, New Mexico, eastern

TABLE 5
Jurassic Formations

	SOUTHERN UTAH AND SOUTHWESTERN COLORADO	WESTERN WYOMING	EASTERN WYOMING
UPPER JURASSIC SERIE	Morrison Fm.--marls are drab, green or gray, lower 2/3 numerous lenticular bodies of ls. of characteristic drab color, 800+', non-marine, seleniferous.	Probably absent	Morrison Fm.--variegated siliceous clays, sh. and sss., 300', non-marine, seleniferous.
	Summerville Fm.--thin-bedded chocolate-colored sss., earthy red-brown ss. and sh., some gyp. and in some sec. a little ls., 0-400', non-marine, seleniferous.	Stump Ss.--mainly thin-bedded gray to greenish-gray, fine-grained sss., some beds of compact calc. ss., 200-600', marine in part, non-seleniferous.	Sundance Fm.--marine gray sh., lss. and sss., abundantly fossiliferous, gray blue and pink calc. sh., thin lss., lower part largely buff to reddish sss., 300', marine, seleniferous in part in southern Wyoming and northern Utah.
	Curtis Fm.--green-gray cgl. and sh., and heavy-bedded gray ss., 0-253', marine, seleniferous.		
	Entrada Ss.--thin-bedded red sh. and ss. at base, heavy massive, red-brown earthy ss. above, which weathers into rounded forms and steep cliffs, 50-1000', non-marine, seleniferous?	Preuss Ss.--very fine even-grained sss., pale reddish-gray to deep dull red, usually calc. and more or less argil. becoming very shaly in places, weathers to dull-red soil, 1300', marine in part, seleniferous?	
	Carmel Fm.--dense ls. and buff, red ss. at base, toward top dominantly red and green sh. with thin sss. and heavy beds of gyp., 0-650', marine, non-seleniferous.	Twin Creek Ls.--black and gray calc. sh. and thin-bedded shaly lss. with occasional beds of yellow ss., 2500-3800', marine, non-seleniferous.	
MIDDLE JURASSIC SERIES		Gypsum Spring Mbr.--red sh., earthy dols. and gyp., marine in part, seleniferous.	Gypsum Spring Fm.--red sh., earthy dols. and gyp., marine in part, 0-250', seleniferous.
LOWER JURASSIC SERIES	Navajo Ss.--(upper part) red ss., massive, exceedingly cross-bedded and greatly reduced in thickness, 50-2000', non-marine, non-seleniferous.	Nugget Fm.--(possibly upper part) yellow, pink and red sss. bounded below by brown to dark-red sss. and sh. of Ankareh Sh. and above by dark-colored fossiliferous sh. and lss. of Twin Creek Fm., 1900', non-marine, non-seleniferous.	Absent

NOTE: For explanation of abbreviations, see Table 2.

Wyoming, Montana, North Dakota, South Dakota, Kansas, and Nebraska. This formation is composed of river flood plain deposit and consists of soft shales and sandstones in varying colors from green, beige, or gray to pink and white. Sulfides in the Morrison and Entrada formations are high in selenium (*34*).

All of the vegetation rooted in the Salt Wash Sandstone of the Morrison Formation is potentially dangerous to grazing livestock due to the presence of large amounts of soluble selenium compounds (selenates) in the soil. The origin of this selenium was considered by Beath (*14*) to be analogous to that of the vanadium, uranium, and chromium with which selenium is associated. The only known seleniferous rocks which exceed the Salt Wash Member in selenate content are the Tertiary tuffs near Lysite, Fremont County, Wyoming (*15, 69*).

Cretaceous

Rocks of the Cretaceous age in the United States consist of shales, sandstones, chalky limestones, conglomerates, altered volcanic ash, and coal. Outcrops of Cretaceous rocks comprise a total area of about 300,000 square miles in the western United States. They are, by far, the most widespread of all rocks of Mesozoic age and are exposed from Texas north along the Rocky Mountains and far into Canada, east to Iowa, and west intermittently to California.

More is known regarding the distribution of seleniferous plants on Cretaceous formations in the western interior of the United States than on rocks of any other period. Cretaceous formations in southern Utah, southwestern Colorado, western central and southeastern Wyoming are indicated in Table 6.

The Cretaceous System is represented in western Wyoming by sandstones and shales with minor amounts of conglomerates, altered volcanic ash beds, and coal seams. The Gannett Group (in part) has several species of seleniferous plants with low selenium content (Table 6).

The Frontier Formation in western, eastern, and central Wyoming (Table 6) consists of beds of black shale that become progressively more sandy upward and culminate at the top in one or more tan sandstones (Wall Creek). Seleniferous plants are abundant.

In the Black Hills region and northeastern Wyoming, there is moderate seleniferous plant growth on the dark gray and black Carlile Shale (Table 6). In the Laramie Basin of southeastern Wyoming, the Carlile consists of dark gray shales and thin sandy layers with many concretions; plants on these rocks contain moderate amounts of selenium.

The Niobrara Formation (Table 6) when traced westward into central Wyoming becomes less calcareous. Further west the chalky members disappear and are replaced by sandy shales of the Hilliard. The Niobrara supports the growth of highly seleniferous vegetation.

In South Dakota, Kansas, and Nebraska, the Niobrara Formation has been divided into lower (Fort Hayes) and upper (Smokey Hill) members (*76, 77*). The lower member is low in selenium and the upper mem-

TABLE 6
Cretaceous Formations

	SOUTHERN UTAH AND SOUTHWESTERN COLORADO		WESTERN WYOMING	CENTRAL AND SOUTHEASTERN WYOMING	
UPPER CRETACEOUS SERIES	Animas Fm.--yellowish-brown clays, tuffs, sss. and cgls. in which andesitic material greatly predominates, 700', non-marine, seleniferous.	Tuscner Fm.--qtz., sss., massive, cross-bedded, friable light-gray to creamy white, 0-600', non-marine, seleniferous.	Evanston Fm.--(lower part) gray, yellow and black sh. and yellow sss., some coal, 0-9500', non-marine, seleniferous?	Lance Fm. (NE Wyo.) friable sss., sh. and coal beds, 0-3000', non-marine, seleniferous in areas.	Medicine Bow Fm.-(SE Wyo.) alter. beds of light-colored to gray carb. sh., gray to brown ss., 5000', partly marine, selenif-erous in areas.
	McDermott Fm.--a series of lenticular sss., sh. and cgls. containing much andesitic debris and usually in part purple color, 200-400', non-marine, seleniferous in areas.	Williams Fork Fm.--alter beds of ss., sandy ss., coal, 550-5050', non-marine, seleniferous	? ?		
	Kirkland Sh.--predominantly clayey, easily weathering gray-white ss., 303-1984', non-marine, selen. in areas				
	Fruitland Fm.--consists of ss. and coal, ranging from sandy sh. and shaly or clayey ss., 500+', partly marine, selen. in areas.	Iles Fm.--alter. thick beds of ss., sandy sh., a few thick coal beds, 1350-1700', non-marine, selenif.	Absent		
	Pictured Cliffs Ss.--massive, sss. and white brownish and yellowish sss. and shs., 281', marine, seleniferous.			Lewis Sh.--contains at many places thick fresh-water deposits with coal beds and heavy sss., 2000-3000', partly marine, seleniferous.	
	Lewis Sh.--contains at many places thick fresh-water deposits with coal beds and heavy sss., 2000-3000', partly marine, seleniferous				
	Mesaverde Group			Mesaverde Fm.--alter. sss. and sh. with occasional marls or thin lss. and a number of coal seams, 2000', partly marine, selen. marine portion	
	Mancos Sh.--dark-gray or lead-colored sh., somewhat sandy, thin calc. layers, in places almost lss., 5000', marine, seleniferous.		? ? Adaville Fm.--yellow, gray and black carb. clays, with irregularly bedded brown and yellow ss. and numerous coal beds, 4000+', marine in part, seleniferous?	Cody Sh.--dark-gray sh., sss. in upper half, 3000-4000', marine, seleniferous.	Steele Sh.--dark-gray sh., thin sss., 2500-3000', marine, more selenif. in lower half.
			Hilliard Fm.--gray to black sandy sh., sandy white sss., 3000-6800', marine, seleniferous.		Niobrara Fm.--gray to buff calc. sh., some sandy sh. and soft fissile sh. in places, chiefly gray ls. and chalky ls., 100-500', marine, seleniferous.
			Frontier Fm.--alter. beds of yellow and gray ss. and yellow, gray and black carb. clay with coal beds, 2200-3800', partly marine, seleniferous.	Carlile Sh.--dark sh., thin sss. ls. concretions, 100-425', marine, seleniferous.	
	Dakota Ss.--yellowish, reddish and occasionally white ss. with alter. beds of various colored clays and lignite, 100-200', non-marine, seleniferous.			Frontier Fm.--sss. and sh., 700', partly marine, seleniferous.	
LOWER CRETACEOUS SERIES			Aspen Fm.--gray and black sh., shaly ss., compact sss., fish scales, 1200-2000', marine, seleniferous.	Mowry Sh.--(upper) hard bluish-gray sh., fish scales, 150', marine, seleniferous. --(lower) black sh., small concretions, 150', marine, selenif.	
			Bear River Fm.--black sh., shaly sss. and lss., some coal, 500-5000', non-marine, seleniferous.	Muddy or Newcastle? Ss.--yellow, red, and white ss., alter. beds of var. colors of clays and lignite, 200', non-marine, seleniferous.	
				Thermopolis Sh.--black sh., 150', largely marine, seleniferous.	
			Gannett Group (in part) non-marine, 3000', seleniferous.	Cloverly Fm.	Rust beds--rusty fucoidal ss. & interbedded black and gray sh., 20-75', partly marine, selenif.?
					Var. Sh.--var. sh. and claystones interbedded with ss., 50-100', non-marine, seleniferous.
					Cgl.--cgl. and sparkly rusty coarse ss., 20-75', non-marine, seleniferous.

NOTE: For explanation of abbreviations, see Table 2.

ber is highly seleniferous. The Niobrara Formation or its equivalent likewise extends into North Dakota, Montana, Wyoming, Colorado, and New Mexico. In all of the above states this formation supports the growth of seleniferous plants.

The Pierre Shale in northeastern Wyoming, South Dakota, North Dakota, eastern Montana, eastern Colorado, Nebraska, and western Kansas is seleniferous. Composed of dark shales, friable brown sandstones, and bentonite, the most extensive outcrops occur in South Dakota where they make up about one third of the area west of the Missouri River. A detailed discussion of the Pierre Shale in South Dakota is given by Moxon *et al.* (*76, 77*) and Searight *et al.* (*94*). Grains and grasses grown on soils derived from the Pierre Shale contain available selenium compounds. Such grains and grasses produce alkali disease in livestock (Chapter V).

On the Bearpaw Shale in Montana, specimens of seleniferous vegetation contained rather high concentrations of selenium.

The marine Mancos Shale in southern Utah, northern New Mexico, and southwestern Colorado (Table 6) supports the growth of a variety of selenium indicator plants.

The Steele Shale in southeastern and central Wyoming (Table 6) supports the growth of a variety of highly seleniferous plants on its basal portion.

The selenium concentrations in plants from the Pierre-Benton Shale in New Mexico are higher than those from the Mancos Shale. Although the weedy type of vegetation is primarily responsible for selenium poisoning, seleniferous grasses occur on localized areas in the vicinity of Springer, New Mexico, on the Pierre-Benton Shale. The presence of selenium in grasses is probably due to the absorption of selenium which was made available by converter plants including *Astragalus bisulcatus.*

The sandstones, shales, and coal beds of the Iles and Williams Fork formations in the Mesaverde Group extend to southern Utah and northwestern Colorado (Table 6). Growth of seleniferous plants occurs on formations of the Mesaverde Group.

The lower marine portion of the Mesaverde Formation in central and southeastern Wyoming (Table 6) consists of alternating sandstones and shales with occasional marls or thin limestones and a number of coal beds.

The Lance Formation (Table 6) in northeastern Wyoming is composed of gray shales interbedded with white and brown sandstones and coal beds. Indicator plants with low selenium content are present on this formation.

In southeastern Wyoming the Medicine Bow Formation, a southern equivalent of the Lance Formation, has a few seleniferous plants (Table 6). The carbonaceous shales along the east flank of the Medicine Bow Mountains contain a very high concentration of selenium.

Tertiary and Quaternary

Tertiary and Quaternary rocks of the western interior region of the United States are widely distributed. They are nonmarine, weakly consolidated deposits distributed chiefly by streams and are mainly composed of reworked debris from all older rocks plus volcanic rocks such as tuffs and lava flows.

Paleocene and Eocene strata alone occupy an area of about 200,000 square miles and are widespread in New Mexico, Colorado, Utah, Wyoming, Montana, and North Dakota.

The present Rocky Mountains began to rise during the latter part of the Cretaceous Period, but erosion of uplands and deposition in basins made the region a nearly level plain by middle or late Tertiary time. The Rocky Mountains were exhumed to their present form as the result of an upward movement in very late Tertiary or early Quaternary time. The Quaternary Period was marked by extensive erosion and minor deposition of unconsolidated glacial drift, loess, and dune sand, alluvium, and volcanic ash. The Tertiary formations in central eastern Utah and western and southeastern Wyoming are indicated in Table 7.

The Fort Union Formation (Table 7) is present in southeastern and central Wyoming and also occupies a large area in North Dakota, northwestern South Dakota, northwestern Colorado, Montana, and Alberta. It includes bluish-white and yellow sandstones, gray shales, and coal. Many of the extensive outcrops of the Fort Union Formation support dense growths of selenium indicator plants.

The Green River Formation (Table 7) of early or middle Eocene age occurs in the Uinta Basin of Colorado and central and eastern Utah and the Green River Basin of Wyoming. These rocks were deposited in a series of great lake basins and are composed of calcareous shales, oil shales, and sandstones. Although most of its exposures are nonseleniferous, those of the Tipton tongue support the growth of a variety of plants with moderate to high selenium content.

The Bridger Formation is exposed in western Wyoming, northwestern Colorado, and central and eastern Utah (Table 7). Comprising gray and green tuffaceous shales and sandstones, white marls, thin tuff beds, and some conglomerates, the Bridger locally has highly seleniferous vegetation.

The White River Group of Oligocene age is widespread in Wyoming, the Dakotas, and Nebraska. The Chadron Formation, lower subdivision, has a number of indicator plants with moderate amounts of selenium.

The Arikaree Sandstone of Miocene age is composed of sand, gravel, and boulder beds admixed with volcanic ash (Table 7). It extends through western Nebraska, southeastern Wyoming, southern South Dakota, and northeastern Colorado. Seleniferous plants with low selenium content were collected from localized areas.

TABLE 7
Tertiary Formations

Epoch	CENTRAL EASTERN UTAH	WESTERN WYOMING	SOUTHEASTERN WYOMING
PLIOCENE	Absent	Absent	Absent
PLIOCENE–MIOCENE	Browns Park Fm.--cgls. at base, tuffaceous mudstone and ss., white ss. and white glass tuff, 0-1200', seleniferous in areas.	Browns Park Fm.--cgls. at base, tuffaceous mudstone and ss., white ss. and white glass tuff, 0-1200', seleniferous in areas.	North Park Fm.--whitish sand and shale, volcanic ash, some ls., cgl. at base, 0-2000', non-marine, seleniferous in areas.
MIOCENE	? ? Bishop Cgl.--boulders and pebbles of ss., qtzite. and crystalline schists, 0-500', non-marine, non-seleniferous.	Bishop Cgl.--boulders and pebbles of ss., qtzite. and crystalline schists, 0-300', non-marine, non-seleniferous.	Arikaree Fm.--sand, gravel, boulder beds, locally ls. lens. 0-700', non-marine, slightly seleniferous in areas.
OLIGOCENE	? ? Duchesne River Fm.--reddish-orange sh., buff-gray sss. and cgl., 0-1500', non-marine, seleniferous in areas.	Absent	WHITE RIVER GROUP: Brule Fm.--pinkish clay, gravely-streaked, 0-300', non-marine, non-seleniferous. Chadron Fm.--gray to brown ss., sh., sand, gravel, 0-100', non-marine, selenif. areas
EOCENE	Uinta Fm.--coarse brown sss. with alter. clays, light reddish stratum, hard brown sss., 0-1500', non-marine, seleniferous in areas.	Uinta Fm.--lower member rough, gritty cgl., fine-grained ss., creamy calc. beds, 0-90', non-marine, seleniferous in areas.	Absent
EOCENE	Bridger Fm.--greenish sand and sh., largely volcanic ash, white beds, 0-2000', non-marine, seleniferous in areas.	Bridger Fm.--greenish sand and sh., largely volcanic ash, white beds, 0-2000', non-marine, seleniferous in areas.	
EOCENE	Green River Fm.--consists of calc. shs., sss. of fresh-water origin, limy, 0-4000+',non-marine, selenif-erous in areas.	Green River Fm.--thin-bedded calc. shs., some ss. light-colored ls., 0-2000', non-marine, selenif. in areas.	
EOCENE	Wasatch Group--var. sands and clays, very little calc. matter, cgls., 0-5000', non-marine, seleniferous in areas.	WASATCH GROUP: Knight Fm.--red and yellow sandy sh. and ss., some conc ls., 0-1750', non-marine, non-seleniferous. Almy Fm.--red and yellow ss., shs., cgl. at base, 0-2500', non-marine, non-seleniferous.	Wind River Fm.--soft, var. sh., coarse brown ss., arkose and cgls., 0-500', non-marine, highly seleniferous in areas. Hanna Fm.--cgl., brown ss., gray sh., and coals, 0-6000+', non-marine, non-seleniferous.
PALEOCENE	Absent	Evanston Fm.--(upper part) gray, yellow and black sh. and yellow sss., some coal, 0-9500', non-marine, seleniferous?	Fort Union Fm.--bluish white sss. and sand, gray sh., ferr. sss. and coals, 0-2400+', non-marine, seleniferous in areas.

NOTE: For explanation of abbreviations, see Table 2.

Latest Miocene or Pliocene rocks are represented in eastern Wyoming by the upper part of the North Park Formation (Table 7) which is characterized by white calcareous sandstones, shales, and ash beds. In localized areas there is abundant growth of seleniferous plants.

In the Imperial Valley of California, near Truckhaven, the Cenozoic sediments support an abundant growth of seleniferous *Astragalus crotalariae.* Plants of several other species rooted in these sediments also contain toxic amounts of selenium.

In Texas and eastern Colorado, the Ogallala Formation of Pliocene age supports the growth of highly seleniferous plants in localized areas (*12*). In Colorado, a sample of *Astragalus pectinatus* from this formation contained 1340 ppm selenium.

In Arizona, the Verde Formation of Pliocene or Pleistocene age near Jerome has an abundant growth of highly seleniferous *Astragalus pattersoni* var. *praelongus.* A Tertiary outcrop in the Tonto Basin near the Roosevelt Reservoir has localized growths of *Stanleya pinnata* with low selenium content.

Pleistocene deposits are accumulations of glacial drift boulder and cobble veneers on pediments, and river terrace and flood plain accumulations. In cases where parent rock is selenium bearing, the soil, likewise, supports the growth of seleniferous vegetation (*94*).

Some alluvial as well as glacial deposits in Wyoming, Nebraska, Colorado, South Dakota, and New Mexico contain enough selenium to support the growth of indicator plants (*5, 50, 92*). Table 8 indicates selenium content of plants grown on these deposits.

TABLE 8

Selenium Content of Indicator Plants Grown on Deposits of the Quaternary Period

Type of deposits	Number of samples	Selenium content of plants (ppm)[a]		
		Minimum	Maximum	Average
Alluvium	56	166	854	437
Glacial	5	65	3,134	763

[a] Air-dried basis.

SELENIFEROUS ROCKS AND MINERALS

The selenium content of rocks varies in different geological formations, in different beds of the same formation, and even in different parts of the same bed (*7*). In some instances it varies according to the nature of the materials—claystones, limestones, etc.—making up the bed. Variation in selenium content within a bed of rock in some cases is due to the occurrence of relatively high secondary concentrations of selenium emplaced after the host bed had been deposited.

Krauskopf (*62*) reviewed the distribution of rare metals (exclusive of the radioactive metals but including selenium) in sedimentary rocks. He discussed four general processes by which minor constituents can be deposited in sedimentary rocks. These processes are mechanical enrichment, precipitation, adsorption, and substitution, and presence of organic materials in deposits. All of these processes probably in some degree contribute to the enrichment of selenium in the geological materials discussed in this section.

Carbonaceous Shales and Materials

Shales usually contain more selenium than limestones and other sedimentary rocks (*6, 8, 14, 20, 67, 74*). The selenium content of indicator plants on Niobrara shale is indicated in Table 9. High concentrations of

TABLE 9

Absorption of Selenium by Astragalus bisulcatus *from Niobrara Shale*[a]

Location	Selenium (ppm)[b]		Depth
	Plants	Shales	(ft)
Wyoming			
Albany County			
Sec. 5, T. 16 N., R. 74 W.	6,200	10.1	1
		8.7	2
Sec. 19, T. 22 N., R. 74 W.	6,950	14.9	1
		22.9	2
Sec. 32, T. 22 N., R. 76 W.	5,500	2.3	1
		3.4	2
		7.5	3
		10.6	4
Sec. 31, T. 15 N., R. 74 W.	10,824	52.0	1
		32.0	2
Sec. 15, T. 15 N., R. 74 W.	5,330	20.0	1
		16.0	2
		12.0	3

[a] Shale derived exclusively from the Niobrara Formation.
[b] Air-dried basis.

selenium occur in some carbonaceous laminae and shales. These may represent the selenium compounds accumulated or absorbed by plants that gave rise to carbonaceous deposits. This suggests that plants or decaying organic matter had the capacity to accumulate or absorb selenium probably as early as Paleozoic time (*8*).

Information on the selenium content of shales from other continents indicates that the Mesozoic and Paleozoic were the eras of most extensive selenium deposition (*74*).

The seleniferous character of carbonaceous beds in the basal part of the Dakota Sandstone in Albany County, Wyoming, has been studied in detail (*7*). Here an arkosic carbonaceous sandstone which contained 8 ppm selenium overlies a ferruginous conglomerate with the same selenium content. Next above the sandstone is a carbon lamina, about 2 inches thick, containing 21 ppm selenium. Above this is a compact carbonaceous sandstone which contained 13 ppm selenium. Ferruginous carbonaceous shale 20 feet above the carbonaceous sandstone is 3 feet in thickness and contained 10 ppm selenium.

The carbonaceous shale from Provo Canyon, Utah, in the Manning Canyon Shale contained 96.3 ppm selenium, and the amount of water-extractable selenium was 16.0 ppm as selenate (*15*). Total selenium content of some carbonaceous shale collected in Albany County, Wyoming, was 150 ppm selenium (*6*).

In uranium-bearing coal the ratio of selenium to uranium was very high. One sample collected on the La Ventana Mesa (New Mexico) contained 600 ppm selenium (*32*). Studies on the selenium content in carbonaceous beds in the Pierre Shale indicate that selenium was present in all samples. Only one sample contained 50 ppm, and the average selenium content of other samples was 2 ppm. All samples contained more arsenic than selenium (*101*).

Analyses of carbonaceous marine shale samples from 6 geological formations of the western United States were reported by Davidson and Lakin (*40*). The selenium content of shales ranged from < 1 to 277 ppm with a maximum of 675 ppm selenium. Data on other elements were also included.

Lignite Beds

Lignitic material is less seleniferous than associated carbonaceous shale or carbon laminae. Specimens from the Bear River Formation in western Wyoming contained 2–7 ppm selenium. Lignitic coal from the Medicine Bow Formation, Albany County, Wyoming, had 1–6 ppm selenium, and similar coal from the Fort Union Formation in northeastern Wyoming had 3 ppm (*7*).

Volcanic Materials

Tuffs

In 1934 Beath (unpublished) noted some highly seleniferous tuffaceous sedimentary rocks near Lysite, Fremont County, Wyoming (Fig. 4), an area where the native forage was toxic to grazing livestock.

Tuffs (5 samples) collected from Lysite were analyzed and contained 12.5, 29, 112, 117, and 187 ppm selenium. In the last three samples the water-soluble selenium, mostly selenate, was 84 and 96 per cent of the total selenium (*15*). The seleniferous tuffaceous strata in the Lysite area were described as being middle or late Eocene age by Love (*69*). The selenium in these tuffs is erratic and its distribution is not confined to any one bed (*43*). Of 206 samples assayed from 11 drill holes only eight samples contained more than 0.005 per cent selenium (50 ppm selenium). Tuffs (trachyte) from the vicinity of Lysite, reported by Davidson and Powers (*38*), contained from 2 to 7 ppm selenium with the exception of one sample which contained 40 ppm selenium. However, the low sele-

FIG. 4. Seleniferous tuffs (Lysite) in north-central Wyoming.

nium content reported by these investigators may have been due to the method of analysis. They reported semi-quantitative data based on a field method of analysis.

Volcanic rocks in the northwestern United States with selenium content of 0.1 to 0.6 ppm were reported by a number of investigators (*20, 26, 65*). Volcanic rocks from California, Colorado, New Mexico, Idaho, and Alaska contained less than 1.0 ppm selenium; from Hawaii the rocks contained less than 2 ppm selenium (*38*).

Impure Bentonite

Bentonite is a rock consisting of clay derived from alteration of volcanic ash (*101*). Bentonite beds in shales are commonly nonseleniferous unless they contain ferric oxide which readily adsorbs selenium (*49*). An iron-stained specimen from the Bear River Formation near Cokeville, Wyoming, contained 5 ppm selenium (*7*). Bentonite and gypsum in the Pierre Shale of Nebraska contained 22 ppm selenium, and bentonite free of gypsum from the same area contained from 9 to 76 ppm selenium (*20, 22*). In these earlier studies all the bentonite analyzed was located in shale beds which contained varying amounts of selenium, in some cases over 100 ppm. The purity or contamination of bentonite with other minerals was not indicated.

Phosphate Rock

Analyses of high-grade phosphate rock in the Phosphoria Formation of western Wyoming showed that light-colored rock contained from 1 to 95 ppm and that darker (low-grade) rock contained a maximum of 212 ppm selenium (*9*). The selenium distribution was highly variable ranging from 1.0 to over 200 ppm. Subsequent studies on phosphate rocks indicated that small amounts of selenium in the rocks were water-soluble selenium compounds (selenates). There was no selenite or organic selenium present (*15*).

Davidson and Gulbrandsen (*37*) reported that the selenium content of phosphate rocks ranged from a few to 300 ppm and of carbonaceous mudstone from a few to 1500 ppm. There was no correlation between selenium and P_2O_5 content of the phosphatic rocks analyzed. The selenium contents of phosphate rocks from different localities have been published by Rader and Hill (*86*). Phosphate rock from Florida, Tennessee, Kentucky, Arkansas, Oklahoma, Australia; light-colored phosphates from the western United States; and apatites from Virginia and Canada contained 1 ppm or less selenium. Brown phosphate rock from Wyoming and Algeria contained 55 ppm selenium. Only small amounts of selenium from the raw phosphate rock is present in superphosphates and phosphoric acid.

Ferruginous Sandstone

Some sandstones in contact with carbonaceous shale beds in the Medicine Bow Formation are highly seleniferous. In one profile, the carbonaceous shale directly above the sandstone layer contained 14 ppm selenium (*7*). Sandstones in close contact with the shale had 112 ppm, whereas sandstone 25 cm below the contact contained only 3 ppm selenium. Enrichment of the sandstone may have resulted by leaching of selenium from the overlying shales.

Sandstones

The Browns Park Formation in southwestern Carbon County, Wyoming, supports growth of highly seleniferous vegetation. Selenium concentration in the finely divided material of the sandstone was 112 ppm, and 91 per cent was a water-soluble compound (selenate) (*15*). Sandstone samples from New Mexico had variable amounts of selenium. The selenium content of the samples varied from 0.2 to 46 ppm (*117*).

Limy Sandstone

A lens of limy sandstone in the Chugwater Formation in Albany County, Wyoming, contained 2–10 ppm selenium, and soils derived from it support the growth of two native seleniferous plants (*7*).

Limestone

The selenium content of limestone in some cases was less than 0.1 ppm with a maximum of 6 ppm selenium (*20, 48, 76*). However, limestone beds in the Phosphoria Formation of western Wyoming contained 14 ppm selenium. A limestone from the Frontier Formation had 7 ppm and one from the Thaynes Formation had 1.5 ppm selenium (*7*). Limestone from Provo Canyon, Utah, contained from 0.6 to 12.0 ppm selenium. Blue-gray limestone from the same area mixed with brownish shale contained 12.0 ppm selenium (*10*).

Selenium in Vanadium-Uranium Ores

That selenium deposits may have had a genesis more or less parallel to that of vandium deposits has been suggested by Beath (*14*). A vanadium-bearing siltstone in the phosphatic member of the Phosphoria Formation at Afton, Wyoming, was found to contain 580 ppm selenium (*15*). The selenium content of uranium-vanadium ores in the Salt Wash Member of the Morrison Formation varied widely with a maximum of 2630 ppm. A uranium-vanadium ore specimen contained 563 ppm selenium, and the water extract of this specimen contained about 8 per cent selenate and 6 per cent selenite (*15, 28*). Vanadium-uranium ore samples collected from southeast of Thompson, Utah, contained 526 to 1995 ppm; carnotite, 810 ppm; and blue-black vanadium ore, 565 ppm selenium. The carbonaceous vanadium-uranium ore contained 2630 ppm selenium. Low-grade ore surrounded by "flowers of uranium" contained 526 ppm selenium (*14*). Native selenium was identified in three localities with sandstone type of uranium-vanadium deposits (*100*).

Uranium minerals in sandstone of the Browns Park Formation of Miocene age (6 miles west of Baggs, Wyoming) contained from 12 to 80 ppm selenium (*106*). The association of uranium and selenium in the ore is probably not due to chemical combination in a specific mineral but to a common mode of deposition.

Limonitic Concretions

High concentrations of selenium are frequently associated with "limonitic" concretions which are spherical or irregular brown masses of ferric oxide and hydroxide formed with various types of rocks. Seven such concretions from the basal portion of the Niobrara Formation had the following selenium contents: 548, 292, 127, 115, 86, 53, and 23 ppm (*7*). The concretion that had 127 ppm of selenium contained no elemental selenium, ferrous selenide, calcium selenite, or calcium selenate (*7*). The shale in which the concretions were embedded contained only 2–10 ppm selenium. A concretion from the Medicine Bow Formation contained 57 ppm selenium. A composite sample of associated shale contained 1.5 ppm selenium. Limonitic concretions from the Steele Shale are not markedly seleniferous (*4*). Solid masses or concretions frequently occur in seleniferous shales, and they usually have a higher selenium content than that of adjacent shales (*4, 26*). Concretions with selenium content from 10 to 100 ppm were also reported by Moxon (*75*).

Sulfides and Selenides

The elements selenium and sulfur are closely related crystallochemically and also in certain aspects of their distribution in minerals and rocks. Some sulfide ores or impure sulfur are enriched with selenium. Selenium forms selenides and sulfoselenides of silver, copper, lead, and mercury, and selenites with copper, cobalt, and lead. Selenium frequently occurs as impure selenides or as an impurity in most sulfides.

Fleischer (*44*) summarized the data in the literature on the selenium content as well as other minor elements in some sulfide minerals. He listed references and type of analysis and arbitrarily selected concentration ranges for minor elements as well as for selenium. The selenium contents of galena (PbS), sphalerite and wurtzite (ZnS), chalcopyrite ($CuFeS_2$), pyrite and marcasite (FeS_2), pyrrhotite and troilite (FeS), and arsenopyrite (FeAsS) are given.

Sulfides decompose readily so that they rarely occur on exposed surfaces. During weathering of seleniferous sulfide deposits, selenium is oxidized to selenite. In sediments where the redox potential is very high, selenium is oxidized to selenate. Both selenates and selenites are readily reduced to elemental selenium and various selenides (*87*).

Selenium commonly occurs in pyrite (FeS_2) and in marcasite (FeS_2)

(*111*). It is not always possible to identify specimens of these minerals in shales, because they are difficult to distinguish from limonitic concretions. Pyrite concretions from the Niobrara Formation contained up to 548 ppm selenium and averaged 250 and 350 ppm selenium. Pyrite from other formations contained from 0.5 to 4.1 ppm selenium (*4*).

The sulfides of copper, iron, mercury, and silver frequently contain high concretrations of selenium. Tiemannite from Utah contained about 24 per cent selenium (*79*). A sample of naumannite from Silver City, Idaho, contained 23 per cent selenium (*95*). Davidson (*39*) reported that common epithermal silver-gold and antimony deposits are highly seleniferous but that less common gold-silver and mercury deposits rarely contain high concentrations of selenium. Analyses of 98 samples of pyrite and sulfide ores from Utah, Nevada, Idaho, and Oregon were reported by Lakin and Byers (*65*). One sample of ore from Park City, Utah, contained 540 ppm selenium.

The selenium content of pyrites from Japanese mines ranged from 0.2 to 39 ppm. Copper pyrite ($CuFeS_2$) had the highest average selenium content of 18.8 ppm. There was no correlation between selenium and sulfur contents of pyrites (*104*). The distribution of selenium in sulfide ores of the Skellefte district (Sweden) was reported by Bergenfelt (*17*). Arsenopyrite (FeAsS) and galena (PbS) generally have high selenium content and chalcopyrite ($CuFeS_2$) is richer than pyrite in selenium. There was considerable variation in the selenium content of ores from different deposits, and it was attributed to the selenium content of mineralizing solutions.

Minerals in which selenium forms an essential constituent have been identified only in a few deposits in the Skellefte district (*47*). In pure sulfide minerals, the selenium content varied from 10 to 1400 ppm. The succession galena-chalcopyrite-sphalerite-pyrite indicates an order of decreasing selenium content.

The possibility of using sulfur-selenium ratios as a method of differentiation between the origin of sulfide deposits was tested by Edwards and Carlos (*42*). The sulfur-selenium ratios of sedimentary thermal pyrites ranged from 9000 to 13,000. Their results indicated that high selenium content is associated with some sulfides of hydrothermal origin, but low selenium content is not positive evidence of sedimentary origin.

Among the sulfide ores investigated, chalcopyrite ($CuFeS_2$), pyrite, bornite ($FeS \cdot 2Cu_2S \cdot CuS$), and arsenopyrite (FeAsS) were most seleniferous. The authors (*42*) considered these to be early-formed minerals. The later-formed minerals, sphalerite (ZnS), galena (PbS), and tetrahedrite (Cu_2SbS_3 or $3Cu_2S \cdot Sb_2O_3$) were less seleniferous. Stibnite (Sb_2S_3), cinnabar (HgS, red), and barite ($BaSO_4$) were poor in selenium and they were considered as low temperature minerals (*42*).

Selenium in 50 sulfide ores and their products was analyzed by Kaiser (*55*). Selenium is relatively more abundant in sulfide deposits of the mountainous region of central Arizona than other areas. There was no apparent connection between the concentration of selenium in epigenetic ore deposits and that in sedimentary rocks in the samples analyzed. Selenium minerals (naumannite, tiemannite, and eucairite) in California were described by Murdoch and Webb (*78*).

Sulfoselenides of mercury, onofrite [Hg(S,Se)], tiemannite (HgSe), and metacinnabar (HgS, black) form a complete isomorphous series and were found in their entirety at Marysvale, Utah, by Bethke (*18*). It was suggested by Bethke (*18*) that selenium is unable to replace sulfur in the cinnabar structure except in trace amounts and that the distribution of selenium between cinnabar and metacinnabar is related to differences in bond type.

Sulfides analyzed from some sedimentary rocks of the Morrison, Entrada, and Wind River formations had variable amounts of selenium (*34*). These sulfides had the following maximum selenium content: chalcopyrite and pyrite, 5 per cent; marcasite, 0.65 per cent; and galena-clausthalite (PbS-PbSe), 18 per cent. The sulfides from the Shinarump and Chinle formations of Triassic age usually contained less than 3 ppm except in the Temple mining district, Utah, where they had as much as 5000 ppm selenium. Sulfides from the same stratigraphic zone usually contain the same relative amounts of selenium. The selenides, clausthalite and eucairite, have been identified from uranium ore deposits in the Morrison Formation (*34*).

Iron sulfides from mineralized rocks of Jurassic age had the highest selenium content (2000 ppm) and of Triassic age, the lowest (19 ppm) (*35*). Some copper sulfides of Jurassic age contained small inclusions of clausthalite and had a high selenium content. Ferroselite was found in two deposits on the Colorado Plateau. The selenium content of the many sulfides from sedimentary rocks of Triassic, Jurassic, Cretaceous, and Tertiary ages described by the authors in the western United States is above that reported for sulfides from other ages or locations (*34, 35*).

There is no significant difference in the selenium content of sulfides (pyrite and marcasite) from barren and mineralized rocks of the Morrison and Chinle formations (*110*). Sulfides from Tertiary mineralized rocks contained 60 times more selenium than sulfides from barren rock. Highly seleniferous deposits contained clausthalite (PbSe), eucairite (CuAgSe), ferroselite, and cobaltial ferroselite.

The oxidation of these seleniferous sulfide minerals in underground or damp cool places and the formation of characteristic pinkish crusts of native selenium were reported by a number of investigators (*34, 35, 100, 103*). The native selenium forms either monoclinic or hexagonal crystals intermixed with soluble sulfates. Under normal oxidizing conditions, native selenium is more stable than selenates or selenites (*35*). Native selenium (3 mines) was described as purple-gray metallic acicular crystals, usually forming aggregates of small crystals (*100*). The mines are located in South Dakota, Utah, and Colorado.

The substitution of selenium for sulfur in a number of sulfide minerals has been suggested by a number of investigators (*34, 35, 39, 110*). This substitution has been postulated on the basis of the similarity of the chemical and physical properties of selenium and sulfur. The radii of S^{2-}(1.74 Å) and of Se^{2-}(1.92 Å) are so close that selenium can and does substitute in the lattices of sulfides. The substitution may have occurred during mineralization of the rocks or it may have derived from volcanic debris deposited with the sediments. Goldschmidt and Strock (*48*) analyzed a number of pyrrhotite-pentlandite ores and showed that the selenium content ranged from 17 to 57 ppm with a calculated S:Se ratio of 4400 to 12,400 by weight. In the oxidation zones of sulfur-selenium ores, heavy metal salts of selenious acid are rarities and selenites are reduced to free selenium. Therefore, selenium cannot be expected to take part in the geochemical cycle of sulfur, but it can be expected to pass into the sediments as the free element or form of heavy metal selenides (*49*).

Selenides were found in uranium deposits of the western part of the Goldfields-Martin Lake area, from the Gil Group northward through Martin Lake and Ato Bay to Hal Lake and the Stream Fault in Canada (*90*). The Hal Lake and Ato Bay deposits are not radioactive. The selenide deposits include umangite ($Cu_2Se \cdot CuSe$), klockmannite, and berzelianite (Cu_2Se) with some clausthalite ($PbSe$), chalcomenite, and native copper. The selenides cement and partly replace brecciated host rock and are largely free of gangue minerals. Selenides are associated with pitchblende at Martin Lake mine, the Eagle Group, and the Gil Group. The selenides are associated with calcite, and in these areas sulfides are rare or lacking.

Impure Sulfur

Elemental selenium occurs as an impurity in some sulfur. Crude sulfur from the Vulcan mine, Colorado, contained 8350 ppm selenium (*20*), but the range of other samples was from 220 and 1400 to 5 ppm selenium (*26*).

Jarosite

Jarosite [$KFe_3(SO_4)_2(OH)_6$], an alteration product that occurs extensively in thin seams along bedding, joint, and fracture surfaces in shale beds, may contain appreciable quantities of selenium. The selenium probably substitutes for sulfur in the structure. A specimen from the Thermopolis Shale in the Big Horn Basin contained 3 ppm selenium, one from the Pierre Shale had 10 ppm selenium, and one from the phosphate beds in the Phosphoria Formation of western Wyoming contained 18 ppm selenium (*7, 9*).

Selenium in Meteorites

The chemical and mineralogical composition of stony meteorites indicates that the parent body of the meteorites was similar in composition to the earth's crust.

Eighteen meteorites of various composition were analyzed for selenium. Stony meteorites (stone, chondrite, pallasite, and mesosiderite) contained from 3 to 15 ppm selenium. Concretions of troilite (iron sulfide) found in octahedrite meteorites contained 23 and 200 ppm selenium (*25*).

Samples of meteorites from various parts of the world were analyzed by Williams *et al.* (*118*). Of the 22 samples examined, 15 contained selenium in comparable amounts to those found in analogous materials from the earth's crust. All samples of stony meteorites had appreciable quantities of selenium, whereas iron-alloy samples of octahedrite contained none. In a sample of troilite from the Cañon Diablo meteorite, the selenium content was high with an atomic ratio of S : Se of 4215. The results are in agreement with those of Goldschmidt and Strock (*48*).

THE FORMATION OF SELENIFEROUS SOILS

Chemical and mechanical factors, and, to a lesser extent, biological modifications of parent rocks determine the selenium content of soils.

In soil formation there are so-called passive factors which are the parent rocks, topography, and age of the land surface. The active factors of soil formation are precipitation and temperature. Interrelated with these are evaporation, humidity, wind, microorganisms in soil, plants, and animal life (*54*).

Selenium in the soil may be derived from (1) formations or rock outcrops, (2) formations lying beneath soil mantle, (3) decomposition of parent rocks by wind and water and subsequent transport by ground or surface water, (4) indicator plants, or (5) man-made enrichment of the soil with selenium in mining operations.

In regions of low humidity the effect of parent material on the resulting soils is probably greater than in regions of high precipitation. The chemical constituents of bedrock thus remain in the soil as a result of decomposition of these rocks.

Throughout the arid and semi-arid seleniferous areas of the western United States, there is a notable absence of a mantle of transported soil.

Most of the soils are composed of rock fragments resulting from weathering *in situ.* Transported soils are restricted to (1) comparatively narrow flood plains of streams, (2) gently sloping surfaces (pediments) that extend from mountain fronts into basins, (3) accumulations of glacial drifts in valleys of the higher mountain ranges, and (4) limited areas covered by wind-blown deposits. It is estimated that less than one tenth of the total area in Wyoming is covered with a mantle of geologically recent, unconsolidated, water-transported or wind-transported soil (*59*).

During the formation of transported soils there is considerable mixing of parent material. Selenium content of soil resulting from weathering of rocks depends in part on the degree of mixing of parent materials as well as selenium content of these materials.

Moxon *et al.* (*77*) estimated that 60 to 80 per cent of selenium from the original formation was lost in soil-forming processes. Calculation showed that the reservoir of selenium in seleniferous subsoils and rocks is so high that successive crops of accumulator plants harvested over long periods of time would have only a negligible effect in reducing the selenium content of the soil (Rosenfeld and Beath, unpublished).

The most pronounced influence of topography on soil formation is in mountainous areas. On level surfaces, surface runoff would be small compared to that on the slopes. If level surfaces were downslope from seleniferous rocks, leaching by water and erosion of the rocks would increase the selenium content of the resulting soil (*77, 94*).

In the absence of a thick protective covering of vegetation on steep slopes, strong winds and rain can remove disintegrated soils with only slight chemical change in the soil. Although most seleniferous soils are formed *in situ* (from underlying rocks) some seleniferous material may be carried for short distances from the site. Wind-blown materials derived from seleniferous rocks may produce drifts short distances from wind-eroded sources (*77*).

Leaching of soluble selenium from the soils is relatively unimportant in semi-arid seleniferous regions of the western United States because of insufficient rainfall. However, by percolation and evaporation of surface water, soluble selenium compounds may be redeposited on or near the surface. Deposition of soluble selenium compounds at various soil horizons was reported by Beath *et al.* (*4*).

Soil crust derived by surface evaporation of water has higher soluble selenium content than the original rock. Much of the selenium in the crust is in a water-soluble form. If salt deposits do not appear on the surface, there is a tendency toward concentration of selenium compound(s) in the upper soil layers (*22*).

Over a long period of time, leaching may be significant in some seleniferous areas (*77*). Indirect evidence for loss of selenium from the soil by leaching is indicated by a higher selenium content in bedrock than in derived soils. In regions of high rainfall (e.g. Hawaii, New Jersey, and Oregon), leaching may account for the absence of available selenium in the soil and vegetation (*23, 26, 91*).

The movement of water tends to increase the selenium content of alluvial deposits in valleys where subsurface drainage moves down or laterally from seleniferous soils or rocks. If there is an increase in annual rainfall, movement of selenium in ground waters is increased (*105*). Irrigation ditches that pass through seleniferous shales may produce seeps at lower levels and may increase available selenium in the seepage water. The accumulation of selenium in undrained pools presents evidence of seepage from upper levels.

Owing to the impervious nature of some seleniferous rocks, Knight and Beath (*60*) doubted that ordinary weathering processes and bacterial action had any appreciable effect on converting selenium present in rocks of the semi-arid areas into an available form. This conversion is carried out mainly by indicator plants.

Much of the Niobrara Formation around the Black Hills in South Dakota is covered with a nonseleniferous alluvium (*77*). In many places the alluvial deposit is so thin that deep-rooted selenium-converting plants reach the seleniferous rock and thereby increase the selenium content of the soils.

Impurities in superphosphate and ammonium sulfate fertilizers of selenium compound(s) may increase the selenium content of soils (*86*). There is no conclusive evidence that fertilizers have produced toxic crops except in Japan (*98*). Insecticides containing selenium compound(s) are known to contaminate the soil; they are discussed in Chapter V. Health hazards caused by selenium that result from mining and processing of ore are discussed in Chapter VIII.

CHEMICAL FORMS OF SELENIUM IN SOILS

Owing to physical and chemical properties of the soil, selenium compounds are difficult to separate and identify. The results of analysis for selenium compounds in soils suggest at best that there are differences in their solubility in water and in some other solvents. There is considerable evidence that selenides, selenates, organic selenium compounds, some elemental selenium, and probably some selenites are present in soils. Some of these compounds are readily absorbed by all types of vegetation.

The maximum quantity of selenium found in several thousand soil samples in the United States was less than 100 ppm and the majority of the seleniferous soils analyzed contained on the average less than 2 ppm. Swaine (*99*) summarized published data on the selenium content of surface soils and subsoils in the United States as well as in other countries.

Lack of information concerning selenium compounds in soil may explain divergent results obtained on the selenium content of vegetation growing on seleniferous soils. The low selenium content of soils presents further difficulties in determining the presence of any specific compound(s).

The presence of small amounts of elemental selenium in the soil was reported by several investigators (*8*, *26*). Elemental selenium may be present in some soils due to bacteria and fungi which are capable of reducing selenites and selenates to elemental form. The elemental selenium could be converted, under suitable conditions, into selenites or selenates by microorganisms. A rod-shaped autotrophic bacterium isolated from nonseleniferous soil was described which was able to convert elemental selenium to selenic acid (*68*). There is no evidence at the present time that there is significant microbial activity in seleniferous soil.

Soils of semi-arid areas are usually immature and such soils may have insoluble selenides. In areas where the sulfide is in a form analogous to a marcasite which weathers more rapidly, it may release selenium in a water-soluble form. Soils containing sulfides or pyrites would likely contain some selenides. Studies on the water solubility of selenium in 100 soil samples indicated that only a small fraction of the selenium was water soluble (*23*, *26*).

Selenium in some soils may be associated with iron oxide in an insoluble form (*26*). A small amount of soluble selenium compounds present in the soil was in the form of $CaSeO_4$. Shale soil from Cove County, Kansas, contained 22 ppm selenium, of which only about one per cent was water soluble; the soil sample contained 57 per cent of calcium carbonate, 4.4 per cent of iron oxide and only 0.2 per cent of organic matter. About 0.6 per cent of the sample was water-soluble matter, mostly calcium sulfate, with traces of chlorides and bicarbonates. Only 2 per cent of the total selenium was soluble in various solvents (*26*). Experimental studies with clay loam containing 11 per cent iron oxide indicated that iron oxide reduced solubility of selenate and selenite (*26*).

Soils also may contain some selenium in the form of insoluble ferric selenites. Byers *et al.* (26) attempted to synthesize a compound *in vitro* similar to insoluble selenium-containing iron compounds that are present in soils. The addition of ferric chloride to selenite formed a precipitate with the approximate composition of $Fe_2(SeO_3)_3$. This salt, however, was not sufficiently insoluble in water to account for the known persistence of selenium in ferruginous humid soils. They found that in dilute solutions selenites reacted with ferric chloride and an insoluble precipitate was formed that approximated the composition of basic ferric selenite [$Fe_2(OH)_4SeO_3$], suggesting that the insoluble selenium compounds in iron oxide may be basic ferric selenites.

Studies of loam soil derived from the Pierre Shale indicate that water-soluble selenium in the soil was selenate (*83*). The presence of selenate in the soil was reported as being responsible for highly poisonous vegetation indigenous to the areas (*15*).

A number of investigators reported that there were organic selenium compounds in the soil. Beath *et al.* (*4*) suggested that soluble organic selenium compounds present in the soils are due to decay of seleniferous plants. This report was disputed by Byers and Knight (*21*) since the amount of organic selenium they detected in their earlier studies was low. Subsequent studies by Byers *et al.* (*26*) confirmed the original observation of Beath and co-workers that seleniferous plant decay contributes considerable amounts of soluble organic and inorganic selenium compounds to the soil. Part of these soluble selenium compounds may be removed from the soil by leaching in areas of high or moderate rainfall, or part of the organic selenium compounds may be volatilized as indicated by noxious odors characteristic of growing seleniferous plants as well as of decaying plants with high selenium content. In most semi-arid seleniferous areas, much of the selenium remains in the soil in available form.

Subsequent studies confirmed that considerable amounts of water-soluble selenium present in the soils were in organic combination (*8, 80*). Olson and Moxon (*80*) presented data showing that water-soluble and organic selenium content of soils can be used as a relative measure of availability of selenium to grains and grasses.

Selenium in the soils may be present as selenates, elemental selenium, pyritic selenium, ferric selenites, and organic selenium compounds of unknown composition. The most available for plant absorption are organic selenium compounds and selenates. Slow hydrolysis of elemental selenium, selenides, and ferric selenites in soils can take place and thereby become available for absorption by crop plants (*114*).

SELENIUM CONTENT OF SOILS

The selenium content of soils bearing seleniferous vegetation shows wide variation. Seleniferous soils are usually alkaline in reaction and contain free $CaCO_3$. Annual rainfall in these areas is less than 20 inches. Non-seleniferous soils are characterized by a zone of accumulated iron and aluminum compounds and a pH range of 4.5 to 6.5 (*66*). There is no definite relation between total selenium in the soils and absorption of selenium by vegetation from these soils.

The selenium content of surface soil as well as subsoil was studied most extensively in those seleniferous areas of Wyoming and South Dakota which produce toxic vegetation dangerous to livestock.

That the distribution of selenium in surface soil (to 9 inches or less) as well as in subsoil in Wyoming and other seleniferous areas is not uniform was indicated by studies by Beath *et al.* (*4, 10*), Byers (*20, 22*), and Byers and Knight (*21*). In a "toxic" area, both surface soil and subsoil (any horizon below 9 inches) contained high concentrations of selenium, 22 and 33 ppm, respectively (*15*). In so-called highly seleniferous areas, surface soils contained from 1.5 to 20 ppm selenium, while the selenium content of subsoils varied from 0.7 to 16 ppm selenium.

In eastern Wyoming, total selenium on the upper horizon of soil derived from the Niobrara Formation was 22 ppm. Separation of selenium compounds from the upper horizon of the soil indicated that about 30 per cent of the total selenium was in organic form and 12 per cent was selenate (Beath, unpublished).

Byers (*20*), Byers and Knight (*21*), Miller and Byers (*72*), and Pugsley and Cox (*85*) carried out primary investigations on the selenium content of more than 600 soil samples in South Dakota. The maximum selenium content of the surface soil at various parts of South Dakota was 20, 13, 3, 38, 40, and 44 ppm and the minimum ranged from 0 to 2 ppm. Maximum selenium in 50 samples of subsoils was 2 and 12 ppm with a minimum of 0.2 and 2 ppm. Subsequent studies by Olson and Moxon (*80*), Olson *et al.* (*81, 82*), Lakin and Byers (*64*), Williams *et al.* (*118*), Searight and Moxon (*92*), and Searight *et al.* (*93*) indicated similar variations in the selenium content of surface soil and subsoil in various areas studied. In a few instances soils containing more than 10 ppm of selenium were found in areas where selenium poisoning in livestock was a serious problem. A few toxic soils contained more than 5 ppm selenium. Soils derived from the Mobridge Member of the Pierre Shale produced toxic vegetation in certain counties in South Dakota (*77*).

Most soils derived from the Niobrara Formation around the Black Hills are highly seleniferous. The Sharon Springs Member of the Pierre Shale in the above region is highly seleniferous, while the Mobridge Member of the Pierre is very low in selenium (*77*). Although other formations in South Dakota contain selenium, they do not weather into seleniferous soils.

In addition to the studies in Wyoming and South Dakota, distribution of selenium in surface and subsoil was studied in the following western states: Arizona (*12, 20, 26, 116*), New Mexico (*20, 26, 73, 115, 116*), Colorado (*20, 22, 26, 73, 115, 116*), Nebraska (*20, 22, 118*), Kansas (*20, 22, 26, 73, 115, 116, 118*), North Dakota (*65, 118*), Montana (*20, 22, 117, 118*), and Utah (*12, 26, 65, 116*). In these areas toxic vegetation and indicator plants are less widespread than in Wyoming or South Dakota. Surface and subsoil in these areas on the average contain less than 2 and 5 ppm of selenium, respectively. All of the surface soils and subsoils in Oklahoma, Texas, Missouri, Nevada, Idaho, and California analyzed had low selenium content.

Trelease (*102*) collected 500 samples of soil from seleniferous areas in the western United States. Fifty per cent of the soils contained from 1 to 6 ppm of selenium and the remainder had higher and lower selenium content. The average selenium content of 500 soil samples was 4.5 ppm with a maximum of 80 ppm selenium.

Localized variations in selenium content of soils may be produced by leaching or transportation of previously formed seleniferous deposits. Soils derived from the heterogeneous glacial deposits and other debris within the greater portion of Big Horn, Yellowstone, and Carbon Counties in Montana were analyzed for their selenium content (*117*). The average selenium content of 448 surface soil samples was 0.8 ppm. The variations in soil samples were from 0.1 to 5.0 ppm selenium. The selenium content of 14 samples of subsoils was 0.2–5 ppm with an average of 1.4 ppm.

The selenium content of alluvium and the absorption of selenium by indicator plants grown on this alluvium are shown in Table 10. There was no correlation in selenium content of soils collected in the same locality but in different sections of the same county.

TABLE 10

Absorption of Selenium by Astragalus bisulcatus *from Alluvium*[a]

Location	Selenium (ppm)[b]		Depth
	Plants	Soils	(ft)
Wyoming			
Albany County			
Sec. 5, T. 16 N., R. 74 W.	57	3.2	1
		6.4	2
Sec. 26, T. 22 N., R. 77 W.	560	0.5	1
		Trace	2
Sec. 15, T. 19 N., R. 75 W.	187		
Sec. 11, T. 17 N., R. 76 W.	1,364		
Sec. 15, T. 15 N., R. 74 W.	2,640	5.1	1
		5.0	2
Carbon County			
Sec. 2, T. 22 N., R. 79 W.	37	1.4	1
		1.6	2
Campbell County			
Rozet-Gillette Area	94	1.5	1
		1.7	2
Natrona County			
Casper Bishop Area	180		

[a] Alluvium derived by transport from all available rock sources.
[b] Air-dried basis.

Soils derived from glacial drift by wind erosion were analyzed from six counties in northern South Dakota and surrounding regions (*93*). Soils on Arlington loess and loess-like silts contained little selenium in upland and hilltop positions, but more in low, poorly drained areas. Selenium content in these soils ranged from 0.6 to 8.9 ppm. Soils on the Wisconsin outwash valley train contained from 0.5 to 1.9 ppm selenium and on the de Smet outwash, from 1.0 to 1.5 ppm selenium.

Soils derived mainly from glacial, lacustrine, and alluvial materials in North Dakota, Idaho, Nevada, and Oregon had comparatively low selenium content. The selenium content of surface soils (170 samples) in these four states on the average varied from 0.05 to 8 ppm. The selenium content of subsoils (30 samples) was on the average from 0.4 to 1.2 ppm (*65*). In North Dakota the selenium content of soils ranged from 0.1 to 8 ppm.

Hawaiian soils differ from most continental United States soils in that they are low in silica and high in iron, aluminum, and titanium (*51*) and selenium compounds are insoluble. These highly ferruginous soils in the Hawaiian Islands contain selenium, but it is unavailable for vegetation (*23, 26*). The selenium content of Hawaiian surface soils varied from 1 to 20 ppm and that of the subsoil from 0.4 to 26 ppm. Surface soils derived from lava or volcanic ash contained from 0.4 to 14 ppm selenium and the subsoils varied from 0.1 to 14 ppm selenium (*51*).

Soil samples collected from a number of locations in Puerto Rico contained only small amounts of selenium with the exception of one sample of subsoil from near Fajardo, which contained 10 ppm selenium (*26*). There was no selenium present in the plants analyzed. The soils analyzed were derived from Cretaceous shales and the presence of selenium in the clay soil of the Fajardo area suggests that under favorable conditions this soil may produce toxic vegetation.

Distribution of selenium in soil profiles—that is, different depths below the surface—was determined by a number of investigators (*4, 10, 20, 22, 26, 64, 77, 81, 83, 115–118*).

The selenium content of twenty soil profiles from eastern Colorado indicated no apparent uniformity in selenium distribution with origin of soils, location of soils, or depths of soil profiles (*26*). Some soils from the surface to 40 inches depth had high but variable concentrations of selenium, while soils from other sections in the same locality contained only small amounts of selenium at all horizons. These variations of the selenium content were apparently related to four or more different selenium compounds in the soil—the insoluble pyritic forms of selenium, soluble selenates, and organic selenium compounds or their decomposition products. No true colloidal selenium was found in the soils examined. The amount of selenium in 20 soil profiles from six counties in eastern Colorado varied from 0.1 to 98 ppm selenium.

Soil profiles representing a wide range of soil types were studied for distribution of trace elements including selenium (*96*). Samples of soil were collected from Wisconsin, Kansas, Iowa, Washington, Missouri, Texas, Ohio, Oklahoma, and North Carolina. The selenium content of the soils ranged from 0.01 to 2.5 ppm. Pierre clay loam contained 8 and 10 ppm selenium and Niobrara sandy clay loam, 18 and 22 ppm. The Niobrara soils were higher in free iron oxide than the Pierre series. Some eluviation was indicated by distribution of selenium in soils which contained much iron oxide.

Soils derived from Niobrara and Mancos shales and alluvium on Niobrara and Morrison formations showed variations in total selenium content of surface soils and soil profiles at different depths as indicated in Table 11. There was no consistent relationship as to the origin of the soil and the water solubility of selenium at different depths.

The total selenium and water-soluble selenium contents of surface soil to a depth of 3 feet were studied by Olson *et al.* (*83*) in six seleniferous

TABLE 11
Selenium in Soil Profiles

Location	Soil derived from	Soil depth (inches)	Total Se (ppm)	Water-soluble Se	
				ppm	%
Wyoming					
Shirley Basin	Niobrara Shale	0–12	9.5	0.4	4.2
		12–24	26.0	1.0	3.8
		24–36	37.0	1.8	4.9
Laramie	Niobrara Shale	0–12	3.7	0.5	13.5
		12–24	4.0	0.3	7.5
		24–36	3.8	0.5	13.2
Laramie	Alluvium	0–6	6.0	0.8	13.3
	(on Niobrara Shale)	6–18	14.0	2.2	15.7
		18–30	28.0	11.0	39.3
		30–40	21.0	6.4	40.0
Utah					
Cisco	Mancos Shale	0–12	5.6	0.7	12.5
		12–24	4.4	0.5	11.4
		24–36	4.0	0.2	5.0
Thompson	Alluvium	0–12	35.0	9.1	26.0
	(on Morrison Fm.)	12–24	82.0	41.4	50.5
		24–36	40.0	25.0	62.5
		36–48	90.0	14.8	16.4

areas and correlated with selenium content of grains and grasses. The water-soluble selenium in the soil varied in different locations from 0.05 to 19 ppm, and total selenium varied from 2.7 to 38 ppm. There was no correlation between the total or water-soluble selenium content of soil and the selenium content of western wheat grass. This lack may have been due to the inadequacy of present field methods of soil sampling (*82*). In greenhouse tests with homogeneous soils, absorption of selenium by plants is correlated with the amount of water-soluble selenium in the soil (*80*).

Well-developed soil profiles usually contain less than 5 ppm selenium even in highly seleniferous areas (*77*). Variations in selenium content of soils at different locations and depths may be due to variations in the selenium content of beds or strata from which the soil was derived or to mixing of soil material by movement of alluvium and loess. At the present time the methods of sampling such soils as well as the methods of soil selenium determination are inadequate.

The presence of soluble selenium in the soil profiles at certain horizons may be more important in producing seleniferous grains and grasses than variations of total selenium in the soil.

SELENIUM IN SOILS OF OTHER COUNTRIES

The presence of selenium in soils and rocks in these areas is discussed only in those instances where the studies were correlated with chronic or acute selenosis. Such correlations were reported from Canada, Mexico, Colombia, Ireland, Israel, South Africa, and Australia.

Canada

Cretaceous rocks crop out in large areas of Alberta, Saskatchewan, and Manitoba. A survey in 1941 (*118*) to locate seleniferous areas of Cretaceous age in these provinces was based on the distribution of *Astragalus bisulcatus* and *Astragalus pectinatus*. About 300 samples of shales, soils, and vegetation were collected for selenium analysis. Soils (80 samples, mostly surface) contained from 0.1 to 6 ppm, and 30 per cent had 1 or >1 ppm selenium. Specimens of *A. bisulcatus* and *A. pectinatus* contained from low to high concentrations of selenium. The selenium content of these indicator plants ranged from 15 to 4190 ppm.

The selenium content of surface soils (9 inches or less) derived from glacial drift in Alberta ranged from 0.3 to 0.7 ppm and that of subsoil (any horizon below 9 inches) from 0.3 to 0.5 ppm (*107*). These soils derived from Cretaceous shales cover large areas in Saskatchewan and Alberta and a small area in Manitoba. Acute poisoning and chronic selenosis in livestock were observed or reported by various livestock operators in these areas (*36, 118*).

Mexico

Toxic vegetation in the valley of the Guanajuato River near the town of Irapuato was traced to artificial introduction of selenium in contrast to natural seleniferous soils. Selenosis in humans and animals first appeared when mines in a neighboring area started to process ores. Samples of ore had a mean selenium content of 16 ppm. The discarded slimes from the mines accumulated in dumps and contained on the average 4.6 ppm selenium (*117*). These dumps were eroded by floods that distributed selenium over the river flood plain. River water which was used for irrigation contained 0.2 ppm and the deposited silt 8 ppm selenium.

Surface soil contained from 0.3 to 20 ppm and subsoil from 0.1 to 6 ppm selenium. Soils not contaminated by waste products from mines contained from 0.3 to 0.4 ppm selenium. Manure used as fertilizer on one ranch contained 20 ppm selenium (*24, 117*).

Cultivated crops and native plants on several ranches on the river flood plain contained high quantities of selenium: mustard, 120 ppm; groundcherry, 35 ppm; alfalfa, 3–30 ppm; milkweed, 3–20 ppm; lambsquarter, 2–15 ppm; sweet clover, 15 ppm; and alfalfa hay, 18 ppm (*117*). Samples of vegetables purchased at random in the Irapuato market had the following selenium content: cabbage, 70 ppm; radish tops and roots, 30 and 15 ppm, respectively; spinach, 7 ppm; parsley, 5 ppm; beans and pomerillo, 2 ppm; green peas and popcorn, none. The peas and corn may have been grown in a nonseleniferous area. The high selenium content of the vegetation indicates that most of the selenium in the soil was present in a water-soluble or available form.

No other such highly seleniferous area in Mexico was observed in surveys of several regions including Juarez, Chihuahua, Torreon, Saltillo, and Mexico City (*71, 117*). Kamffer and Ancona (*56*) found *A. bisulcatus* and *A. haydenianus* in the states of Coahuila, Chihuahua, and Sonora. The occurrences of the above plants indicate that there are seleniferous formations in the three counties.

Kellum *et al.* (*57*) correlated some Cretaceous strata in the state of Coahuila in Mexico with the Eagleford of Texas and the Niobrara of the Great Plains. Analytical data, reported by Williams *et al.* (*117*), on soils and vegetation included locations which they considered to be of Cretaceous age. Although many of the soils analyzed by Williams *et al.* (*117*) in Mexico contained low concentrations of selenium (0.1–0.5 ppm), no selenium indicator plants were identified in the areas they studied.

Colombia, South America

The "peladero soils" or toxic soils were described by Wills (*119*) as being fertile, black, dusty, and rich in graphite. The corn and fruits raised on a "strong peladero" produced loss of hair and nails of people consuming these foods. Seleniferous areas in Colombia are on formations ranging in age from Jurassic to Quaternary or Recent (*16*).

Ancizar-Sordo (*1*) analyzed soil samples from the Leiva district, Boyaca State, where a disease similar to chronic selenosis was reported in men and animals. Surface soils collected from this area contained from 1 to 14 ppm and subsoil from 2.5 to 7 ppm selenium.

Selenium determinations of a large number of soils from the area located between the Negro and Negrito (Salgar) rivers showed that region to be seleniferous (*16*). Soils in this area are alluvial, derived from black slate of the Villeta Formation. On the average from 2 to 7 ppm selenium was found in soil samples. The maximum selenium content of surface soil ranged from 12.6 to 20 ppm. The seleniferous areas in Colombia are in humid areas where rainfall is high. This contrasts with selenium occurrences in arid and semi-arid regions of the western United States. It is also significant that no known selenium indicator plants have been reported in Colombia and there are no specimens of known indicator plants in the Herbarium Science Institute.

Analyses of grains and forages collected from seleniferous areas showed high concentrations of selenium. The selenium content of grass was 280 ppm, of wheat 155 ppm, of barley 25 and 137 ppm, of corn 40 ppm, and of common vetch 110 and 136 ppm selenium.

Ireland

A disease condition in livestock similar to alkali disease has been observed for a number of years in certain parts of Limerick, Tipperary, and Meath counties. In 1951, Walsh *et al.* (*108*) reported from County Limerick toxic amounts of selenium in soils and vegetation. New toxic areas were reported by Walsh and Fleming (*45, 109*).

The occurrence of selenium in toxic amounts under humid conditions is again in contrast to the seleniferous areas of the western United States. It is also of interest that water available to livestock contained appreciable amounts of selenium. A botanical survey of the area did not reveal any known selenium indicator plants.

The formations in all the toxic areas of Ireland are upper and middle Carboniferous limestones associated with shale and sandstone of the Yoredale and Pendleside Series. The seleniferous formation in County Limerick is low-lying valley soil in a glaciated area with underlying upper Carboniferous limestone. Composition of the soil is influenced by wash from the Yoredale beds (Avonian shales) which lie west of the seleniferous area. These beds contain considerable deposits of iron pyrite which may be the source of the selenium (*45, 109*).

Shales collected from Leitrim, Clare, Dublin, and Mayo counties contained on the average 6.3, 6.1, 1.3, and 1.5 ppm selenium, respectively. The selenium content of rock from other areas was the following: Limerick County, pyritiferous shale, 8.9 and 28.5 ppm, and shale limestone, 0.97 and 1.55 ppm; Tipperary County, shale bed, 0.1 and 0.25 ppm; Meath County, weathered shale, 13.0 ppm, and weathered limestone, 2.0 and 13.0 ppm (*45*).

Soils with the highest selenium content were found in low-lying poorly drained meadows rich in organic residues. The positive correlation of the amount of selenium in organic-rich lake bed sediments suggests that decomposition of seleniferous vegetation increased the selenium content of the areas.

Soils and plants from the seleniferous areas contained the following amounts of selenium: Limerick County soils, 1.7, 2.0, 2.9, 5.5, and 324.0 ppm, and on these soils the herbage contained 0.8–450 ppm selenium; Tipperary County soils, 1.2–132 ppm selenium, and herbage grown on this soil, 0.9–115.0 ppm selenium; Meath County soils, 1.8–3.3 ppm, and herbage, 10.6–14.5 ppm selenium.

Studies of soil profiles indicated that selenium content varied at different depths and from different counties: Meath differed from 359 to 1200 ppm at a pH of 6.5 and 8.1; Tipperary varied from 0.6 to 175 ppm when the pH was 7.1 to 7.9; and Limerick varied from 13.5 to 105.0 ppm when the pH of the soil differed from 6.5 to 8.1 (*45*).

There was no apparent correlation between depth of soils and selenium content. The soils which contained the highest percentage of organic matter contained the most selenium. The soils from Limerick and Tipperary counties had high molybdenum content, 53 and 50 ppm, respectively. The soil from County Meath which contained 1200 ppm selenium contained only 4 ppm molybdenum.

Water-soluble selenium in these highly seleniferous soils was very low and varied from 0.33 to 2.82 per cent of the total selenium. Nevertheless, the actual available selenium in these soils was sufficient to produce toxic vegetation in the areas investigated (*45*).

Israel

In 1957, Ravikovitch and Margolin (*88*) reported a disease diagnosed as alkali disease in cattle herds in the Huleh Valley.

In these areas the soil, mostly alluvial, originated from limestone of the Cenomanian and Turonian formations of Cretaceous age. The soils vary from clay to sandy. The climatic conditions in this region are subhumid; annual precipitation averages about 20 inches. The valley soils are moderately alkaline with a pH of 7.8 to 8.2. Soils of calcareous origin had a maximum of 6 ppm selenium. The largest amount of selenium in soil profiles was usually found in the upper layers. The amount of water-soluble selenium varied from traces to 0.6 ppm and was from 7.5 to 30 per cent of the total selenium.

In seleniferous areas of Naot-Mordechai, alfalfa absorbed on the average 11.1 ppm selenium from soils containing only 0.1–0.3 ppm total selenium; alfalfa grown on soils containing 3.8 and 2.1 ppm selenium accumulated up to 44 ppm selenium. There was a correlation between age of alfalfa and selenium content of plants. The young growth of alfalfa was uniformly more seleniferous than the older growth. Among other forage plants growing on seleniferous soils were clover, vetch, oats, peas, rye grass, and beans (maximum amounts of selenium ranged from 0.4 to 27 ppm). In wheat and oats (grains) the maximum selenium content was 22 ppm.

A survey of native plants was carried out in a seleniferous area in the Naot-Mordechai region. Of the plants analyzed, the *Prosopis faracata* (Leguminosae) contained a minimum of 135 ppm, an average of 215 ppm, and a maximum of 311 ppm selenium. In the opinion of the investigators, this plant could be considered a selenium-accumulating plant. Because its roots penetrate to considerable depths, the usefulness of this species as a selenium indicator is limited. In Israel the shallow-rooted annuals are best in evaluating soils for agriculture crops.

The plant, *Cynodon dactylon* (Gramineae), was capable of accumulating selenium from 0.2 to 8.9 ppm. The soils contained from traces to 6.0 ppm selenium. There were positive correlations between amounts of selenium in the soil and growth of *C. dactylon.* This plant is widespread in Israel and may serve as a reliable index for evaluation of soils with respect to their selenium content.

South Africa

The Karoo "System" is the most widespread sequence of sedimentary rocks in South Africa. These rocks as a whole cannot be older than late Carboniferous and they are probably much older than Cretaceous formations in the Americas (*19*). The Karoo is generally considered to be of Triassic age. The authors conclude, therefore, that the selenium content of soils derived from the Karoo "System" would be less than that in the more seleniferous soils in the Americas.

In the areas located on the Karoo, a disease syndrome resembling chronic selenosis in livestock was described. Analyses of animal tissues and native plants indicated that they contained selenium. The selenium content of the plants varied from 0 to 2.8 ppm on a dry basis. Liver and kidney of animals having the disease contained amounts of selenium similar to those reported in livestock having chronic selenosis in the United States.

Australia

In Queensland in the Cape York Peninsula, the shrub *Morinda reticulata* (Rubiacae) is designated as a selenium indicator. The selenium content on a moisture-free basis of old leaves was 1.5–720 ppm and of succulent young leaves 151–1141 ppm. Typical symptoms of alkali disease were reported in horses that consumed the green plants (*61*). The soils from the seleniferous area were described as brown sandy loam, reddish sandy loam, and reddish-brown clay loam. The air-dried soils contained from 0.02 to 0.4 ppm selenium. The higher selenium content was associated with plant debris in the soil.

In northwestern Queensland, selenium is associated with certain limestones. Vegetation grown on soils receiving the runoff from these limestones produced acute toxicity in livestock. One plant belonging to the Leguminosae (*Neptunia amplexicaulis*) is considered as a selenium accumulator and possibly as an indicator plant. The selenium content ranged from 10 to 4000 ppm on dry basis.

SELENIUM IN WATER

No evidence has been obtained up to the present time that selenium occurs in water in sufficient amounts to produce selenosis in man or animal except in isolated cases. Occasionally water from seleniferous areas may contain high concentrations of selenium, but this water is generally unpalatable to livestock.

Analyses of water from a number of lakes, springs, and streams suspected to be the cause of livestock poisoning failed to indicate the presence of either arsenic or selenium. In undrained basins with long sloping banks bearing seleniferous plants, water contained less than 0.1 ppm selenium (*4*). The selenium in the water was due to leaching of some selenium from seleniferous plants. In a few cases drainage water from irrigated areas has been found to contain appreciable quantities of selenium (*20, 22*).

Seepage deposits of salts on banks of drainage ditches in Colorado sometimes had as much as 260 ppm selenium (*22*). Selenium content of drainage water from the Belle Fourche area, South Dakota, was 1.2 ppm (*20*). Water from a shallow well near Fallon, Nevada, had 0.6 ppm selenium (*22*).

Spring water contained 1.6 ppm selenium (*14*) and this water was used for drinking and household purposes. Water from an intermittent spring on the Niobrara Formation (Custer, South Dakota) contained 0.4 ppm selenium, while another spring contained 0.07 ppm selenium (*72*).

The water-soluble and suspended selenium of the Colorado River and its tributaries was studied by Williams and Byers (*112*). Water samples from upper parts of the Colorado River had a maximum selenium content of 0.001 ppm, but irrigation drainage from seleniferous lands increased this amount from 10 to 70 times. Drainage waters from irrigated lands contained as much as 2.7 ppm selenium. Drainage waters from irrigated seleniferous lands increased the selenium content of the Colorado River to 0.003 ppm, despite dilution from several tributaries. Analyses of water from all important tributaries of the Colorado River showed that selenium was absent from these streams at points above the influx of irrigation drainage from soils derived from Mancos shales, but was present in the Colorado, Gunnison, and San Juan rivers at points below such drainage (*26*). The selenium content of daily composite samples from the Gunnison River (Grand Junction, Colorado) contained from 0.005 to 0.055 ppm selenium. Samples of water from the San Juan River (Shiprock, New Mexico) below irrigated areas contained 0.4 ppm selenium. The selenium content of water samples from other parts of the Colorado River and its tributaries differed with the location of the river. The Colorado River water at Yuma, Arizona, contained 0.004 ppm selenium. The Colorado River and its tributaries carry considerable amounts of selenium into the Gulf of California and the chief sources of this selenium are the irrigated seleniferous soils (*64*).

SELENIUM ON THE SEA FLOOR AND IN SEA WATER

The amount of selenium which is carried to sea water is so great that serious poisoning of the ocean would have occurred if there were no mechanism in the sea to remove selenium from sea water. Selenium is removed from aqueous solution by adsorption on precipitated hydroxides of iron and manganese, organic matter, and iron sulfides (*49*).

Selenium does not follow sulfur into sea water but is absorbed by ferric hydroxide and rich marine sediments, thus accounting for seleniferous sedimentary iron ores (*97*). This process of enrichment by selenium of sedimentary iron ores may explain larger amounts of selenium in these ores than average crustal abundance of the element.

Water from the North Sea contained 3.8 μg selenium per liter (*48*). Water samples from various oceans analyzed by Byers *et al.* (*26*) contained no selenium except one sample from the mouth of the river Elba (1.0 μg per liter) and the sample from Puget Sound (0.25 μg per liter).

Nine deep sea samples from the Bering Sea and the Arctic Ocean off the coasts of Alaska and Siberia contained 0.03–0.7 ppm selenium in bottom sediments (*113*). Surface core samples from the Atlantic Ocean contained about 0.2–0.6 ppm selenium; the content usually increased with depth of the core to 2 ppm selenium at 200 cm. With the increase of selenium content there was a corresponding increase in sulfur (*117*). Sediments from the Gulf of California contained 0.1–5 ppm and the Gulf of Mexico sea-floor core (6 to 9 inches) contained 0.6–1.0 ppm selenium (*64*). Core samples of sea-floor sediments containing volcanic ash from the Bering Sea contained 0.25–0.7 ppm; from Ocean City, Maryland 0.6–2.0 ppm; from the North Atlantic <0.1–0.8 ppm; and from the Caribbean Sea at Bartlett Deep <0.08–0.2 ppm selenium. There was no relation between volcanic activity and selenium accumulation in the cores (*41*).

Marine waters at Shirahama, Japan, contained 4–6 μg selenium per liter (*52*). Selenium content of Japanese coastal water ranged from 4 to 6 μg per liter (*53*).

Nearly all sea-floor samples analyzed contained selenium. This would suggest that suspended and dissolved selenium in river water is precipitated when it reaches the sea. The selenium content of these recent sediments is similar to the selenium content of older sedimentary formations.

GEOBOTANY

The interrelation of geological origin of rocks and growth of selenium indicator plants was recognized by Beath *et al.* (*2*). They correlated the distribution of selenium accumulator plants with certain formations and indicated that rocks of different formations vary in their ability to supply

FIG. 5. A Niobrara outcrop (the Chalke Butte, near Rock River, Wyoming) showing dense seleniferous vegetation at the base of the outcrop.

selenium to plants. In the early field work, rocks of Cretaceous age—the Steele and Pierre shales and the Niobrara Formation—were studied in relation to the distribution of selenium in vegetation. The distribution of seleniferous vegetation at the base of the Niobrara outcrop is indicated in Fig. 5. Subsequent surveys indicated that rocks and soils derived from other formations likewise support the growth of seleniferous vegetation (*10–13*).

TABLE 12
Selenium Content of Indicator Plants[a]

Periods[b]	Formations[b]	Selenium (ppm)[c]		
		Minimum	Maximum	Average
Tert. and Quat.	Verde	197	2,002	1,270
Tertiary	Ogallala	118	2,362	1,258
	Arikaree	58	530	185
	Chadron	134		72
	Bridger	192	3,320	1,392
	Wasatch	77	2,310	725
	Fort Union	93	3,683	711
Cretaceous	Lance	151	1,890	693
	Mesaverde	154	543	320
	Pierre-Benton	53	4,474	716
	Judith River	53	1,195	316
	Pierre	157	2,849	744
	Steele	62	4,450	953
	Mancos	68	1,999	504
	Colorado	51	1,815	366
	Niobrara	199	3,939	689
	Benton	74	640	279
	Carlile	86	519	299
	Greenhorn	100	640	275
Jurassic	Morrison	63	3,360	557
	Sundance	84	1,612	667
	Kayenta	126	864	402
Triassic	Chinle	79	914	425
	Moenkopi	142	3,060	713
Permian	Phosphoria	199	904	440
	Rico-Cutler	139	313	226
	Cutler	96	233	165
Carboniferous	Hermosa	142	171	157
	Paradox			364
	"Amsden"			177

[a] *Astragalus, Stanleya* and a limited number of sections *Oonopsis* of *Haplopappus* and *Xylorhiza* of *Machaeranthera.*

[b] Data were compiled from references *4, 10–12, 14, 77, 102, 118.*

[c] Parts per million dry weight.

The primary aim of these studies was to map seleniferous areas, thereby determining the location of toxic vegetations which produce selenosis in livestock. The geological mapping of selenium distribution by indicator plants or selenium accumulator plants was originated for its importance to agriculture, but contributed a practical method for geologists for botanical prospecting as well. Selenium indicator plants are used to locate uranium deposits (*28–31, 33, 46, 58*).

As has already been discussed, in addition to some formations of Cretaceous age, certain formations of Permian, Triassic, Jurassic, Tertiary, Quaternary, and to a limited extent Carboniferous age can support the growth of these indicator plants (*2–6, 11–14, 22, 27, 50, 76, 77, 92*).

The selenium content of the plants and their distribution on formations are shown in Table 12. The data indicate that the most seleniferous formations occur in the Cretaceous Period. The table summarizes the minimum, maximum, and average selenium contents of a number of species in four genera of indicator plants known to require selenium for their growth. These are seleniferous species of *Astragalus*, *Stanleya* and sections *Oonopsis* of *Haplopappus* and *Xylorhiza* of *Machaeranthera*. The taxonomy and selenium accumulation in these plants are discussed in detail in Chapters III and IV.

References

1. Ancizar-Sordo, J. 1947. Occurrence of selenium in soils and plants of Colombia, South America. *Soil Sci.* **63**:437–438.
2. Beath, O. A., J. H. Draize, H. F. Eppson, C. S. Gilbert and O. C. McCreary. 1934. Certain poisonous plants of Wyoming activated by selenium and their association with respect to soil types. *J. Am. Pharm. Assoc. Sci. Ed.* **23**:94–97.
3. Beath, O. A., J. H. Draize and C. S. Gilbert. 1934. Plants poisonous to livestock. *Wyoming Agr. Expt. Sta. Bull. No.* **200**:1–84.
4. Beath, O. A., H. F. Eppson and C. S. Gilbert. 1935. Selenium and other toxic minerals in soils and vegetation. *Wyoming Agr. Expt. Sta. Bull. No.* **206**:1–55.
5. Beath, O. A. 1936. Selenium in native range plants occurring on soils derived from Permian and Triassic (?) sediments. *Science* **83**:104.
6. Beath, O. A. and C. S. Gilbert. 1936. Selenium-bearing vegetation during late Cretaceous time. *Science* **84**:484–485.
7. Beath, O. A. 1937. The occurrence of selenium and seleniferous vegetation in Wyoming. II. Seleniferous vegetation. *Wyoming Agr. Expt. Sta. Bull. No.* **221**:29–64.
8. Beath, O. A., H. F. Eppson and C. S. Gilbert. 1937. Selenium distribution in and seasonal variation of type vegetation occurring on seleniferous soils. *J. Am. Pharm. Assoc. Sci. Ed.* **26**:394–405.
9. Beath, O. A., C. S. Gilbert and H. F. Eppson. 1937. Selenium in soils and vegetation associated with rocks of Permian and Triassic age. *Am. J. Botany* **24**:96–101.
10. Beath, O. A., C. S. Gilbert and H. F. Eppson. 1939. The use of indicator plants in locating seleniferous areas in western United States. I. General. *Am. J. Botany* **26**:257–296.

11. Beath, O. A., C. S. Gilbert and H. F. Eppson. 1939. The use of indicator plants in locating seleniferous areas in western United States. II. Correlation studies by states. *Am. J. Botany* **26**:296–315.
12. Beath, O. A., C. S. Gilbert and H. F. Eppson. 1940. The use of indicator plants in locating seleniferous areas in western United States. III. Further studies. *Am. J. Botany* **27**:564–573.
13. Beath, O. A., C. S. Gilbert and H. F. Eppson. 1941. The use of indicator plants in locating seleniferous areas in western United States. IV. Progress report. *Am. J. Botany* **28**:887–900.
14. Beath, O. A. 1943. Toxic vegetation growing on the Salt Wash Sandstone Member of the Morrison Formation. *Am. J. Botany* **30**:698–707.
15. Beath, O. A., A. F. Hagner and C. S. Gilbert. 1946. Some rocks and soils of high selenium content. *Geol. Survey Wyoming, Bull. No.* **36**:1–23.
16. Benavides, S. T. and R. F. S. Mojica. 1959. Seleniosis: Ocurrencia de selenio en rocas, suelos y plantes. Intoxicacion por selenio en animales y en humanos. *Inst. Geograf. Colombia Publ. No.* **IT–3**:1–145.
17. Bergenfelt, S. 1953. Om forekomst av selen i Skelleftefaltets sulfidmalmer. *Geol. Fören. i Stockholm Förh.* **75**:327–359. (English summary.)
18. Bethke, P. M. 1956. Sulfo-selenides of mercury (Abs.) *Geol. Soc. Am. Bull. No.* **67**:1671.
19. Brown, J. M. M. and P. J. de Wet. 1962. A preliminary report on the occurrence of selenosis in South Africa and its possible role in the aetiology of Tribulosis (Geeldikkop), enzootic icterus and some other disease conditions encountered in the Karoo areas. *Onderstepoort J. Vet. Res.* **29**:111–135.
20. Byers, H. G. 1935. Selenium occurrence in certain soils in the United States with a discussion of related topics. *U. S. Dept. Agr. Tech. Bull. No.* **482**:1–47.
21. Byers, H. G. and H. G. Knight. 1935. Selenium in soils in relation to its presence in vegetation. *Ind. Eng. Chem.* **27**:902–904.
22. Byers, H. G. 1936. Selenium occurrence in certain soils in the United States with a discussion of related topics. 2nd report. *U. S. Dept. Agr. Tech. Bull. No.* **530**:1–78.
23. Byers, H. G., K. T. Williams and H. W. Lakin. 1936. Selenium in Hawaii and its probable source in the United States. *Ind. Eng. Chem.* **28**:821–823.
24. Byers, H. G. 1937. Selenium in Mexico. *Ind. Eng. Chem.* **29**:1200–1202.
25. Byers, H. G. 1938. Selenium in meteorites. *Ind. Chem. Eng., News Ed.* **16**:459.
26. Byers, H. G., J. T. Miller, K. T. Williams and H. W. Lakin. 1938. Selenium occurrence in certain soils in the United States with a discussion of related topics. 3rd report. *U. S. Dept. Agr. Tech. Bull. No.* **601**:1–74.
27. Byers, H. G. and H. W. Lakin. 1939. Selenium in Canada. *Can. J. Res.* **17**: 364–369.
28. Cannon, H. L. 1952. The effect of uranium-vanadium deposits on the vegetation of the Colorado Plateau. *Am. J. Sci.* **250**:735–770.
29. Cannon, H. L. 1953. Geobotanical reconnaissance near Grants, New Mexico. *U. S. Geol. Survey Circ.* **264**:1–8.
30. Cannon, H. L. 1954. Botanical methods of prospecting for uranium. *Trans. Am. Inst. Mining Met. Engrs.* **199**:217–220.
31. Cannon, H. L. and F. J. Kleinhampl. 1956. Botanical methods of prospecting for uranium. *U. S. Geol. Survey, Profess. Paper No.* **300**:681–686.
32. Cannon, H. L. and W. H. Starrett. 1956. Botanical prospecting for uranium on La Ventana Mesa, Sandoval County, New Mexico. *U. S. Geol. Survey Bull. No.* **1009–M**:391–407.

33. Cannon, H. L. 1957. Description of indicator plants and methods of botanical prospecting for uranium deposits on the Colorado Plateau. *U. S. Geol. Survey Bull. No.* **1030–M**:399–516.
34. Coleman, R. G. 1956. The occurrence of selenium in sulfides from sedimentary rocks of the western United States (Abstr.) *Econ. Geol.* **51**:112.
35. Coleman, R. G. and M. Delevaux. 1957. Occurrence of selenium in sulfides from some sedimentary rocks of the western United States. *Econ. Geol.* **52**:499–527.
36. Davidson, W. B. 1940. Selenium poisoning. *Can. J. Comp. Med. Vet. Sci.* **4**:19–25.
37. Davidson, D. F. and R. A. Gulbrandsen. 1957. Selenium in the Phosphoria formation in Idaho, Wyoming, Utah and Montana. (Abstr.) *Geol. Soc. Am. Bull. No.* **68**:1714.
38. Davidson, D. F. and H. A. Powers. 1959. Selenium content of some volcanic rocks from the western United States and Hawaiian Islands. *U. S. Geol. Survey Bull. No.* **1084–C**:69–81.
39. Davidson, D. F. 1960. Selenium in some epithermal deposits of antimony, mercury and silver and gold. *U. S. Geol. Survey Bull. No.* **1112–A**:1–15.
40. Davidson, D. F. and H. W. Lakin. 1961. Metal content of some black shales of the western United States. *U. S. Geol. Survey Res., Profess. Paper. No.* **424–C**:329–331.
41. Edgington, G. and H. G. Byers. 1942. Geology and biology of North Atlantic deep-sea cores between Newfoundland and Ireland. Part 9. Selenium content and chemical analysis. *U. S. Geol. Survey Profess. Paper No.* **196–F**:151–155.
42. Edwards, A. B. and G. C. Carlos. 1954. The selenium content of some Australian sulphide deposits. *Proc. Australasian Inst. Mining and Met. No.* **172**:31–64.
43. Everett, F. D. and L. C. Bauerle. 1957. Investigation of tuffs near Lysite, Wyoming, for selenium. *U. S. Bur. Mines Rept. Invest.* **5296**:1–30.
44. Fleischer, M. 1955. Minor elements in some sulfide minerals. *Econ. Geol., Anniv. Vol.* **50** (Pt. 2):970–1024.
45. Fleming, G. A. and T. Walsh. 1957. Selenium occurrence in certain Irish soils and its toxic effects on animals. *Proc. Roy. Irish Acad.* **58**:151–167.
46. Froehlich, A. J. and F. J. Kleinhampl. 1960. Botanical prospecting for uranium in the Deer Flat area, White Canyon district, San Juan County, Utah. *U. S. Geol. Survey Bull. No.* **1085–B**:51–84.
47. Gavelin, S. 1955. Sulphide mineralization in the Skellefte district, northern Sweden and its relation to regional granitization. *Econ. Geol.* **50**:814–831.
48. Goldschmidt, V. M. and L. W. Strock. 1935. The geochemistry of selenium. *Nachr. Ges. Wiss. Göttingen, Jahresber. Geschäftsjahr Math.-physik. Kl., Fachgruppen II.* **1**:123–142.
49. Goldschmidt, V. M. 1954. "Geochemistry," pp. 532–540. Oxford Univ. Press, London.
50. Hershey, A. L. 1945. Some poisonous plant problems of New Mexico. *New Mexico Agr. Expt. Sta. Bull. No.* **322**:1–23.
51. Hough, G. J., P. L. Gile and Z. C. Foster. 1941. Rock weathering and soil profile development in the Hawaiian Islands. *U. S. Dept. Agr. Tech. Bull. No.* **752**:1–43.
52. Ishibashi, M. 1953. Minute elements in sea-water. *Oceanog. Works Japan Rec.* [N. S.] **1**:88–92.
53. Ishibashi, M., T. Shigemetsu, and Y. Nakagawa. 1953. Determination of selenium in sea water. *Oceanog. Works Japan Rec.* [N. S.] **1**:44–48.

54. Joffe, J. S. 1949. "Pedology," pp. 124–157. Pedology Publications, New Brunswick, New Jersey.
55. Kaiser, E. P. 1954. Selenium in sulfide ores. *Geol. Soc. Am. Bull.* **65**:1379.
56. Kamffer, R. M. and L. Ancona. 1942. A contribution to the knowledge of plants poisonous to livestock in Mexico, *Astragalus*. *Pecuario Inst. Rev.* **1**:1–46.
57. Kellum, L. B., R. W. Imlay and W. G. Kane. 1936. Evolution of the Coahuila peninsula, Mexico. *Geol. Soc. Am. Bull.* **47**:969–1008.
58. Kleinhampl, F. J. and C. Koteff. 1960. Botanical prospecting for uranium in the Circle Cliffs area, Garfield County, Utah. *U. S. Geol. Survey Bull. No.* **1085–C**: 85–104.
59. Knight, S. H. 1937. Occurrence of selenium and seleniferous vegetation in Wyoming. I. The rocks of Wyoming and their relations to the selenium problem. *Wyoming Agr. Expt. Sta. Bull. No.* **221**:2–27.
60. Knight, S. H. and O. A. Beath. 1937. Occurrence of selenium in seleniferous vegetation in Wyoming. I. and II. *Wyoming Agr. Sta. Bull. No.* **221**:2–64.
61. Knott, S. G., C. W. R. McCray and W. T. K. Hall. 1958. Selenium poisoning in horses in North Queensland. *Queensland Dept. Agr. and Stock, Div. Animal Ind., Bull.* **41**:1–16.
62. Krauskopf, K. G. 1955. Sedimentary deposits of rare metals. *Econ. Geol., Anniv. Vol.* **50** (Pt. 1):411–463.
63. Kulp, J. L. 1961. Geologic time scale. *Science* **133**:1105–1114.
64. Lakin, H. W. and H. G. Byers. 1941. Selenium occurrence in certain soils in the United States with a discussion of related topics: 6th report. *U. S. Dept. Agr. Tech. Bull. No.* **783**:1–27.
65. Lakin, H. W. and H. G. Byers. 1948. Selenium occurrence in certain soils in the United States with a discussion of related topics: 7th report. *U. S. Dept. Agr. Tech. Bull. No.* **950**:1–36.
66. Lakin, H. W. 1961. Selenium in agriculture. Selenium content of soils. *U. S. Dept. Agr. Handbook* **200**:27–34.
67. Leutwein, V. F. and R. Storke. 1957. Über die Moglichkeit der Geochemischen Prospektion auf selen, Untersucht am Beispiel des Kupferschiefers und des Tilkersder Erzbezirks. *Geologie* **6**:349–378.
68. Lipman, J. G. and S. A. Waksman. 1923. The oxidation of selenium by a new group of autotrophic microorganisms. *Science* **57**:60.
69. Love, J. D. 1954. Preliminary report on uranium in the Gas Hills area, Fremont and Natrona Counties, Wyoming. *U. S. Geol. Survey Circ.* **352**:1–11.
70. Luttrell, G. W. 1959. Annotated bibliography on the geology of selenium. *U. S. Geol. Survey Bull. No.* **1019–M**:867–972.
71. Miller, J. T. and I. C. Brown. 1938. Observations regarding soils of northern and central Mexico. *Soil Sci.* **46**:427–452.
72. Miller, J. T. and H. G. Byers. 1935. A selenium spring. *Ind. Eng. Chem., News Ed.* **13**:456.
73. Miller, J. T. and H. G. Byers. 1937. Selenium in plants in relation to its occurrence in soils. *J. Agr. Res.* **55**:59–68.
74. Minami, E. 1935. The rare earth content of European and Japanese clay shales. *Nachr. Ges. Wiss. Göttingen, Jahresber. Geschaftsjahr Math.-physik. Kl., Fachgruppen IV* **1**:155–170.
75. Moxon, A. L. 1937. Alkali disease or selenium poisoning. *South Dakota Agr. Expt. Sta. Bull. No.* **311**:1–91.
76. Moxon, A. L., O. E. Olson, W. V. Searight and K. M. Sandals. 1938. The stratigraphic distribution of selenium in the Cretaceous formations of South

Dakota and the selenium content of some associated vegetation. *Am. J. Botany* **25**:794–809.

77. Moxon, A. L., O. E. Olson and W. V. Searight. 1950. Selenium in rocks, soils, and plants. *South Dakota Agr. Expt. Sta. Tech. Bull. No.* **2**:1–94.
78. Murdoch, J. and R. W. Webb. 1956. Minerals of California. *California Dept. Nat. Resources Div. Mines Bull.* **173**:150, 239, 327.
79. Newberry, J. S. 1881. The silver reef sandstones. *Eng. Min. J.* **31**:4–5.
80. Olson, O. E. and A. L. Moxon. 1939. The availability to crop plants of different forms of selenium in the soil. *Soil Sci.* **47**:305–311.
81. Olson, O. E., L. L. Sisson and A. L. Moxon. 1940. Absorption of selenium and arsenic by plants from soils under natural conditions. *Soil Sci.* **50**:115–118.
82. Olson, O. E., D. F. Jornlin and A. L. Moxon. 1942. Field studies on methods for determining availability of selenium to plants. *Soil Sci.* **53**:365–368.
83. Olson, O. E., E. I. Whitehead and A. L. Moxon. 1942. Occurrence of soluble selenium in soil and its availability to plants. *Soil Sci.* **54**:47–53.
84. Phillips, A. H. 1918. A possible source of vanadium in sedimentary rocks. *Am. J. Sci.* **46**:473–475.
85. Pugsley, C. W. and T. H. Cox. 1937. Selenium problems in South Dakota. *South Dakota State Planning Board* pp. 1–30.
86. Rader, L. F., Jr. and W. L. Hill. 1935. Occurrence of selenium in natural phosphates, superphosphates and phosphoric acid. *J. Agr. Res.* **51**:1071–1083.
87. Rankama, K. and Th. G. Sahama. 1949. "Geochemistry," pp. 743–755. Univ. of Chicago Press, Chicago, Illinois.
88. Ravikovitch, S. and M. Margolin. 1957. Selenium in soils and plants. *Agr. Res. Sta., Rehovot* **7**:41–52.
89. Robinson, W. O. 1936. Selenium content of wheat from various parts of the world. *Ind. Eng. Chem.* **28**:736–738.
90. Robinson, S. C. 1950. Mineralogy of the Goldfields district, Saskatchewan. *Canada Geol. Survey Paper* **50–16**:1–38.
91. Schubert, J. R., O. H. Muth, J. E. Oldfield and L. F. Remmert. 1961. Experimental results with selenium in white muscle disease of lambs and calves. *Federation Proc.* **20**:689–694.
92. Searight, W. V. and A. L. Moxon. 1945. Selenium in glacial and associated deposits. *South Dakota Agr. Expt. Sta. Tech. Bull. No.* **5**:1–33
93. Searight, W. V., A. L. Moxon, R. J. Hilmoe and E. I. Whitehead. 1946. Occurrence of selenium in Pleistocene deposits and their derivatives in South Dakota. *Soil Sci.* **61**:455–463.
94. Searight, W. V., A. L. Moxon, E. I. Whitehead and F. G. Viets, Jr. 1946–1947. Detailed mapping of seleniferous vegetation on soils of Pierre origin. *Proc. South Dakota Acad. Sci.* **26**:87–98.
95. Shannon, E. V. 1920. An occurrence of naumannite in Idaho. *Am. J. Sci.* **50**: 390–391.
96. Slater, C. S., R. S. Holmes and H. G. Byers. 1937. Trace elements in the soils from the Erosion Experiment Stations, with supplementary data on other soils. *U. S. Dept. Agr. Tech. Bull. No.* **552**:1–23.
97. Strock, L. W. 1935. The distribution of selenium in nature. *Am. J. Pharm.* **107**: 144–157.
98. Suzuki, Y., K. Nishiyama, Y. Takano, T. Tajiri and K. Sakurayama. 1959. Studies on the selenium content of various foodstuffs, fertilizers and human hair. *Tokushimi J. Exptl. Med.* **6**:243–249.

99. Swaine, D. J. 1955. The trace-element content of soils. Selenium. *Commonwealth Bur. Soil Sci. (Gt. Brit.) Tech. Comm. No.* **48**:91–99.
100. Thompson, M. E., C. Roach and W. Braddock. 1956. New occurrences of native selenium. *Am. Mineralogist* **41**:156–157.
101. Tourtelot, H. A. 1962. Preliminary investigation of the geologic setting and chemical composition of the Pierre Shale, Great Plains region. *U. S. Geol. Survey, Profess. Paper No.* **390**:1–74.
102. Trelease, S. F. 1945. Selenium in soils, plants and animals. *Soil Sci.* **60**:125–131.
103. Trites, A. F., Jr. and H. W. Lakin. 1956. Behavior of selenium in the zone of oxidation. *Intern. Geol. Congr. 20th, Mexico,* pp. 377–378 (Abstr.)
104. Tsuge, T. and S. Terada. 1950. The selenium content of pyrites and soils in Japan. *J. Agr. Chem. Soc. Japan* **23**:421–425. (In Japanese, with English summary).
105. U. S. Geological Survey. 1954. Compilation of records of surface waters of the United States through September, 1950. *U. S. Geol. Survey Water-Supply Paper No.* **1313** (Pt. 9):1–749.
106. Vine, J. E. and G. E. Prichard. 1954. Uranium in the Poison Basin area, Carbon County, Wyoming. *U. S. Geol. Survey Circ.* **344**:1–8.
107. Walker, O. J., W. E. Harris and M. Rossi. 1941. Selenium in soils, grains and plants in Alberta. *Can. J. Res.* **19B**:173–178.
108. Walsh, T., G. A. Fleming, R. O'Connor and A. Sweeney. 1951. Selenium toxicity associated with an Irish soil series. *Nature* **168**:881.
109. Walsh T. and G. A. Fleming. 1952. Selenium levels in rocks, soils and herbage from a high selenium locality in Ireland. *Trans. Intern. Soc. Soil Sci., Comm. II and IV,* **2**:178–185.
110. Weeks, A. D. 1956. Mineralogy of uranium deposits, in Geologic investigations of radioactive deposits. *U. S. Geol. Surv.* **TEI–620,** issued by U. S. A. E. C. Comm. Tech. Inform. Service, Oak Ridge, Tennessee, pp. 123–127.
111. Williams, K. T. and H. G. Byers. 1934. Occurrence of selenium in pyrites. *Ind. Eng. Chem., Anal. Ed.* **6**:296–297.
112. Williams, K. T. and H. G. Byers. 1935. Occurrence of selenium in the Colorado River and some of its tributaries. *Ind. Eng. Chem., Anal. Ed.* **7**:431–432.
113. Williams, K. T. and H. G. Byers. 1935. Selenium in deep sea deposits. *Ind. Eng. Chem., News Ed.* **13**:353.
114. Williams, K. T. and H. G. Byers. 1936. Selenium compounds in soils. *Ind. Eng. Chem.* **28**:912–914.
115. Williams, K. T. 1937. Selenium and its relation to soil, plants and animals. *Tabul. biol., Hague* **14**:194–208.
116. Williams, K. T. 1938. Selenium in soils. *U. S. Dept. Agr. Yearbook,* House doc. 398, 75th Congr., 2nd Sess., pp. 830–834.
117. Williams, K. T., H. W. Lakin and H. G. Byers. 1940. Selenium occurrence in certain soils in the United States with a discussion of related topics: 4th report. *U. S. Dept. Agr. Tech. Bull. No.* **702**:1–59.
118. Williams, K. T., H. W. Lakin and H. G. Byers. 1941. Selenium occurrence in certain soils in the United States with a discussion of related topics: 5th report. *U. S. Dept. Agr. Tech Bull. No.* **758**:1–69.
119. Wills, G. 1857. "Compendio de Geología," Capítulo VIII, pp. 28–41. Imprenta Ortiz, Bogotá.

CHAPTER III

SELENIUM INDICATOR PLANTS

Certain native plants accumulate high concentrations of selenium when they grow on seleniferous soils or geological formations. Species of plants that have this unique characteristic are known as "Beath's selenium indicators"; they are primary selenium indicators since their growth is restricted to seleniferous areas (*2, 3*).

Primary selenium indicators known at the present time include about 24 species and varieties of *Astragalus* (milk vetch, with pealike flowers); section *Xylorhiza* (woody aster) of *Machaeranthera;* section *Oonopsis* (goldenweed) of *Haplopappus;* and *Stanleya* (prince's plume). Experimental studies with solution and sand cultures corroborated the field observations that these species require selenium for their growth and development (*14*).

A number of primary indicator plants have an offensive odor. Brandegee (*4*) called attention to the similarity in odor between the flowers of *A. haydenianus* and *A. bisulcatus.* Jones (*5*) referred to *A. pattersoni* as a nauseous poisonous weed; Wooton and Standley (*20*) characterized it as malodorous. Beath (*1*) noted that the water extracts of *A. bisulcatus* were markedly odoriferous. The intensity of the odor of a species may be used as a qualitative indication as to the amount of selenium present in the plants.

There are other species of native plants that absorb moderately large quantities of selenium when they grow on soils that contain high concentrations of available selenium and they are called *secondary selenium absorbers.* These species belong to a number of plant genera (including *Aster, Atriplex,* and *Grindelia*) and are an aid in locating seleniferous regions.

Reports from outside the United States, Canada, and Mexico show that there are few, if any, primary selenium indicator plants present in seleniferous areas. Nevertheless, the occurrence of seleniferous soils and vegetation in Israel, Ireland, South America, South Africa, and Australia was reported and is discussed in Chapter II.

GENUS *Astragalus*

Among the selenium indicator plants, *Astragalus* shows the greatest diversity of form and the most extensive geographical distribution. This

TABLE 13

Selenium Indicator Species of Astragalus *and Their Distribution*

Species	Distribution
Bisulcati	
A. *bisulcatus* (Hook.) Gray	Alberta, Sask., Manitoba, Montana, North Dakota, Idaho, Wyoming, South Dakota, Nebraska, Colorado, Oklahoma, Kansas, New Mexico
A. *diholcos* (Rydb.) Tidestrom	Wyoming, Colorado
A. *haydenianus* (Gray)	Wyoming, Utah, Colorado, Nevada, New Mexico
A. *oocalycis* Jones	Colorado, New Mexico
Galegiformes	
A. *racemosus* Pursh	Alberta, Montana, North Dakota, Wyoming, South Dakota, Nebraska, Utah, Colorado, Kansas, New Mexico, Oklahoma, Texas
Lonchocarpi	
A. *osterhouti* Jones	Colorado
Ocreati	
A. *albulus* Woot. & Stand.	Arizona, New Mexico
A. *argillosus* Jones	Utah, Arizona
A. *confertiflorus* Gray	Wyoming, Utah, Colorado, Arizona, New Mexico
A. *confertiflorus* var. *flaviflorus* (Kuntze) Jones	Wyoming, Utah, Colorado
A. *moencoppensis* Jones	Utah, Arizona
Podo-sclerocarpi	
A. *grayi* Parry	Wyoming, Montana
A. *pectinatus* Dougl.	Alberta, Sask., Manitoba, Montana, North Dakota, South Dakota, Utah, Wyoming, Colorado, Kansas
A. *pectinatus* var. *platyphyllus* Jones	Wyoming
A. *toanus* Jones	Idaho, Utah, Nevada
Preussii	
A. *beathii* Porter	Arizona
A. *eastwoodae* Jones	Utah
A. *ellisiae* Porter	New Mexico
A. *crotalariae* (Benth.) Gray	California, Nevada, Arizona
A. *pattersoni* Gray	Utah, Colorado, Arizona, New Mexico, Texas
A. *pattersoni* var. *praelongus* (Sheld.) Jones	Nevada, Utah, Arizona, New Mexico
A. *preussii* Gray	Nevada, Utah, California, Arizona, New Mexico
A. *recedens* (Jones) n. comb.	Colorado, New Mexico
A. *sabulosus* Jones	Utah, Arizona

genus includes about 300 species in North America, and 1200 species are known in other parts of the world. Only the North American species have been analyzed for selenium. Distribution of primary indicator species of *Astragalus* is given in Table 13. Field studies by Beath *et al.* (*3*) have shown so far that 21 of these species and 3 varieties are selenium accumulators and indicators, whereas 81 other species absorb only small amounts of selenium and are not limited to seleniferous soils. North American indicator species fall into 6 of the 29 sections of Jones' (*6*) division. The 81 nonindicator species are found in 19 of these sections.

Astragalus L. MILK VETCH

PEA FAMILY

Perennial herbs with alternate compound leaves usually bearing many (though rarely only 1 or 3–5) odd-pinnate leaflets and white, pale-yellow, violet or purple pealike flowers in racemes or spikes. Calyx a 5-toothed tube. Petals, 5 with claws; the upper, or standard, broader than the rest. On each side of the standard, and a little below it, are the two wings. The keel is formed by the two lower petals, which are joined along their lower edges. Stamens, 10 (9 united and 1 free). Pistil simple; ovary 1-celled, or in some species partially or completely 2-celled. Stigma terminal, minute. Fruit a pod, 1-celled or perfectly or partially 2-celled by a false septum formed by the partial or complete intrusion of the lower suture or of both sutures. Seeds kidney-shaped, borne on slender stalks along the upper suture or seam. Texture of pods ranges from papery to fleshy, usually becoming hard, leathery, or woody when dry. *Astragalus* usually has a blunt keel, while the closely related *Oxytropis* has a keel that bears a sharp beak.

KEY TO SELENIFEROUS SPECIES OF *Astragalus*

The accompanying key provides a means of identifying the selenium indicator species and varieties of *Astragalus*. The descriptive terms used in the key are illustrated in Fig. 6. The key is based primarily upon the character of the mature pod. The summary of characters in Table 14 and the drawings of Figs. 7 and 8 will be useful for the identification of species. Complete descriptions of most of the species may be found in the publications of Jones (*6*) and Rydberg (*13*).

Key to the seleniferous species of *Astragalus* described by Porter (*9–12*) is as follows:

Pods 2-grooved above (ventrally bisulcate) and stipitate . . . . Group I

Pods not 2-grooved above (bisulcate), or if so then nonstipitate

TABLE 14

Summary of Characters of Seleniferous Species of Astragalus *(Porter)*

Group and species	Mature pods: Body length (mm)	Mature pods: Body width (mm)	Mature pods: Stipe length (mm)	Flowers: Color	Flowers: Length (mm)	Height of plants (dm)
Group I						
A. *bisulcatus*	12–20	3	3–4	Purple to white	12–20	4–8
A. *haydenianus*	8–10	2–3	3–5	Cream to white	8–12	3–7
A. *diholcos*	8–9	2–3	3–4	Cream to white	6–7	2–5
A. *oocalycis*	5–7	3–4	0.5	Cream to white	15–18	3–6
Group II						
A. *argillosus*	6–7	3–4	0	Purple	9–10	1–2
A. *confertiflorus*	9–11	4	0	Cream to white	9–11	1–3
A. *confertiflorus* var. *flaviflorus*	9–11	4	0	Cream to yellow	9–11	1–3
A. *moencoppensis*	5–7	3	0	Purple	7–8	2–3
A. *toanus*	17–20	4–5	0	Purple	15–19	3–5
A. *grayi*	10–14	4–6	0	Cream	20	3–4
A. *pectinatus*	15–20	6–8	0	Cream to white	20–22	2–5
A. *pectinatus* var. *platyphyllus*	13–20	8–10	0	Cream	25–28	2–4
Group III						
A. *albulus*	12–15	4	2	Cream	13–15	4–6
Group IV						
A. *osterhouti*	40–50	4–5	4	Cream to white	15–22	4–6
Group V						
A. *preussii*	15–28	9–12	4–6	Purple	20–23	3–6
A. *crotalariae*	25–30	11–13	2–3	Purple	20	4–7
A. *eastwoodae*	15	10	2–3	Purple	20–23	2–4
Group VI						
A. *racemosus*	20–27	4	5–6	Cream to white	12–15	6–8
Group VII						
A. *sabulosus*	40–45	12–15	0	Cream	25	1–2
A. *pattersoni*	15–20	5–8	0–0.5	Cream to white	18–20	3–6
A. *pattersoni* var. *praelongus*	35	15	0–0.5	Cream	18–20	4–7
A. *beathii*	30–40	7	0–1	Purple	20–22	4–6
A. *ellisiae*	30	6–8	0–0.5	Cream to white	18	3–5
A. *recedens*	25–30	8–12	0–0.5	Cream	20	3–5

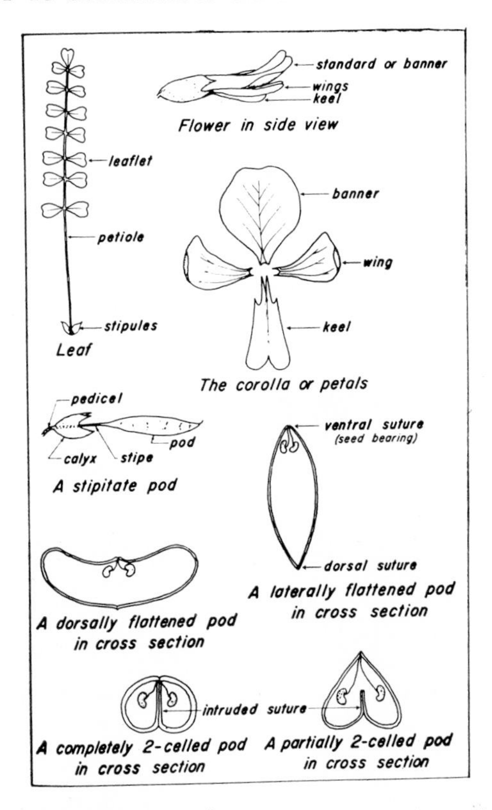

FIG. 6. Diagram illustrating descriptive terms in *Astragalus* key.

Fruit stipitate, thin in texture, and dorsally flattened or triangular in cross section, the ventral suture prominent
- Legume 12–15 mm long, the stipe about 2 mm long; foliage gray . . . . Group III
- Legume 20–27 mm long, the stipe about 5 mm long; foliage green . . . . Group VI

Fruit stipitate or nonstipitate, leathery or fleshy in texture if dorsally flattened, never triangular in cross section, but the ventral suture sometimes prominent
- Legume essentially nonstipitate, the stipe 1 mm long or less
  - Dorsal suture not raised as an internal ridge . . . . Group II
  - Dorsal suture somewhat intruded as an internal ridge . . . . Group VII

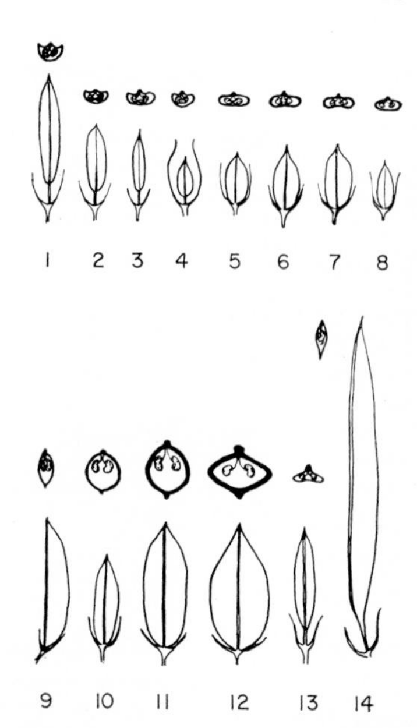

FIG. 7. Pods of seleniferous species of *Astragalus*.

1. *bisulcatus*
2. *haydenianus*
3. *diholcos*
4. *oocalysis*
5. *argillosus*
6. *confertiflorus*
7. *confertiflorus* var. *flaviflorus*
8. *moencoppensis*
9. *toanus*
10. *grayi*
11. *pectinatus*
12. *pectinatus* var. *platyphyllus*
13. *albulus*
14. *osterhouti*

Legume stipitate, the stipe 2–6 mm long
 Body of pod 40–50 mm long, not inflated, laterally flattened, both sutures prominent externally . . . . Group IV
 Body of pod 15–30 mm long, inflated, rounded in cross section, neither of the sutures prominent externally . . . . Group V

GROUP I

Calyx completely enclosing the mature fruit *A. oocalycis*
Calyx not completely enclosing the mature fruit
 Flowers purple or rarely white; pods 12–20 mm long . . . . *A. bisulcatus*
 Flowers white or cream-colored, only the keel purple tipped; pods 10 mm long or less

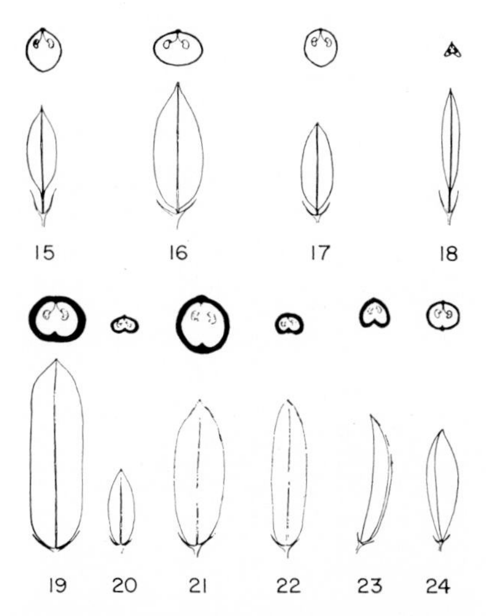

FIG. 8. Pods of seleniferous species of *Astragalus*.

15. *preussii*
16. *crotalariae*
17. *eastwoodae*
18. *racemosus*
19. *sabulosus*
20. *pattersoni*
21. *pattersoni* var. *praelongus*
22. *beathii*
23. *ellisiae*
24. *recedens*

Fruits cross-veined, blunt-pointed . . . . A. *haydenianus*
Fruits not cross-veined, acute at the tip A. *diholcos*

GROUP II

Flowers 7–11 mm long
  Corolla purple
    Stems densely gray-pubescent; flowers 9–10 mm long . . . . A. *argillosus*
    Stems green and merely strigose; flowers 7–8 mm long . . . . A. *moencoppensis*
  Corolla white to pale yellow or merely tinged with purple
    Leaflets mostly 1–2 mm wide, linear; flowers white, fading to cream-colored . . . . . A. *confertiflorus*
    Leaflets often 3–4 mm wide, oblong to elliptic; flowers cream-colored, fading to yellow . . . . A. *confertiflorus* var. *flaviflorus*

FIG. 9. *Astragalus bisulcatus,* with purple flowers and young pods. × ⅔.

Flowers 15–28 mm long
  Pods erect or ascending
    Calyx lobes more than half as long as the tube . . . . Nonseleniferous spp.
    Calyx lobes less than half as long as the tube

Corolla purple; leaflets linear, about 1 mm wide or less . . . . *A. toanus*
Corolla cream-colored; leaflets linear, about 3–4 mm wide . . . . *A. grayi*

FIG. 10. *Astragalus bisulcatus*. Mature green pods with two longitudinal grooves giving rise to common name—two-grooved vetch. × ⅔.

FIG. 11. *Astragalus haydenianus,* with long spikes of small white flowers. × 1/6.

Pods pendulous
- Leaflets mostly 1–2 mm wide . . . . . *A. pectinatus*
- Leaflets mostly 3–4 mm wide . . . . . *A. pectinatus* var. *platyphyllus*

GROUP III

Stems much branched, 4–6 dm long, ends erect. Stipules large and membranous, united around the stem. Plants covered with silvery-white hairs. Flowers several in dense head-like or spikelike clusters about 1 dm long. Corolla cream-colored, 13–15 mm long. Pod of a thin texture . . . . *A. albulus*

GROUP IV

Corolla cream-colored, 15–22 mm long. Stipe 4 not long enough to carry pod wholly out of the calyx. Body of pod hairless (glabrous), 40–50 mm long, nearly linear, tapering more toward the base than the apex . . *A. osterhouti*

GROUP V

Pod papery, remaining closed or only tardily splitting open . . . . Nonseleniferous spp.
Pod more or less leathery, at maturity 2-valved at the apex
  Stipe 4–6 mm long . . . . *A. preussii*
  Stipe 2–3 mm long
    Body of pod 25–30 mm long . . . . . . *A. crotalariae*
    Body of pod about 15 mm long . . . . . *A. eastwoodae*

GROUP VI

Plant stout, 6–8 dm high. Foliage green, set with short stiff hairs; leaflets oblong. Calyx bear-

FIG. 12. *Astragalus oocalycis.* Hairy egg-shaped calyx nearly encloses the white corolla. This species is found in southwestern Colorado between Durango and Pagosa Springs and in adjacent northern New Mexico. × 4/5.

FIG. 13. *Astragalus confertiflorus,* with small white or pale-yellow flowers. × ¾.

ing short white hairs (not black hairy). Corolla cream to white, rarely with purple-tipped keel, 12–15 mm long; standard moderately arched; lower edge of keel-petals abruptly arched upward near apex. Pod triangular in cross section, about 4 mm broad, pendent, the body linear or lance linear in outline; stipe 5–6 mm; upper suture sharply raised, lower suture decidedly grooved . . . . *A. racemosus*

GROUP VII

Leaflets single . . . . Nonseleniferous spp.
Leaflets several or many
Flowers purple . . . . *A. beathii*

Flowers cream-colored, or only the keel purple tipped
  Pods 40–45 mm long; flowers about 25 mm long; plants mostly 2 dm high or less . . *A. sabulosus*
  Pods 15–35 mm long; flowers 18–20 mm long; plants mostly 3 dm high or more
    Fruits strongly grooved below (dorsally), somewhat curved when mature . . . *A. ellisiae*
    Fruits not strongly grooved below (dorsally), rounded in cross section, straight
      Body of pod tapering from the middle to the narrow base . . . . *A. recedens*
      Body of pod merely rounded at the broad base, not tapering
        Pods 15–20 mm long, 5–8 mm wide *A. pattersoni*
        Pods about 35 mm long, 15 mm wide *A. pattersoni* var. *praelongus*

FIG. 14. *Astragalus grayi,* with cream-colored flowers. A species abundant in central and northwestern Wyoming. × ⅕.

FIG. 15. *Astragalus pectinatus* (narrow-leaved vetch). Procumbent stems bearing white or cream-colored flowers and leaves with narrowly linear leaflets. × ½.

NONINDICATOR SPECIES OF ASTRAGALUS

The nonindicator species of *Astragalus* occur on both nonseleniferous and seleniferous soils. Even when growing in proximity to the selenium-accumulating species on seleniferous soils, they are free from selenium or contain mere traces. There is no explanation for the striking differences in the ability of closely related species to absorb and accumulate selenium.

Table 15 shows the selenium indicators and nonindicators of North American species of *Astragalus.*

Astragalus saurinus Barneby, collected on the Curtis Formation in the Dinosaur National Monument, Utah, was found to be a selenium absorber. It would be included in the Podo-sclerocarpi section.

TABLE 15
Selenium Indicator and Nonindicator Species of Astragalus *in Jones' Sections of the Genus*

Section	*Astragalus* species		
	Se indicators	Nonindicators	Unexamined
Bisulcati	4	0	0
Galegiformes	1	2	0
Lonchocarpi	1	1	2
Ocreati	5	1	0
Podo-sclerocarpi	4	6	4
Preussii	8	1	1
Argophylli	0	17	5
Chaetodontes	0	1	3
Collini	0	2	3
Debiles	0	1	4
Flexuosi	0	4	7
Hamosi	0	3	15
Homalobi	0	11	14
Hypoglottides	0	2	0
Inflati	0	15	40
Leptocarpi	0	2	7
Malaci	0	4	2
Mollissimi	0	2	6
Raventi-Arrecti	0	3	4
Sarcocarpi	0	2	2
Uliginosi	0	1	3

Unexamined sections: Triphylli (2), Sparsiflori (5), Alpini (8), Atrati (5), Lotiflori (4), Strigulosi (11), Micranthi (23), Didymocarpi (8).

It is evident that five of the sections—Galegiformes, Lonchocarpi, Ocreati, Podo-sclerocarpi, and Preussii—may need revision as each includes both indicator and nonindicator species. With these exceptions, the sections are in agreement with the results of field observations, seed germination tests, and growth experiments.

Jones' revision of *Astragalus* has proved of great value for the classification of selenium indicators. It allows a fairly accurate prediction as to the selenium-absorbing capacity of different species.

SECTION *Xylorhiza* OF *Machaeranthera*

The various species of woody aster (*Xylorhiza*) resemble one another closely. The species that have been examined have been selenium indicators (Fig. 18). They are abundant in Wyoming, Colorado, and Utah, where they cover literally thousands of square miles of grazing land. In general appearance, woody aster resembles the common oxeye daisy but is not so tall.

FIG. 16. *Astragalus racemosus*. White or cream-colored flowers (sometimes purple tipped) and long pods, triangular in cross-section. × ½.

Fig. 17. *Astragalus pattersoni,* with white or cream-colored flowers and large erect pods. It is widely distributed to the south and west from north-central Colorado. The variety *praelongus* has longer and broader pods. × ½.

SECTION *Xylorhiza* OF *Machaeranthera,* WOODY ASTER

Composite Family

Perennial caulescent herbs, with thick woody taproots and short caudices. *Xylorhiza* means "woody root." Leaves many, spinulose-tipped, entire or spinulose-toothed. Heads large, solitary at the ends of the branches, radiate. Involucres hemispheric; bracts mostly in 2 or 3 series, acuminate, herbaceous, carinate below. Ray-flowers pistillate; ligules

FIG. 18. *Machaeranthera glabriuscula* (woody aster). White (or rarely pinkish) flowers resembling those of the oxeye daisy. × ½.

showy, white, or pinkish, resembling those of the oxeye daisy. Disk-flowers perfect. Appendages of the style-branches lanceolate, acute. Achenes oblong, compressed. Pappus fulvous, simple, of rather few coarse bristles.

The following tabulation lists the known species.

Species	Distribution
Machaeranthera brandegei[a] Rydb.	Colorado
M. coloradensis[a] (Gray) Osterh.	Colorado
M. glabriuscula[b] (Nutt.) Cronq. & Keck	Wyoming, South Dakota, Colorado
M. venusta (Jones) Cronq. & Keck	Utah, Colorado
M. glabriuscula var. *villosa* (Nutt.) Cronq. & Keck	Colorado

[a] Selenium content not determined.

[b] In earlier literature referred to as *Xylorhiza parryi* (Gray) Greene.

SECTION *Oonopsis* OF *Haplopappus*

The species of *Oonopsis* (goldenweed) group of *Haplopappus* are dependable indicators of selenium (Fig. 19). They have yellow flowers and are related to the goldenrods. The seleniferous species of *Haplopappus* are widely distributed in Wyoming and Colorado. They absorb large amounts of selenium. Owing to volatile selenium compounds, they have a very offensive garlicky odor.

SECTION *Oonopsis* OF *Haplopappus*, GOLDENWEED

Composite Family

Perennial herbs with woody caudex or crown, and erect leafy stems. Leaves linear or lanceolate, entire. Heads in terminal cymes or solitary. *Oonopsis* means literally "egg appearance," probably so-named because of the shape of the flower heads. Involucres campanulate or hemispheric; bracts well imbricate, flat, cuspidate-acuminate. Ray-flowers pistillate or wanting; ligules yellow. Disk-corollas yellow, cylindric, with 5 short teeth. Tips of the style branches ovate, shorter than the stigmatic part. Achenes glabrous or strigose, many-nerved. Pappus of rather few coarse bristles.

Fig. 19. *Haplopappus fremontii* (goldenweed) [(*Gray*) subsp. *wardii* (Gray) Hall] with yellow flowers. × ½.

The various species which closely resemble one another are given below.

Haplopappus argillacea A. Nels.	Wyoming, South Dakota
H. fremontii[a] Gray, subsp. *wardii* (Gray) Hall	Wyoming
H. engelmanii (Gray) Hall	Colorado, Kansas
H. fremontii Gray	Colorado, Kansas
H. fremontii subsp. *monocephalus* (A. Nels.) Hall	Colorado
H. multicaulis[b] (Nutt.) Gray	Wyoming

[a] In earlier literature referred to as *Oonopsis condensata* A. Nels.
[b] Selenium content not determined.

GENUS *Stanleya*

Species of prince's plume (*Stanleya*) have variable concentrations of selenium. Their yellow plumes make them easy to recognize (Fig. 20).

FIG. 20. *Stanleya pinnata.* Yellow flowers with long cylindrical pods. × ¾.

Stanleya PRINCE'S PLUME

MUSTARD FAMILY

Leafy perennials, usually more or less glaucous. Leaves extremely variable, from entire to pinnatifid or even pinnate. Flowers perfect, in long racemes. Sepals yellow or yellowish, oblong, widely spreading in anthesis. Petals 4, yellow to creamy or greenish with long claw and narrow elongate blades. Stamens 6; filaments elongate, spreading; anthers linear, curved and spirally coiled. Pods long, roundish in section, long-stalked; valves 1-nerved. Stigma sessile, small, simple. Seeds in one row, oblong; cotyledons incumbent.

About a dozen species of *Stanleya* have been described, some of which are well characterized while others are almost inseparable botanically. The known species are as follows:

Stanleya albescens Jones	Colorado, Arizona, New Mexico
S. *confertiflora*[a] (Robinson) Howell	Oregon, Idaho
S. *pinnata* (Pursh) Britt.	Utah, Wyoming, South Dakota, North Dakota, Kansas, Arizona, California, Colorado, Montana, Idaho, Nevada, New Mexico, Texas
S. *pinnata* var. *bipinnata* (Greene) Rollins	Wyoming, Colorado
S. *pinnata* var. *gibberosa* Rollins	Wyoming
S. *pinnata* var. *integrifolia* (James) Rollins	Utah, Wyoming, Colorado, Kansas, Texas
S. *tomentosa* Parry	Wyoming
S. *viridiflora* Nutt.	Montana, Oregon, Idaho, Wyoming, Nevada, Utah

[a] Selenium content not determined.

The position of *Stanleya* as a primary selenium indicator is not as well established as that of selenium accumulator species of *Astragalus* and seleniferous species in sections of *Haplopappus* and *Machaeranthera*. *Stanleya pinnata* var. *bipinnata* frequently absorbs large amounts of selenium. Although some specimens contain exceedingly low concentrations of selenium, occurrence of *Stanleya* has frequently led to highly seleniferous plants of other genera in the immediate vicinity.

SECONDARY SELENIUM ABSORBERS

Plants of several genera are capable of absorbing considerable quantities of selenium where they grow on highly seleniferous soils, although they are not restricted to such soils.

Aster

Species of *Aster* that have been found to contain toxic amounts of selenium include *Aster adscendens* Lindl., *A. coerulescens* DC., *A. commutatis* Gray, *A. ericoides* L., *A. glaucoides* Blake, *A. laevis* var. *geyeri* Gray, and *A. occidentalis* (Nutt.) T. and G. The asters are largely perennials.

From an economic point of view, they merit attention because of their wide distribution, dense growth, palatability to livestock, resistance to frost, and adaptability to a wide range of climatic and soil conditions. On some grass ranges the seleniferous asters grow in sufficient density to make the associated grasses toxic. The selenium in the asters is soluble in water, mostly as selenate.

Atriplex

Among the saltbushes, *Atriplex canescens* (Pursh) James and *A. nuttallii* Wats. may be seleniferous on certain soils. *Atriplex canescens* has been somewhat better as a secondary selenium indicator than *A. nuttallii*. *Atriplex nuttallii* requires highly seleniferous soil with a high concentration of available selenium to absorb a significant amount. *Atriplex canescens* has been found to be a selenium absorber on many moderately seleniferous soils derived from the Pierre and Niobrara formations. Most of the selenium in the saltbushes is soluble in water, about 80 per cent is selenate. Species that are not normally seleniferous include *A. argentea* Nutt., *A. confertifolia* (Torr.) Wats., and *A. pabularis* A. Nels.

Castilleja

Paintbrushes that belong to various species of *Castilleja* frequently accumulate selenium. Paintbrush is a partial parasite on the roots of a host plant. It is believed that paintbrush obtains its selenium through its own roots directly from the soil.

Comandra

A member of the sandalwood family, *Comandra pallida* A. DC. is a partial parasite on the roots of various plants. Unlike paintbrush, *Comandra* is believed to contain selenium only when its parasitic roots are attached to a seleniferous host. Limited studies have indicated that part of the water-soluble selenium in *Comandra* is selenate.

Grayia

In general, collections of *Grayia spinosa* (Hook.) Moq. from a number of western states have been very low in selenium. Specimens of *G. brandegei* Gray collected near Rifle, Colorado, were rather highly seleniferous. It is possible that the plants accumulated the available selenium from associated vegetation.

Grindelia

The species of *Grindelia* (gumweed) are biennials and perennials. Most of them are unpalatable. Being prolific seed producers, they quickly occupy waste places and abandoned fields. Analyses of many specimens indicate that the species of *Grindelia* absorb selenium from certain soils. *Grindelia squarrosa* (Pursh) Dunal. has been studied more than any other species. One mature specimen contained 102 ppm selenium, 78 per cent was soluble in water, and 33 per cent was present as selenate.

Gutierrezia

Snakeweeds are widely distributed. The species most frequently encountered in selenium studies is *Gutierrezia sarothrae* (Pursh) Britt. and Rusby. Many samples from Kansas, Wyoming, South Dakota, and Colorado have been analyzed. Like other plants in the group of secondary absorbers, it has only moderate ability to take up selenium. But under similar conditions *G. sarothrae* and the species of *Haplopappus* formerly referred to as *Sideranthus* absorb more selenium than species of *Grindelia*. Some specimens have a fairy high concentration of selenium, especially those growing on soils bearing indicator plants. Plants from several areas contained about 75 per cent water-soluble selenium and a considerable amount was selenate. *Gutierrezia diversifolia* Greene collected on the Wasatch Formation near De Beque, Colorado, contained 723 ppm total selenium. Of this, 513 ppm was soluble in water; and about 90 per cent of the soluble selenium was selenate.

Machaeranthera

The species *Machaeranthera ramosa* A. Nels. is a biennial and can absorb the available selenium from the soil in high concentrations. The basal leaves are succulent and palatable to livestock. Nearly all the selenium is water soluble and approximately 85 per cent is selenate. *Machaeranthera grindelioides* (Nutt.) Shinners has occasionally been found to be seleniferous but does not accumulate as high concentrations of selenium as *M. ramosa* A. Nels. This and other species of this group are to be considered as selenium absorbers. The plants yield some water-soluble selenium, most of which is in organic form.

Mentzelia

Specimens of *Mentzelia* rarely absorb selenium in toxic amounts. *Mentzelia decapetala* (Pursh) Urban and Gilg often grows on seleniferous soil, but it rarely contains significant amounts of selenium. Collections from various areas in the western states have shown that the species of this genus are not important as selenium absorbers.

IDENTIFICATION OF INDICATORS BY GERMINATION TESTS

A test was devised by Trelease (*17*) with germinating seedlings to determine whether or not a given species of *Astragalus* is capable of accumulating selenium. This test was based on the observation that selenium indicator species can grow in the presence of selenite, while the growth of nonindicator species is inhibited (*16*).

In making the test, the seeds were treated for from 30 to 60 minutes with concentrated sulfuric acid, then soaked in water for 3 hours, and distributed on moist filter paper in a covered glass dish. Duplicate nutrient solutions (*16*) were prepared for each species of *Astragalus,* one selenium free and the other with 20 ppm of selenium (as sodium selenite). Seedlings about 10 mm in length were placed on paraffined netting with roots dipping in the solution in the glass dishes. The cultures were covered and kept in darkness at room temperature. The covers were removed after the first day, and at the end of 3 days, the lengths of the seedling roots and hypocotyls were measured.

The results of such a test are summarized in Table 16. A *plus* sign indicates a species that accumulates selenium and a *minus* sign denotes a nonaccumulator species. The addition of 20 ppm of selenium to the culture solution had no effect on the growth of the roots of the accumulators due to the presence of stored selenium in the seeds. Growth of the roots of the nonaccumulators was inhibited in the solution containing 20 ppm selenium, but in the selenium-free solution the growth was 25–30 mm. The hypocotyls of the nonaccumulator species in the presence of selenium grew about 5 mm, while in selenium-free cultures they grew 20–30 mm.

The results of these germination tests are in agreement with those of field observations and growth experiments of longer duration.

The chromosome numbers of the species used in the germination tests were reported by Vilkomerson (*19*). These are shown in Table 16. The chromosome numbers are consistent with Jones' division of the genus into sections except for the Galegiformes. The section Galegiformes includes species which differ both in selenium response and in chromosome number. Investigations on the relation of chromosomes to the ability to accumulate selenium would be of scientific interest. Members of the Lonchocarpi or of the Podo-sclerocarpi should be favorable plants for genetic studies, since each of these groups includes species of like chromosome number but unlike characteristics in accumulating selenium.

SELENIUM EFFECT ON PRIMARY INDICATORS

Experiments to obtain direct evidence on whether or not selenium is essential for the growth and development of the indicator plants were carried out by Trelease and Trelease (*15*). The seeds were treated with acid as described in the preceding section, and they were germinated in quartz sand. The seedlings were grown for several months in the greenhouse in the presence or the absence of selenate or selenite. At the conclusion of the experiment the plants were dried, weighed, and analyzed for selenium. The results with *Astragalus racemosus* are indicated in Table 17.

TABLE 16

Capacity of Astragalus *Species for Selenium Accumulation as Indicated by Germination Tests; Chromosome Numbers Are Given*

Section and species	Selenium accumulation	Chromosome number (2*n*)
Bisulcati		
A. *bisulcatus* (Hook.) Gray	+	24
A. *haydenianus* Gray	+	24
A. *oocalycis* Jones	+	24
Galegiformes		
A. *racemosus* Pursh.	+	24
A. *drummondii* Hooker	—	22
Lonchocarpi		
A. *osterhouti* Jones	+	22
A. *lonchocarpus* Torr.	—	22
Ocreati		
A. *confertiflorus* Gray	+	24
A. *confertiflorus* var. *flaviflorus* Kuntze	+	24
Podo-sclerocarpi		
A. *grayi* Parry	+	44
A. *pectinatus* Dougl.	+	22
A. *toanus* Jones	+	22
A. *canonis* Jones	—	22
A. *casei* Gray	—	22
A. *pterocarpus* Watson	—	22
A. *sclerocarpus* Gray	—	22
A. *tetrapterus* Gray	—	22
Preussii		
A. *asclepiadoides* Jones	—	24
A. *beathii* Porter	+	24
A. *crotalariae* (Benth.) Gray	+	24
A. *pattersoni* Gray	+	24
A. *pattersoni* var. *praelongus* Jones	+	24
A. *preussii* Gray	+	24
Inflati		
A. *lentiginosus* var. *palans* Jones	—	22
Sarcocarpi		
A. *succulentus* Rich.	—	22
Uliginosi		
A. *canadensis* L.	—	16

The seedlings of *A. racemosus* in selenium-free culture solution grew slowly in comparison with those that received this element. Marked stunting of the plants was evident in about 3 weeks in the absence of selenium in the culture solution. At the end of a growth period of about 3 months, the plants that received selenium from the culture solution had approximately twice the dry weight as those grown in the selenium-free solution. In a number of plants the selenium in the growth media doubled the

TABLE 17
Influence of Selenium (as Selenite and as Selenate) on the Dry Yields of Astragalus racemosus *Grown in Sand Cultures*

Selenium in culture solution (ppm)	Selenite series		Selenate series	
	Dry weight of plants (gm)	Se content of plants (ppm)	Dry weight of plants (gm)	Se content of plants (ppm)
0	66	3	66	3
3	114	345	114	557
9	131	1,112	127	1,725
27	135	3,118	116	4,170

growth of the plants. The dry weight was increased by factors ranging from 1.5 to 6.2 ppm. Concentrations of 0.3 to 27 ppm of selenium in the solution were effective in increasing the yields. These experiments indicated that selenium has a pronounced stimulating effect on the growth of *A. racemosus* and suggested that selenium may be an essential microtrophic element for the development of the indicator plants.

Similar results were obtained with other selenium indicator species of *Astragalus*, including *A. pattersoni, A. beathii, A. bisulcatus, A. confertiflorus, A. grayi, A. osterhouti, A. pectinatus*, and *A. preussii*. In all studies there was some growth in the absence of selenium due to the selenium content of the seeds. To obtain final proof that selenium is an essential microtrophic element for these plants, it would be necessary to demonstrate that they could not be carried through several generations on a selenium-free culture solution.

Selenium requirement by certain plants appears to be unique among the essential elements in being needed by only a few species of the higher plants—the Leguminosae, the Compositae, and the Cruciferae. This implies an interesting evolutionary development of requirement of selenium by a small number of species belonging to distantly related families.

PHYSIOLOGICAL DIFFERENTIATION IN *Astragalus*

The influence of selenium on one of the nonindicator species of *Astragalus*—*A. succulentus*—has been studied in solution and sand cultures (*18*), and *Astragalus racemosus*, a selenium indicator, was included in the test in order to obtain comparable data on the two types of *Astragalus*. Sodium selenite was added to the culture solution in concentrations of ⅓, 1, 3, and 9 ppm of selenium. After the plants were grown for 3 months in the greenhouse, they were dried, weighed, and analyzed for selenium. Table 18 and Fig. 21 show the influence of selenium on the growth of the plants.

The results of these studies brought out a striking physiological differentiation among the species of the genus *Astragalus*. The two species gave opposite response to selenium. *Astragalus racemosus* growth was stimulated by selenium, whereas *A. succulentus* growth was inhibited by all concentrations of selenium when compared with growth of the plant in selenium-free culture solution. The plant growing in culture solution containing 9 ppm of selenium subsequently died. The plants grew more vigorously in sand cultures owing to better aeration of the roots, but the growth of *A. succulentus* was depressed with increasing concentration of selenium in the same manner as in culture solutions. The toxic effect of relatively low concentrations of selenium (as selenite) on *A. succulentus* resembles the effect on various crop plants, such as wheat, corn, buckwheat, soy beans, and tobacco (7, 8). Subsequent experiments have

TABLE 18

Influence of Selenium (as Selenite) on Dry Yields of Astragalus racemosus *and* Astragalus succulentus *Grown in Solution Culture*

Selenium concentration in culture solution (ppm)	*A. racemosus*			*A. succulentus*		
	Average dry weight per culture of 5 plants		Selenium content of plants (ppm)	Average dry weight per culture of 5 plants		Selenium content of plants (ppm)
	Grams	Relative		Grams	Relative	
0	2.33	1.00	29	1.06	1.00	8
⅓	3.14	1.35	99	0.68	0.64	106
1	3.85	1.65	234	0.37	0.35	335
3	3.78	1.62	355	0.25	0.24	339
9	3.81	1.64	726	0.20	0.19	451

shown that *A. asclepiadoides, A. canadensis, A. drummondii, A. lonchocarpus,* and *A. lentiginosus* growth were inhibited in the same manner as *A. succulentus.*

Analyses of the plants showed that *A. racemosus* accumulated higher concentrations of selenium than *A. succulentus* when the concentration of selenium in the solution was 9 ppm or higher. The pronounced susceptibility of *A. succulentus* to selenium poisoning limits its accumulation of this element to a few hundred parts per million. In contrast, *A. racemosus* has the ability to accumulate selenium in very high concentrations.

The greenhouse tests of growth in artificial media confirmed field observations in showing a physiological differentiation of *Astragalus* species into two groups: selenium accumulators and selenium nonaccumulators.

Physiological response to selenium also provides a new approach to an understanding of the evolutionary relationships of the *Astragalus* species. Response to selenium is useful as a taxonomic character in the classifica-

Fig. 21. Effects of selenium on the growth of two species of *Astragalus*. Above: *Astragalus racemosus* stimulated by selenium. Below: *Astragalus succulentus* growth inhibited by selenium. Concentrations of selenium in the culture solution (left to right): 0, ⅓, 1, 3, 9 ppm.

tion of these plants. It should be a valuable aid in solving problems concerning the taxonomy and evolution of the numerous species now generally included in the genus *Astragalus* or grouped, as by Rydberg (*13*), into a number of closely related genera.

HERBARIUM COLLECTIONS OF *Astragalus*

Identification of species of *Astragalus* often requires comparison with herbarium specimens preserved in a university or botanical institution. Among the institutions having large collections of *Astragalus* are the

Rocky Mountain Herbarium, University of Wyoming, Laramie; New York Botanical Garden, New York; Harvard University, Cambridge, Massachusetts; and Missouri Botanical Garden, St. Louis, Missouri.

References

1. Beath, O. A. 1917. The poisonous properties of the two-grooved milk vetch (*Astragalus bisulcatus*). *Wyoming Agr. Expt. Sta. Bull. No.* **112**:58–67.
2. Beath, O. A., J. H. Draize, H. F. Eppson, C. S. Gilbert and O. C. McCreary. 1934. Certain poisonous plants of Wyoming activated by selenium and their association with respect to soil types. *J. Am. Pharm. Assoc.* **23**:94–97.
3. Beath, O. A., C. S. Gilbert, and H. F. Eppson. 1941. The use of indicator plants in locating seleniferous areas in western United States. IV. Progress report. *Am. J. Botany* **28**:887–900.
4. Brandegee, T. S. 1876. The flora of southwestern Colorado. *U. S. Geol. and Geog. Survey Terr.* **2**:227–248.
5. Jones, M. E. 1895. Contributions to western botany. No. VII. *Proc. California Acad. Sci.* [2] **5**:611–732.
6. Jones, M. E. 1923. Revision of North American species of *Astragalus*. Salt Lake City. (Published by author.)
7. Martin, A. L. 1936. Toxicity of selenium to plants and animals. *Am. J. Botany* **23**:471–483.
8. Martin, A. L. and S. F. Trelease. 1938. Absorption of selenium by tobacco and soy beans in sand cultures. *Am. J. Botany* **25**:380–385.
9. Porter, C. L. 1939. A revision of the subgenus *diholcos* of the genus *Astragalus*. *Am. J. Botany* **26**:690–693.
10. Porter, C. L. 1941. A new species of *Astragalus* from Arizona. *Madrono* **6**:18–20.
11. Porter, C. L. 1945. Two tioid *Astragalus* novelties from the Rocky Mountain region. *Madrono* **8**:99–102.
12. Porter, C. L. 1951. *Astragalus* and *Oxytropis* in Colorado. Univ. of Wyoming Publ. **16**:1–49.
13. Rydberg, P. A. 1929. Fabaceae: Galegeae. *N. Am. Flora* **24**:251–262.
14. Trelease, S. F. and H. M. Trelease. 1938. Selenium as a stimulating and possibly essential element for indicator plants. *Science* **87**:70–71.
15. Trelease, S. F. and H. M. Trelease. 1938. Selenium as a stimulating and possibly essential element for indicator plants. *Am. J. Botany* **25**:372–380.
16. Trelease, S. F. and H. M. Trelease. 1939. Physiological differentiation in *Astragalus* with reference to selenium. *Am. J. Botany* **26**:530–535.
17. Trelease, S. F. 1942. Identification of selenium indicator species of *Astragalus* by germination tests. *Science* **95**:656–657.
18. Trelease, S. F. and O. A. Beath. 1949. "Selenium," 292 pp. The Champlain Printers, Burlington, Vermont. (Published by the authors.)
19. Vilkomerson, H. 1943. Chromosomes of *Astragalus*. *Torrey Botany Club, Bull.* **70**:430–435.
20. Wooton, E. O. and Standley, P. C. 1915. Flora of New Mexico. *Contrib. U. S. Nat. Herb.* **19**:1–794.

CHAPTER IV

ACCUMULATION OF SELENIUM BY PLANTS

Selenium indicator plants play an important part as converters of soil selenium. These plants absorb selenium from geological formations, virgin shales or soils and convert it into soluble compounds which, when returned to the soil, are readily available for absorption by all types of plant vegetation. In many regions, enrichment of the upper soil may have gone through countless cycles of growth and decay of the converter plants. In areas of dense growth the converters contribute considerable amounts of available selenium to crop plants.

The accumulation of selenium in plants depends on the species of plant, environmental factors, age, and phase of growth of the plants and nature of selenium compounds.

The selenium content of plants growing in the same soil represents the relative ability of species to accumulate selenium. Several species of plants collected from the same outcrop of the Niobrara Formation showed marked differences in their selenium content.

Astragalus bisulcatus	5,530 ppm
Stanleya pinnata	1,190 ppm
Atriplex nuttallii	300 ppm
Grasses	23 ppm

SELENIUM-ACCUMULATING CAPACITY OF PLANTS

On the basis of field studies in the western United States, the seleniferous plants are divided into groups according to their ability to accumulate selenium. The division may have been made on the basis of the chemical properties and the biological effects on livestock of the selenium compounds present in these plants.

Group 1. Primary selenium indicator or accumulator or "Beath's selenium indicator" or converter plants contain large amounts of selenium (1000 to 10,000 ppm). The chemical compounds of selenium in the plants are not well defined; however, it is recognized that selenium in *Astragalus* and some other indicators is present in water-soluble, small molecular weight, organic compounds. The disease syndrome of blind staggers or acute selenium poisoning in livestock is the result of the consumption of

TABLE 19

Ranges of Selenium Content of Representative Primary Selenium Indicator Plants[a]

Ranges of selenium (ppm)		Percentage distribution of specimens[b] in each range						
Low	High	*Astragalus bisulcatus* (405 specimens)	*Astragalus pattersoni* and var. *praelongus* (68 specimens)	*Astragalus pectinatus* (385 specimens)	*Astragalus racemosus* (180 specimens)	Section *Oonopsis* of *Hap.* (29 specimens)	Section *Xylorhiza* of *Mach.* (82 specimens)	*Stanleya* spp. (233 specimens)
<1		<1	<1	<1	2.2	<1	1.2	1.7
1	9	6.9	1.5	0	8.3	0	7.3	20.6
10	19	5.4	4.4	0.3	7.8	0	9.8	5.1
20	39	8.9	2.9	0.5	9.5	0	20.7	8.2
40	79	11.9	2.9	4.2	12.2	3.4	4.9	13.3
80	159	16.3	13.2	14.3	11.1	10.3	13.4	11.6
160	319	19.0	25.0	17.9	12.2	13.8	20.7	15.4
320	639	15.1	5.9	23.1	13.9	17.3	4.9	12.9
640	1,279	8.9	16.2	21.0	12.2	27.6	9.8	9.4
1,280	2,559	4.4	17.6	13.8	5.0	10.3	4.9	1.7
2,560	5,119	3.0	10.3	4.7	4.4	13.8	1.2	0
5,210	10,239	0.2	0	0.3	1.2[c]	3.4	1.2	0

[a] Plants collected in 15 states of the western United States.

[b] Air-dried.

[c] One specimen contained 14,920 ppm.

these types of vegetation (see Chapter V). These plants will be referred to in this chapter as indicator plants.

Group 2. Secondary selenium absorbers rarely contain more than a few hundred parts per million of selenium on air-dried bases. A large percentage of selenium in these plants occurs as selenate; only lesser amounts occur in organic form(s). These plants may produce acute or chronic selenosis in livestock. (The taxonomic descriptions of Groups 1 and 2 are given in Chapter III.)

Group 3. Most cultivated crop plants, grains, and native grasses generally accumulate low concentrations of selenium (maximum, 30 ppm). Selenium is associated mainly with plant proteins. Alkali disease in livestock is produced by the form of selenium present in these plants.

SELENIUM ACCUMULATION IN INDICATOR PLANTS

Experimental studies by Trelease and Trelease (*74, 75*) indicated that selenium is an essential element for the growth and development of indicator plants. The ranges of selenium content of indicator plants grown on different types of soil are shown in Table 19.

As evident from the data, there is wide variation in the selenium content in these plants. The samples were collected in widely distributed areas in the western United States (15 states). They were at various stages of growth and there may have been differences in the ages of the plants. The low selenium values in some indicator plants may have been due to loss of selenium by volatilization during drying and the inadequacy of methods of determination for small amounts of selenium or both. In some species, the loss by volatilization may be as high as 60 per cent (*5*).

In general, indicator species of *Astragalus*, sections of *Oonopsis* of *Haplopappus* and *Xylorhiza* of *Machaeranthera* accumulate more selenium than *Stanleya* (*2, 3, 6, 47, 51*).

The secondary selenium absorbers usually have lower selenium content than indicator plants (*6, 51*). The comparative selenium content of primary and secondary selenium absorbers is given in Table 20. Only a limited number of samples were collected but the results show the variations in selenium content of different species of plants as well as of the same species grown within a small area on the same geological formation (*51*).

The variations in selenium content of indicator plants are recognized by all investigators. These differences are not only related to species or genus of selenium indicator plants but also to their environments.

Chemical Environment

On the basis of the geological distribution of indicator plants, Cannon (*16*) suggested that *Stanleya* requires sulfur in addition to selenium for growth. Experimental studies on the growth requirements of *Stanleya pinnata* in nutrient solution indicated that the inclusion of sulfate with selenate enhanced growth and accumulation of selenium in the plants (*24*). When sulfate concentration of the nutrient solution was reduced to 0.1 ppm (sulfur) or less and selenate concentration was increased to 10 ppm (selenium) or more, the growth of *S. pinnata* was inhibited. These limited studies of the genus *Stanleya* indicate that the accumulation of selenium in these plants is influenced by sulfur, and sulfur may have a specific function for the accumulation of selenium in high concentrations in these plants.

The influence of other elements on the absorption of selenium by indicator plants has not been investigated with the exception of some pre-

TABLE 20

Comparative Selenium Content of Primary and Secondary Selenium Absorbers[a]

Plant[b]		Selenium[c] (ppm)		
		Minimum	Maximum	Average
Astragalus racemosus	(25)[d]	3.5	4,100	1,021
Stanleya bipinnata	(8)	250.0	2,380	700
Aster multiflora	(21)	0.0	320	62
Grindelia squarrosa	(8)	0.0	260	38
Gutierrezia sarothrae	(9)	8.0	220	60

[a] Moxon *et al.* (*51*).
[b] Plants were collected within an area of four square rods on the same formation.
[c] Dry basis.
[d] Numbers in parentheses are the numbers of samples analyzed.

liminary studies by Cannon (*16*). The experiment was carried out near Santa Fe, New Mexico. Desert-type soil was treated with sodium vanadate, calcium sulfate, sodium selenite, potash, and carnotite singly and in combination. Some 20 species of plants were grown in these plots and analyzed.

When either sulfur or selenium was added to the carnotite plots or sodium vanadate strip, the solubility of uranium and vanadium increased. This relationship was reciprocal since sulfur and selenium were also more soluble and readily absorbed by the plants in the presence of carnotite. When gypsum and selenium (selenite) were added to the carnotite plot, uranium and vanadium were generally more easily absorbed and transported to the upper part of the plant.

A comparison of uranium, selenium, and vanadium content of four species of plants grown on three plots is given in Table 21.

Absorption of uranium, vanadium, and selenium varied widely depending on the species of plants and the chemical environment in the soil. The growth of *Stanleya pinnata* was inhibited in the presence of carnotite and that of *Grindelia* in the presence of selenite. The addition of selenite to carnotite increased not only the selenium uptake by *A. pattersoni* and *Stanleya* but uranium as well as vanadium absorption.

The effect of other ions on the absorption and accumulation of selenium by indicator plants merits more consideration than it was given in the past. The effect of one ion on the absorption of other ions by higher plants has been demonstrated by a number of investigators. The genus *Stanleya* as well as seleniferous species of other genera could be used for studies on the interaction of ions and their effects on the accumulation of selenium in these plants.

TABLE 21

Uranium, Vanadium, and Selenium Content in the Ash of Plants[a]

Plant genus[b]	Carnotite (ppm)			Carnotite-selenite (ppm)			Sodium selenite (ppm)		
	U	V	Se	U	V	Se	U	V	Se
Descurainia (Tansy mustard)	265	100	206	490	250	29	2.8	35	227
Astragalus (*pattersoni*)	33	25	136	164	95	11,680	2.1	60	5,000
Grindelia (Gumweed)	87	105	159	162	84	150	(1)	(1)	(1)
Stanleya (Prince's plume)	(1)[c]	(1)	(1)	66	50	92	0.5	15	174

[a] Cannon (*16*).
[b] Aerial part.
[c] Numbers in parentheses indicate no growth of plants in plots.

Physical Environment

A favorable growing season, initiated by an abundance of moisture, is usually conducive to high selenium absorption by the deep-rooted indicator plants. Franke and Painter (*19*) reported that the selenium content of plants was higher during seasons of greater rainfall. Byers (*13*), however, presented data indicating that absorption decreased with increasing rainfall. Although high rainfall may tend to reduce absorption by diluting the soluble selenium in soil solution, it also promotes absorption by favoring vigorous growth of some species of the plants.

Astragalus racemosus grows in drier alkali soil than *A. bisulcatus*. *Astragalus pattersoni* grown on raw Mancos Shale has higher selenium content than when grown in the wash of the Mancos. The selenium content of *A. beathii* on the Moenkopi Formation is higher than plants growing in the wash of this formation.

An alteration in the environment affects and controls the process of absorption of selenium by these plants.

Age and Phase of Growth

All indicator plants are perennials with well-developed root systems and great avidity to accumulate and absorb selenium continually during the life of the plant. The selenium content of foliage of young *A. bisulcatus* was 477 ppm; as the plant grew it increased to 2920 ppm (5). The roots of the younger plant had correspondingly lower selenium content (75 ppm) than did the roots of the older plant (444 ppm). The selenium is not stored in the aerial part of the plants but is metabolized during their life cycle. With the development of root systems, more selenium is made available to the plants.

TABLE 22

Seasonal Variations in Selenium Content of Indicator Plants

Indicator plant	Stages of growth	Selenium content (ppm)[a]
Astragalus bisulcatus[b]	Pre-bloom[1]	8,840
	Full bloom[2]	6,590
	Past seeding[3]	595
Machaeranthera glabriuscula[b]	Very early growth[1]	1,800
	Early bud stage[1]	1,200
	Full bloom[2]	700
	Past seeding[3]	79
Haplopappus fremontii[b]	Pre-bloom[1]	2,290
	Full bloom[2]	4,800
	Past seeding[3]	1,585
Aster commutatis[c]	Initial growth[1]	590
	Pre-bloom[1]	273
	Full bloom[2]	233
	Seeding[3]	15

[a] Air-dried.
[b] Primary selenium indicator.
[c] Secondary selenium absorber.
[1] Spring.
[2] Summer.
[3] Fall.

Most indicator plants show seasonal variations in their selenium content. In *Astragalus*, the selenium content is highest at an early growth and then gradually declines. The seasonal variations in the selenium content of three species of indicators and one species of secondary absorbers are given in Table 22.

Haplopappus fremontii (Table 22) and *Grindelia squarrosa* are representative of a small group of plants that do not attain their maximum selenium content until the flowering stage and retain a relatively large amount in the dormant stage (*5, 51, 53*).

A number of species of secondary selenium absorbers (Table 22) are more highly seleniferous in their early growth than in the later stages (*5, 51*).

The distribution of selenium in the various parts of the plant (roots, stems, leaves, flowers, and fruits) differs according to the species, its phase of growth, and its physiological state.

The tops of most selenium accumulators usually contain more selenium than the roots as is shown in Table 23; the exceptions are *Haplopappus*

TABLE 23
Distribution of Selenium in Tops and Roots of Selenium Accumulators

Plant	Selenium (ppm)[a]		Ratio
	Tops	Roots	Tops/roots
Astragalus crotalariae	2,000	45	44
A. beathii	1,963	66	30
A. pattersoni var. *praelongus*	583	26	22
A. argillosus	385	27	14
A. bisulcatus	1,180	130	9
A. preussii	313	40	8
A. beathii (greenhouse, selenate)	524	213	2.5
A. pattersoni	730	296	2.5
A. racemosus (greenhouse, selenite)	1,256	659	1.8
Haplopappus fremontii	4,800	4,800	1.0
Stanleya pinnata	125	429	0.3

[a] Air-dried.

fremontii and *Stanleya pinnata*. The ratio of selenium content of tops to that in roots in *H. fremontii* is unity, while in *S. pinnata* it is 0.3. In species of *Astragalus* there are considerable differences in these ratios, but in all species the selenium content of the tops exceeds that of the roots.

The distribution of selenium in different parts of indicator plants shows variation during reproductive growth. The fruits in early fruiting period have lower selenium content than seeds, while stems, leaves, and roots have more selenium in fruiting stage than at the time seeds are matured. The selenium content in reproductive growth of *A. pectinatus* and regrowth of *A. bisulcatus* is given in Table 24.

Astragalus bisulcatus and related species often produce new shoots and the regrowth in the fall may remain green for a considerable time.

TABLE 24
Selenium Content of Species of Astragalus *in Reproductive and Regrowth Stages*

	Stages of growth	Selenium (ppm)[a]
Astragalus pectinatus	Early Fruiting	
	Fruits	612
	Stems	339
	Leaves	374
	Roots	594
	Mature Stage	
	Seeds	3,250
	Pods	124
	Stems and leaves	260
Astragalus bisulcatus	Pre-bloom	8,840
	Full bloom	6,950
	Regrowth	8,000
	Old stems	225
	Roots	800

[a] Air-dried.

These tender shoots contain high concentrations of selenium, while old stems have comparatively small amounts of selenium (Table 24).

Dry leaves and stems always contain less selenium than green leaves and stems. The selenium content of the leaves and stems is high during vegetative growth, decreases to a low level at senescence, and increases in the maturing seeds.

Seeds of all seleniferous species of *Astragalus* have high concentrations of selenium (Table 25). The differences in the selenium content in seeds

TABLE 25
Selenium Content of Seleniferous Astragalus *Seeds*

	Average selenium (ppm)
Astragalus racemosus	1,659
A. osterhouti	3,000
A. bisulcatus	3,051
A. pattersoni	3,330

of different species may not be due only to environmental factors but may be related to the genetic characteristics of the species.

Experimental Studies

Solution and sand cultures are used to determine the roles of mineral elements or other nutrients in plant nutrition. The physiological differentiation and identification of seleniferous species of *Astragalus* were discussed in a previous chapter.

Trelease and his co-workers (*76–79*) conducted experiments in order to determine whether the unique characteristics of indicator plants could be validated with plants grown in solution culture or sand culture irrigated with solutions. The studies in solution or sand cultures indicated that crop plants as well as indicator plants absorb and accumulate higher concentrations of selenium derived from an aqueous extract of an indicator plant than from inorganic selenium compounds (*76–79*).

The accumulation of selenium by *Astragalus racemosus* grown in culture solution with selenite and organic selenium is shown in Figs. 22 and

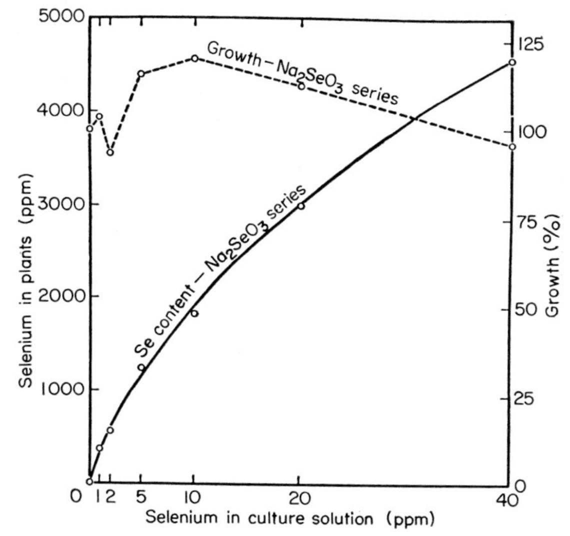

FIG. 22. Influence of selenium as selenite on growth and accumulation in *Astragalus racemosus.*

105105

23. These results indicate the differences in the accumulation of selenium by the plant from the selenite and organic selenium (as *Astragalus* extract). The plants accumulated more selenium from the plant extract than from selenite (*79*). The addition of 5 to 10 ppm selenium as selenite stimulated growth of the plant, but the growth apparently was less than reported in previous experiments by Trelease and Trelease (*75, 76*). The addition of *Astragalus* extract containing organic selenium depressed the growth rate when the selenium content exceeded 1.25 ppm, and 5 ppm completely inhibited the growth of *A. racemosus*. The selenium in the extract of *Astragalus* appears to inhibit the metabolic activity of the plant (as indicated by its effect on growth) more than the same concentrations of selenite or selenate.

Investigations of the enzyme system in *A. racemosus* by Rosenfeld and

Wirtz (67) revealed that the tissue homogenate technique could not be used in these studies. The metabolic activity of *A. racemosus* could be studied only in intact leaves. If the leaves were homogenized in buffer, the respiration was partially or completely inhibited by the tissue juices. The inhibition subsequently was followed by erratic and irregular rates of respiration. This would suggest that by breaking the leaves in the buffer some toxic compound(s) were liberated from the leaves and before respiration could be resumed the plant extract partially removed some of the inhibitor(s). The addition of selenate (30 ppm selenium)

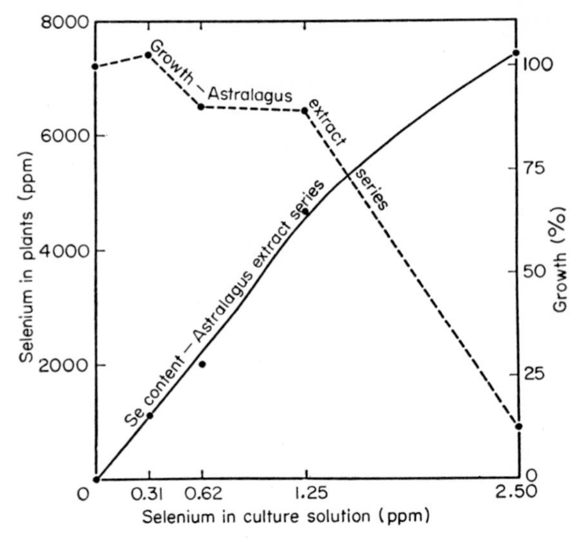

FIG. 23. Influence of organic selenium in *Astragalus* extract on growth and accumulation in *Astragalus racemosus*.

to the substrate of intact leaves also partially inhibited the respiration of *A. racemosus* leaves which contained over 2000 ppm selenium (Rosenfeld, unpublished). It appears that selenium is bound in seleniferous *Astragalus* so that the enzymes or coenzymes may function even when the plants contain high concentrations of selenium. However, the respiratory enzyme(s) of the indicator plant(s) are sensitive to free selenate, selenite, or even the selenium compounds bound within the tissues of these plants.

The growth inhibition of *A. racemosus* by the aqueous extract of *Astragalus* and the inhibition of respiration by homogenization of leaves suggest that *Astragalus* plants may synthesize some water-soluble selenium compounds which, when liberated, can interfere with the metabolic activities of the plants. Since selenium in the aqueous extract of *Astragalus* is present in organic form (4, 5, 78), future studies with organic seleno-compounds as sources of selenium would be of considerable value for metabolic studies.

Astragalus bisulcatus and *Astragalus pectinatus* accumulated 1150 ppm when the soil contained elemental selenium (*5*).

These investigations substantiated field observations that indicator plants can absorb high concentrations of selenium regardless of its chemical structure. Under certain conditions selenium compound(s) may interfere with the metabolic activities of indicator plants which contain high concentrations of selenium.

Tracer Studies

The use of radioactive selenium in studies with indicator plants is limited at the present time. The extreme sensitivity of tracer techniques may be useful for studies to determine chemical and physical factors that influence the translocation of selenium in indicator plants.

Translocation in the present discussion will refer to the movement of selenium from the soil by roots and the movement of Se^{75} in the aerial parts of the plant. The translocation of Se^{75} was studied in selenium accumulator, *A. bisulcatus,* in greenhouse experiments by Rosenfeld and Eppson (*68*). *Astragalus bisulcatus* was grown in soil mixed with Amberlite resins on which Se^{75}-selenite and K_2SeO_4 was absorbed. The plants absorbed the selenium bound to the resins and translocated it to the aerial part of the plant. Radioautographs of the plants demonstrated that there was a definite relation between metabolic activity and the presence of selenium in the plants.

Figure 24 shows the distribution of Se^{75} in leaves harvested 210 days after the seeds were planted. Actively growing young leaves contained large amounts of radioactivity. In older yellow leaves, there was a corresponding loss of selenium from the mesophyll with the loss of chlorophyll. Autoradiographs indicated that selenium was not stored or deposited in the plants but was transported from regions of low to high metabolic activity. The presence of Se^{75} around the veins and nodes of leaflets and stems suggests that at senescence selenium was either withdrawn from the dying leaflets or was not transmitted to the aging tissues. Newly developing stems and leaflets of *A. bisulcatus* contained high concentrations of Se^{75}.

The uptake of Se^{75} ($H_2Se^{75}O_3$) from nutrient solutions by the roots and shoots of five species of plants including *Neptunia amplexicaulis* was investigated by Peterson and Butler (*64*). This plant occurs mainly on seleniferous soils in central Queensland and is considered a selenium indicator. The uptake of Se^{75}-selenite by young *Neptunia* plants was not much greater (from the nutrient solution) than by other plants. There was a considerable difference in the uptake of Se^{75} by young and mature shoots and roots of *Neptunia*. The roots of the mature plants contained 99 per cent of the total Se^{75}, but the Se^{75} uptake by roots of younger plants varied from 64 to 78 per cent.

Lack of differential uptake of Se^{75}-selenite from the young *Neptunia* plant may be correlated with the presence of stored selenium in the seeds. Selenium content of *Neptunia* seeds from Queensland was 123 μg per seed and from New Zealand, 0.45 μg per seed. The presence of stored selenium in the seeds of indicator plants creates specific problems

FIG. 24. Se^{75} autoradiogram of leaves of *A. bisulcatus*. Se^{75} is distributed throughout the young leaves and stems. In chloratic leaflets and interveinal tissue, Se^{75} is decreased. (Rosenfeld and Eppson, *68*.)

in evaluating the selenium accumulation by indicator plants in culture solutions and short-term experiments. Accumulation of specific ions within living cells depends upon the metabolic history of the cells. Rapid accumulation of ions does not occur if the cells already contain relatively high concentrations of the same ions; in such cases the trend is toward an equilibrium between the solution and cells. Conversely, if the initial ion content of cells is low, the concentration of ions in the absorbing cells may exceed that of the ions in the solution (*56*).

Of the numerous mechanisms which have been proposed for active electrolyte absorption by roots, probably the one which most satisfactorily fits the absorption of selenium by indicators is that proposed by Brooks (*11*).

He suggested that the initial step in absorption of either cation or anion involves the exchange of an ion in the culture solution for an ion of like charge which is held on the surface or within the protoplasm.

A similar mechanism was evidenced in the studies of Peterson and Butler (*64*) with *Neptunia* and of Rosenfeld (*69*) with 7- to 8-day-old excised roots of *A. preussii.*

To study the mechanism of Se^{75} absorption by *A. preussii,* the roots were placed in buffer solution containing $Se^{75}O_3$ ions; at various time intervals they were removed and rinsed superficially with water, and the uptake of Se^{75} was determined.

The excised roots rapidly absorbed the $Se^{75}O_3$ ions from the buffer solution, but within 5 minutes equilibrium was established between the incoming and outgoing ions. This was indicated by the constant amount of Se^{75} present in the roots at 10 and 15 minutes or longer. Increase in time or in isotope concentration of the solutions did not increase the percentage of absorption of Se^{75} by the excised roots. In *A. preussii* a high concentration of Se^{75} (87%) was present in the sap in dissolved state, and the remaining selenium was bound within the root skeleton (*69*).

Overstreet and Boyer (*56*) suggested that absorption of potassium in a "high salt plant" was not an accumulation but was the establishment of ionic equilibrium between the solution and the potassium already present in the plants. The initial selenium content of *A. preussii* seeds varied from 761 to 1067 ppm, and in the roots the variations were 369 to 764 ppm. The roots utilized about 50 per cent of the stored selenium in the seeds during embryonic development. The seedlings had the characteristic odor of volatile selenium (probably dimethyl selenide).

The inward as well as the outward movement of ions from the *A. preussii* roots was influenced by the original concentration of selenium in the roots (*69*). The absorption of Se^{75} in live roots was influenced by temperature. Live roots at 0° C and dead roots at 0° and 25° C absorbed $Se^{75}O_3^{=}$ from the substrate at different rates than live roots at 25° C. If the permeability of the cells was impaired, the absorption or exchange was nonmetabolic and no equilibrium was established between the influx and outgo of Se^{75} from the roots. Jacobson and Overstreet (*35*) studied the binding of Sr^{++} by ether-killed roots as well as living roots and observed a similar absorption pattern. Dead roots absorb more Sr^{++} but the ions in these roots were more readily removed than from live roots. On the basis of the exchange curves they suggested that the ions are fixed in the form of chemical compounds with varying degrees of stability.

The effect of sulfur compounds on the uptake of $Se^{75}O_3^{=}$ by *A. preussii* roots indicated that the absorption or exchange of Se^{75} was not influenced by the addition of sulfite or sulfate ions to the absorption or exchange solutions (Rosenfeld, unpublished). The inward and outward movement of

Se^{75} from the roots in the presence of sulfate and sulfite ions was the same as in the absence of sulfur ions. These preliminary experiments suggest that in excised roots of *A. preussii*, the binding site(s) of sulfate or sulfite ions are not the same as those of the selenite ion.

SELENIUM ACCUMULATION IN FARM CROPS

In most farming areas, the virgin soils contain so little available selenium that cultivated crops are unable to absorb more than traces of the element. If seleniferous soils are kept free of indicator or selenium converter plants, they do not become seleniferous under cultivation (*4*).

Farm crops, in order to accumulate and store selenium (5 ppm or more), must be rooted in soils that contain available selenium. Natural soils of this type occur in South Dakota (Fall River, Gregory, Haakon, Hughes, Jones, Lyman, and Stanley counties), along the northern edge of Nebraska (Boyd, Knox, and Sheridan counties), and the northeastern edge of Wyoming (Niobrara County). The occurrence of this type of seleniferous area in other parts of the western United States was not studied as extensively as in the above states.

TABLE 26

Selenium Content of Wheat and Wheat Products[a]

State	Counties	Selenium content (ppm)		
		Minimum	Maximum	Average
Colorado	2 (3)[b]	2.0	3.0	2.5
Kansas	9 (44)	<0.1	5.0	1.3
Montana	16 (363)	<0.1	4.0	0.6
Nebraska	6 (76)	<0.1	10.0	2.3
North Dakota	3 (71)	<0.1	3.0	0.7
South Dakota	14 (149)	<0.1	25.0	2.6
Wyoming	4 (45)	<0.1	3.0	0.6

[a] Williams *et al.* (*85*).

[b] Numbers in parentheses are numbers of specimens analyzed.

Selenium content of wheat and wheat products, barley, corn, oats, and rye from seven western states is given in Tables 26 and 27 (*85*). Among the samples analyzed, the most seleniferous grain and its products were from South Dakota, Nebraska, and Kansas. The maximum amount in a few samples was high, but if the results are evaluated on the basis of the averages, even in these areas the grains contained low concentrations of selenium. Lakin and Byers (*40*) reported that 82.5 per cent of 951 samples of analyzed wheat contained 1.0 ppm or less selenium; 10 per cent contained 2–3 ppm; and 7.5 per cent contained 4 ppm or more selenium (only eight samples contained as much as 8 ppm of selenium or more). Robinson (*66*) reported 26 ppm of selenium in one sample of wheat, but 29 samples contained from 0.1 to 1.5 ppm. These samples were collected from various parts of the world. Selenium content of corn, wheat, and barley analyzed in South Dakota ranged between 25 and 30 ppm (*48*).

Field Studies

The relatively low selenium uptake by wheat from seleniferous soil was indicated by studies in central and eastern Montana. Young wheat plants were collected where *A. pectinatus* and *A. bisulcatus* grew outside of the wheat fields (*7*). The average selenium content of 21 wheat seedlings was 1.9 ppm with a maximum of 8 ppm. The selenium content of *A. pectinatus* ranged from 28 to 2140 ppm and of *A. bisulcatus* from 12 to 1468 ppm. That indicator plants can increase the available selenium for crop plants was evident from field studies in Wyoming (*5*). Composite samples of *A. racemosus* which contained 14,920 ppm and *Stanleya pinnata* which contained 1163 ppm of selenium were plowed under, and the selenium content of grains grown on that field increased. The wheat contained 20 ppm, and the corn of the following year contained 12 ppm of selenium. Roots and stubbles left in crop fields are a potential source of available selenium for succeeding crops. Although some of the available selenium is removed in harvesting, a significant fraction is retained by the residual parts of plants.

TABLE 27

Selenium Content of Grains[a]

State	Counties	Selenium content (ppm)		
		Minimum	Maximum	Average
Colorado	4 (8)[b]	0.5	1.0	0.4
Kansas	2 (5)	1.0	3.0	1.5
Montana	7 (19)	0.1	2.0	1.0
Nebraska	5 (51)	0.1	15.0	1.8
North Dakota	3 (17)	0.2	2.0	0.8
South Dakota	11 (74)	0.1	30.0	2.8
Wyoming	1 (2)	0.5	1.0	0.8

[a] Williams *et al.* (*85*).

[b] Numbers in parentheses are numbers of specimens analyzed.

When barley was grown in an area where a heavy stand of *A. bisulcatus* grew, the straw and grain of the barley contained 20 ppm of selenium (*4*). These studies indicate the mode of selenium enrichment of soils with subsequent accumulation of selenium in crop plants.

Selenium content of various farm crops is indicated in Table 28. The data were obtained on food crops grown in seleniferous areas. Grains, asparagus, onions, and rutabagas contained high concentrations of selenium, but all other food crops contained lesser amounts of selenium.

The selenium content of crop plants at different stages of growth was studied by Moxon *et al.* (*51*). Wheat plants had a higher selenium content at early stages of growth than at maturity, while oats contained no selenium at seeding, heading, and pollinating stages. However, there was an increase in selenium content at early maturity. The selenium content of barley remained fairly constant at all stages of growth.

Grains and roots contain about the same amount of selenium, but there are lesser amounts present in stems and leaves at maturity (*5*). The distribution of selenium in crop plants at early maturity is indicated in Table 29.

TABLE 28

Selenium Content in Grains and Vegetables Grown in Seleniferous Areas[a]

	Selenium (ppm)			Selenium (ppm)	
	Minimum	Maximum		Minimum	Maximum
Wheat	1.15	30.0	Cabbage	2.3	4.5
Corn	1.00	20.0	Peas and beans	0.2	2.0
Rye	0.90	25.0	Carrots	1.3	1.4
Onions	0.40	17.8	Tomatoes	0.2	1.2
Barley	1.70	17.0	Beets	0.3	1.2
Oats	2.00	15.0	Potatoes	0.2	0.9
Asparagus	2.70	11.0	Cucumbers	0.1	0.6
Rutabagas	1.70	6.0			

[a] Compiled from publications discussed in the chapter.

Distribution of selenium in the various mill fractions of wheat was reported by Moxon *et al.* (*50*). Although wheat from South Dakota farms rarely contains more than 30 ppm of selenium, one sample grown on highly seleniferous soil had 63 ppm. Milled and fractionated wheat was analyzed for selenium: bran contained 88 ppm; shorts 77 ppm; and patent flour 53 ppm. The distribution of selenium in milled fractions of 3 other samples with lower selenium content was similar to the above. The nitrogen, sulfur, and selenium content of bran was higher than all other fractions. This would be expected since it has been shown that selenium is closely associated with the proteins of wheat.

There are only limited data on the ability of alfalfa to accumulate high concentrations of selenium. Moxon (*48*) analyzed alfalfa samples from various parts of South Dakota and reported that the maximum selenium content was 10 ppm. Beath (*4*) reported that alfalfa grown on seleniferous raw shale contained little or no selenium. Alfalfa grown on Pierre loam (eastern Wyoming), which had a dense growth of *A. pectinatus*, accumulated considerable amounts of selenium (*4*). Pre-bloom alfalfa on the average contained 57 ppm; at the full-bloom stage the selenium content decreased to 19 ppm. Byers (*14*) reported 200 ppm selenium in alfalfa grown on an irrigated field in Nebraska. Alfalfa samples collected on unirrigated fields contained 25 ppm selenium.

The selenium content of sweet clover varies with the stage of growth (*51*). The highest concentration of selenium was present at the early flowering stage (26 ppm); it decreased at the full-bloom stage to 15 ppm.

TABLE 29

Distribution of Selenium in Crop Plants at Early Maturity

		Selenium (ppm)[a]
Wheat[b]	Grain	35.0
	Stems and leaves	17.0
	Roots	36.0
Oats[c]	Heads	7.3
	Stems	3.8
	Roots	12.7
Barley[c]	Heads	3.6
	Stems	5.5
	Roots	10.5

[a] Dry basis.
[b] Beath *et al.* (*5*).
[c] Moxon *et al.* (*51*).

The plant past flowering stage contained 4 ppm and at maturity contained only 1 ppm of selenium.

It is apparent that alfalfa and clover, like other crop plants, can absorb and accumulate selenium if the selenium is in available form.

Experimental Studies

Selenium accumulation in about 30 kinds of farm crops was studied experimentally by Beath (*4*). The plants were grown on raw Steele, Morrison, Benton, and Niobrara shales. Alfalfa, cabbage, sugar beets, and hairy vetch stored less than 0.1 ppm. Potatoes contained 0.1 ppm; parsnips 0.2 ppm; carrots 0.3 ppm; crested wheat grass 0.3 ppm; beans 0.4 ppm; rutabagas 0.5 ppm; sunflower seeds 0.6 ppm; corn 0.6 ppm; oat heads 0.7 ppm; and peas 1.7 ppm. The highest concentration was 2 ppm in heads of wheat. Experiments were continued for 4 years, and the highest selenium content of any crop plant was 3.6 ppm.

The role of converter plants in increasing the availability of selenium to nonseleniferous plants from raw shales was studied by Beath (*4*).

Farm crops were grown on one plot of Steele shale, and several species of indicators were grown on another plot for 3 years. The foliage of the converters was permitted to fall to the ground, decay, and leach for 3 years in the manner which normally occurs in the field. At the end of the third year, wheat planted on the indicator plot absorbed enough selenium to make the wheat highly seleniferous, whereas the crops on the plot free of indicators remained nonseleniferous or contained only trace amounts.

In experiments where water extracts of *A. bisulcatus* or chopped plants were added to Steele or Niobrara shale, farm crops grown on the plot absorbed comparatively high concentrations of selenium. The selenium content of wheat heads was 95 ppm; stems and leaves 123 ppm; and roots 107 ppm (*5*). In the second year, the grain contained 107 ppm; straw and chaff 38.4 ppm; and roots 35.9 ppm of selenium.

Cereals grown on Thermopolis shales artificially selenized with either sodium selenite or selenium from *A. bisulcatus* uniformly contained less selenium than when grown on Steele, Morrison, or Niobrara shales selenized with the same amount of available selenium (*4*). The decreased availability of selenium to cereals in Thermopolis shale was more pronounced with selenium from *Astragalus* plants than with sodium selenite. The effects of shales or soil derived from different formations on the availability of selenium to crop plants points to the significance of physical as well as chemical factors which may control or regulate absorption of selenium by nonseleniferous plants.

The absorption of selenium by young corn plants grown on seleniferous Pierre clay soil and Pierre shale was studied by Moxon (*48*). Corn accumulated the same amount of selenium whether it was grown on the Pierre soil or shale. The selenium content varied from 14.7 to 28 ppm. Considerable amounts of selenium in the soil were present as selenate. The Pierre Shale appears to differ in its physical and chemical characteristics from other seleniferous shales by the availability of selenium for absorption by crop plants.

Soil colloids remove selenites from the soil solution more readily than selenates. Colloids have been found to reduce the absorption of sodium selenite by wheat and millet, but to have little or no effect on the absorption of sodium selenate (*22*).

Sodium selenate is partially retained in the upper layers of a clay loam when a solution is poured on the surface (*30*). Wheat absorbed sodium selenate more readily when it was added to the naturally seleniferous Pierre clay than when it was added to an originally nonseleniferous clay loam.

Elemental selenium is insoluble in water, but by hydrolysis or bacterial action small amounts may be converted to available form for crop plants (5). Hurd-Karrer (*30*) reported that elemental selenium was not absorbed by wheat from loam containing up to 200 ppm.

These experiments provided evidence that indicator plants or converter plants play an important role in providing available selenium for crop plants. The available selenium compounds for absorption are organic selenium (as the result of decay, volatilization, and leaching of converter plants) and inorganic selenium compounds, but elemental selenium is not absorbed by plants.

Laboratory Studies

Experiments with corn growing in solution or sand cultures have confirmed soil experiments that selenium derived from an aqueous extract of

TABLE 30
Accumulation of Selenium by Alfalfa from Selenite and Astragalus *Extract*

	Sodium selenite		*Astragalus* extract[b]	
Selenium[a] (ppm)	Selenium (ppm)	Dry Weight (gm)	Selenium (ppm)	Dry Weight (gm)
0	0	48.5	0	48.5
1	58	36.5	89	49.1
2	97	29.5	178	44.7
5	164	15.0	441	48.5

[a] Concentrations in culture solution.
[b] Selenium in aqueous extract.

seleniferous species of *Astragalus* was much more readily absorbed and accumulated by crop plants than selenium from selenite (*77–79*).

Alfalfa accumulated 441 ppm selenium from 5 ppm *Astragalus* extract with no apparent injury to growth while selenite reduced the growth rate about one third (Table 30).

Selenium is usually accumulated in larger amounts from solutions containing selenates than from those containing selenites (*33*). A considerable amount of selenite remains in the roots of young wheat plants grown in solution cultures, whereas selenate becomes more evenly distributed throughout the plants.

External concentration of selenium affects the absorption and accumulation of selenium in the plant. The accumulation of selenium in plants decreases with an increase in the concentration of selenium in culture solution (*79*).

The differential rate of absorption of selenite, selenate, and organic selenium from *Astragalus* extract by young corn plants grown in culture solution indicated that the ratio of selenium in the tops to that in the roots was 1:15 with selenite, 2:1 with selenate, and 1:5 with *Astragalus* extract (*80,* p. 137).

The distribution of selenium in corn grown to maturity in sand cultures was influenced by the form of selenium supplied to the plant (Table 31) (*80.* p. 137). The results indicate that translocation to different parts of the plant of the absorbed selenium was, to some degree, influenced by the form of selenium available for absorption.

The differential mobility of the selenium in the plant may be related to the structural configuration of selenium compound(s) or to the presence of some stimulating factors in the plant extract which increased the absorption of selenium.

TABLE 31

Selenium Content of Mature Corn Grown in Sand Cultures

Selenium added (ppm)	Selenium (ppm)							
	Roots		Stems		Leaves		Grain	
	A[a]	B[b]	A[a]	B[b]	A[a]	B[b]	A[a]	B[b]
0.5	135	121	60	78	58	86	77	55
1.0	155	218	105	138	76	153	107	99
2.5	209	817	147	393	141	359	209	325
5.0	321	1,820	182	1,228	134	890	308	694

Selenium added to culture solutions:
[a] A: sodium selenite.
[b] B: selenium as aqueous extract of *A. bisulcatus.*

Experimental studies in the greenhouse on the uptake of selenium by wheat plants from seedling to maturity are limited at the present time. Greenhouse studies with the addition of progressive amounts of selenium (from 2 to 32 ppm as selenite) indicated that the amount of selenium absorbed by the plants depended on the selenium available to the plants and the successive stages of maturity of the plants (*36*). The selenium content at maturity in different parts of plants in decreasing order were: kernels, hulls, and stems, regardless of the amount of selenium present in the soil.

The selenium uptake by wheat grown in soil containing 4 ppm of selenium with varying amounts of Se^{75}-selenate indicated that selenium absorption by the plants increased with the growth of the plants. At 40 days, the entire plant contained less selenium than at 63 and 95 days (*37*). The range of selenium content of the plants at 40 days was from 51 to 54 ppm, while at 60 days the leaves and stems contained 70–73 ppm and the heads contained 110–113 ppm. The selenium content at 95 days ranged from

102 to 125 ppm in leaves and stems, from 111 to 117 in kernels, and from 109 to 119 ppm in hulls.

SELENIUM ACCUMULATION IN NATIVE GRASSES

Native grasses rarely accumulate high concentrations of selenium in grazing areas of the Great Plains, the Rocky Mountains, and the Great Basin. Miller and Byers (*47*) classified plants with reference to selenium absorption and placed grasses among low selenium absorbers. Only in the true "poison areas" where the soil contains substantial amounts of available selenium are the native grasses highly seleniferous. Extensive areas of this kind occur in western South Dakota (*48, 51, 53–55*); localized areas occur in south-central Wyoming, southeastern Utah, and Idaho. The selenium content of grasses on seleniferous soil in South Dakota varied

TABLE 32
Comparison of the Selenium Content of Some Common Grasses in Western South Dakota

Name	Number of specimens	Selenium content (ppm)	
		Range	Average
Western wheat grass (*Agropyron smithii*)	135	0.0–84.0	11.5
Needle grass (*Stipa* spp.)	49	0.0–40.0	5.6
Side oat grama (*Bouteloua curtipendula*)	17	0.0–32.0	3.6
Buffalo grass (*Buchloe dactyloides*)	9	0.0–12.0	2.7
Blue grama (*Bouteloua gracilis*)	8	0.0– 3.6	1.4
Little bluestem (*Andropogon scoparius*)	76	0.0– 6.0	1.1

from 0 to 84 ppm selenium. Over 72 per cent of the samples analyzed had a minimum of 1.0 ppm and a maximum of 15 ppm selenium.

The plant population or plant association is of importance as to the amount of selenium grasses accumulate. Native grasses absorb high concentrations of selenium when growing in proximity to selenium-bearing weeds (*4*). Grasses grown close to *Astragalus* contained 70 ppm selenium; at a short distance away, 62 ppm; and at a distance too far to receive the leached selenium from *A. bisulcatus*, 11 ppm.

That primary and secondary selenium accumulators increase the selenium content of grasses has been reported by a number of investigators (*5, 13, 51*).

Western wheat grass (*Agropyron smithii*) is the most highly seleniferous of the grasses in western South Dakota as indicated in Table 32. This is the dominent grass of the region and it is used extensively for hay as well as for pasture (*51*). Olson *et al.* (*53*), on the basis of their studies, suggest that *A. smithii* may be used as an indicator for the availability of selenium from the soil for other species of grasses. In western wheat grass (*A. smithii*), there is a decrease of selenium content in later stages of growth (*51, 53*), owing to the combined effects of leaching, loss of volatile selenium, and shedding of seeds (Table 33).

TABLE 33
Selenium Content of Western Wheat Grass (Agropyron smithii) *at Different Stages of Growth*[a]

Stages of growth	Selenium content (ppm)
Pre-heading	28
Early heading	23
Heading	18
Maturing	14
Late maturity	12
Dry	3

[a] Collections in two subsequent years were made, and the selenium content in the different stages of growth were approximately the same.

There have been no experimental studies to determine the differential uptake and accumulation of selenium in different types of grasses.

COMPARATIVE SELENIUM ACCUMULATION BY PLANTS

It is evident from the preceding discussion that plants differ in their relative capacities to absorb selenium. Factors other than species of plant control selenium absorption (*21, 28–30, 33, 39, 43, 44, 47, 51, 64, 74, 78, 79*). The comparative selenium accumulation in indicators and in crop plants was studied experimentally.

A comparison of accumulation of selenium from selenite and organic selenium (as *Astragalus bisulcatus* extract) by corn and *Astragalus racemosus* in culture solution was made by Trelease and Greenfield (*79*). *Astragalus racemosus* growing in culture solution absorbed higher concentrations of selenium from plant extract (*A. bisulcatus*) and selenite than corn (Fig. 25). There were not only variations in absorption of selenium by different plants but there were also variations in the uptake of selenium from different seleno-compounds.

The availability of different forms of selenium compounds to crop plants and indicators, *A. racemosus* and *Stanleya pinnata,* was studied by Moxon *et al.* (*51*) in experimental plots. $CaSeO_4$ was more readily absorbed than Na_2SeO_4 by all plants. Indicator plants as well as wheat, barley, and corn absorbed more selenium from selenates than from selenites. $Fe(OH)SeO_3$ and Na_2SeO_3 were readily absorbed by the indicator plants, but the uptake by crop plants was low. FeSe was not absorbed by crop plants and only a limited amount was absorbed by the young indicator plants. Organic selenium (water extract of *A. racemosus*) and $CaSeO_4$ were more readily absorbed by barley than Na_2SeO_4.

Similar differences in the accumulation of selenium by wheat, oats, alfalfa, and *A. racemosus* from different selenium compounds were indicated by studies of Ganje and Whitehead (*21*). Selenium uptake by crop plants was highest when sodium selenate was added to the soil. The accumulation by *A. racemosus* and crop plants of selenium from the different seleno-compounds in increasing order was: basic iron selenite (structure not indicated), selenite, and selenate.

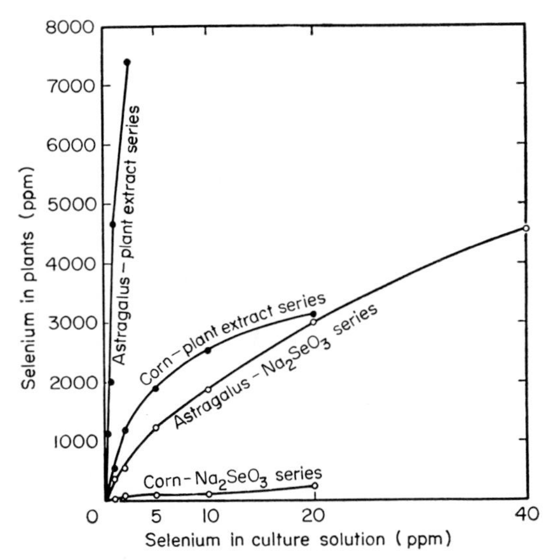

FIG. 25. Comparison of the ability of corn and *A. racemosus* to accumulate selenium from selenite and from organic selenium in *Astragalus* extract.

In a 10-day experiment, *Neptunia amplexicaulis* (indicator plant), white clover, red clover, wheat, and rye grass showed only slight differences in accumulating selenium (*64*). Red clover, white clover, and rye grass accumulated more selenium in short-term experiments than either *N. amplexicaulis* or wheat plants grown in nutrient solution. A high percentage of selenium was present in the roots of all plants. Differences in the ability of selenium indicators of genera *Astragalus* and *Neptunia* to accumulate selenium from selenite may be due to differences in the function of selenium in these plants. It would be of interest to determine the uptake of selenium from selenate and seleniferous plant extract by *Neptunia*. Seleniferous species of *Astragalus* can accumulate over 1000 ppm selenium from selenite in relatively short-term experiments. The limited uptake of selenium by *Neptunia* would suggest some basic metabolic difference between these indicator plants.

FACTORS THAT INFLUENCE SELENIUM ACCUMULATION IN PLANTS

Proteins and Amino Acids

At the present time there is considerable evidence to indicate that selenium is involved in the protein metabolism in crop plants.

The differences in the accumulation of selenium by corn from selenite and from the aqueous extract of *Astragalus* are indicated in Fig. 26.

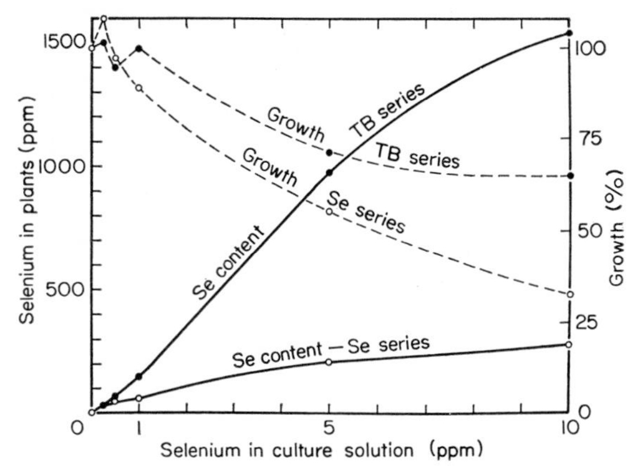

Fig. 26. Effects of selenium as selenite (Se series) and as organic selenium in *Astragalus* extract (TB series) on growth and selenium accumulation in corn plants.

The effect of nitrogenous organic substances on the absorption of sodium selenite was investigated by Trelease and co-workers (77–79). Various proteins, protein derivatives, and amino acids were added in a concentration of 50 ppm to a culture solution containing 5 ppm selenium as sodium selenite (Table 34). Four of these nitrogenous substances—bactotryptone, neopeptone, sodium caseinate, and proteose peptone—approximately doubled the accumulation of selenium by corn plants. Similar increases were obtained with addition of aqueous extracts of alfalfa hay and string beans.

Increasing the concentration of sodium caseinate in a solution containing 5 ppm of selenium as sodium selenite resulted in a progressive increase in the accumulation of selenium in corn plants (Fig. 27). With 200 ppm of sodium caseinate, the corn stored 830 ppm selenium or 4 times the amount accumulated in the absence of protein. As selenium accumulation increased, there was a decrease in dry weight of the plants.

TABLE 34

Influence of Various Proteins and Amino Acids in the Culture Solution on the Accumulation by Corn Seedlings of Selenium Supplied as Sodium Selenite

Protein or amino acid in culture solution 50 ppm	Selenium series (5 ppm Se as Na_2SeO_3)		Control series[a] (no Se)
	Se content of plants (ppm)	Ave. dry wt. of tops (gm)	Ave. dry wt. of tops (gm)
Bactotryptone	471	0.90	2.23
Neopeptone	420	0.87	2.10
Sodium caseinate	413	0.92	2.26
Proteose peptone	396	0.95	3.37
Alanine	324	0.78	2.27
Tyrosine	264	1.02	2.63
Cystine	253	1.00	2.87
Tryptophan	205	1.12	2.20
Control	192	1.14	2.47
Alfalfa hay extract	319	0.80	1.17
Control	143	1.27	2.20
String-bean extract	285	0.84	0.83
Control	132	0.66	1.04

[a] Analysis showed that these plants contained no selenium.

A marked increase in the accumulation of selenium from sodium selenite by corn was produced by the addition of the extracts of nonseleniferous plants (78).

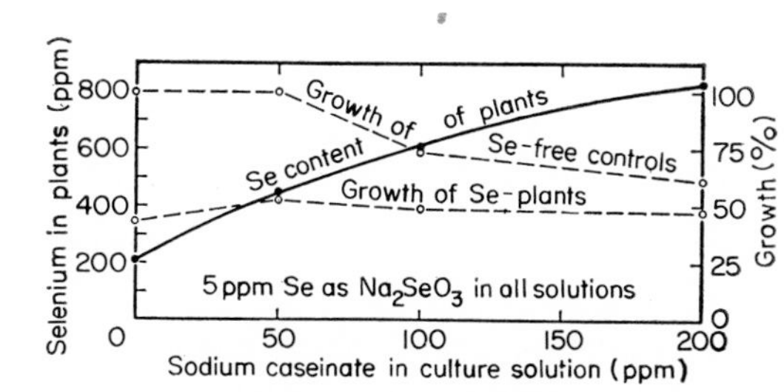

FIG. 27. Influence of sodium caseinate on selenium accumulation and growth of corn plants in solutions containing 5 ppm selenium as selenite.

These experiments suggest that large amounts of nitrogenous organic substances allow greater selenium accumulation by crop plants, but do not prevent growth inhibitory effects of selenium.

SULFUR

Up to the present time, there is no evidence to indicate that the application of sulfur or sulfate to cultivated land would provide a practical means of preventing crop plants from accumulating high concentrations of selenium. Sulfur-selenium antagonism with analogous compounds, i.e., selenate and sulfate, has been demonstrated by Hurd-Karrer (*28, 29, 33, 34*). Selenium is generally present in soils as selenides, sulfide ores, iron pyrites, pyritic concretions, selenates, organic seleno-compounds, selenites, and small amounts of elemental selenium. There is no theoretical

TABLE 35
Sulfur and Selenium in Three-Month-Old Crop Plants[a]

Plant[b]	Leaves or entire tops[c]		Stems[c]		Seed[c]	
	S(%)	Se(ppm)	S(%)	Se(ppm)	S(%)	Se(ppm)
Cabbage	3.83	760	0.95	200	—	—
Kale	3.72	720	0.97	220	—	—
Rape	3.41	720	1.15	250	—	—
Cauliflower	3.38	630	0.84	220	—	—
Sunflower	1.97	420	0.75	100	0.21	100
Black mustard	2.64	480	1.24	220	1.38	320
Onion	1.62	420	—	—	—	—
Flax	1.23	250	—	—	0.15	110
Alfalfa	1.09	220	—	—	—	—
Red clover	0.95	230	—	—	—	—
Vetch	0.89	250	—	—	—	—
Wheat	0.78	120	—	—	0.17	70
Rye	0.64	110	—	—	0.19	30
Corn	0.63	160	0.30	50	0.13	40
Millet	0.62	150	—	—	0.19	110
Lettuce	0.61	90	—	—	—	—
Kafir	0.54	110	—	—	0.15	30
Soybean	0.46	110	—	—	—	—
Sorgo	0.36	110	0.29	80	0.12	50

[a] Hurd-Karrer (*32*).
[b] Grown in Keyport loam with 4 ppm of selenium as sodium selenate.
[c] Air-dried weight.

basis to suggest that the absorption of these seleno-compounds would or could be regulated by the addition of sulfur or sulfate to the soil.

Many seleniferous soils are saturated with sulfur (as gypsum); the addition of more sulfate or sulfur would be of doubtful value in reducing selenium absorption by plants. Field and experimental studies with seleniferous soils failed to show that sulfate, sulfur, or gypsum treatments influenced the absorption of selenium by plants (*4, 5, 19*).

Crop plants, according to Hurd-Karrer (*32*), accumulate selenium from selenate in direct proportion to their sulfur requirement. This direct relationship is indicated by the data in Table 35. In general, variations in selenium content are parallel to corresponding variations in sulfur. The Cruciferae accumulated about four times as much sulfur as the legumes and the latter about twice as much as the cereals. The five members of the Cruciferae—cabbage, cauliflower, mustard, rape, and kale—had the highest concentration of sulfur and selenium. Flax, sunflower, and legumes (except soybean) were intermediate, and the cereals were low in both elements.

The analogous behavior of selenate to sulfur in crop plant metabolism is indicated in the above results. Accumulation of selenium by native seleniferous plants is not associated with high sulfur requirements of these plants. *Haplopappus fremontii* contains 100 times as much selenium as corn, but only twice as much sulfur (*59*). There is no evident correlation between sulfur and selenium accumulation in the five native plants (Table 36) (*80* p. 131). Sulfur:selenium ratios for the various species ranged from 1.4 for *Haplopappus fremontii* to 218 for white sweet clover. *Astragalus bisulcatus* (a legume) contained over 90 times more selenium than yellow sweet clover (also a legume), but only 4.4 times as much sulfur.

TABLE 36
Comparison of Plants with Respect to Their Sulfur and Selenium Content[a]

Plant	Sulfur (%)	Selenium (%)	S/Se
Astragalus bisulcatus[b]	1.58	0.2224	7.1
Haplopappus fremontii[b]	0.45	0.3228	1.4
White sweet clover	0.37	0.0017	218.0
Yellow sweet clover	0.36	0.0024	150.0
Gumweed (*Grindelia*)[c]	0.25	0.0293	8.5

[a] Plants were grown close together on soil derived from Niobrara shale.
[b] Primary selenium indicator.
[c] Secondary selenium absorber.

The effect of sulfur on selenium accumulation in plants is not related to the sulfur content of the plant or to the S:Se ratio present in soil, but to competition between structural analogs. Studies by Hurd-Karrer (*28, 29, 33, 34*) with sand or culture solutions demonstrated that sulfate decreased the absorption of selenate by crop plants. This was the first demonstration of competitive antagonism between structural analogs in plants. The antagonism between selenate and sulfate during absorption was studied by Leggett and Epstein (*41*), who investigated the kinetics of sulfate absorption by barley roots. The data on the rate of S^{35} uptake in the presence of selenate were analyzed by the classical Michaelis-

Menten analysis for enzyme action. They interpreted the results as an indication of competition between the ions on approximately even terms for a site or carrier at the cell membrane. Other ions, PO_4, NO_3, and Cl showed no measurable affinity for the binding site of SO_4-SeO_4. Earlier studies with plants suggested that there are other factors which may regulate the absorption of these two ions besides the affinity of the ions for absorption site. Studies by Hurd-Karrer (*34*) indicated that the rate of $SO_4^{=}$ absorption was greater than that of $SeO_4^{=}$ and that the internal S:Se ratio always exceeded that of the external ratio.

Sulfur or sulfate treatments of artificially selenized soils or culture solution with selenate markedly reduced selenium uptake by crop plants (*30, 31, 34*), but in no instance was the selenium absorption entirely prevented by sulfate (Table 37).

TABLE 37

Selenium and Sulfur Absorption by Wheat[a]

Selenium[b] in culture solution (ppm)	Sulfur[c] in culture solution: 16 ppm		32 ppm		96 ppm		192 ppm	
	Accumulation in plant[d]							
	Se (ppm)	S (%)	Se (ppm)	S (%)	Se (ppm)	S (%)	Se (ppm)	S (%)
0	0	0.54	0	0.430	0	0.72	0	1.105
1	146	0.775	76	0.71	38	0.83	12	1.125
2	322[1]	0.880	165	0.84	50	0.95	48	1.095
4	1,333[3]	1.195	429[1]	0.975	113	1.09	103	1.10
6			746[2]	1.1	188	1.075	143	1.235
8			1,280[3]	1.80	328	1.01	278	1.145
12					538[1]	1.17	396	1.155
24					1,253[3]	1.225	1,004[1]	1.335
48							2,046[2]	1.47

[a] Hurd-Karrer (*34*).
[b] Added as Na_2SeO_4.
[c] Added as $MgSO_4$.
[d] Air-dried.
NOTE: [1, 2, 3] Indicate the appearance and increase of chlorosis.

Absorption of selenium derived from seleniferous plant extract was not affected by the addition of sulfate or gypsum to soil plots (*4, 5*). In fact, selenium absorption increased with the addition of sulfate. Wheat grown in soil mixed with *A. bisulcatus* accumulated 484 ppm, whereas on a similar plot treated with one per cent sulfate it contained 845 ppm selenium. The accumulation of selenium in plants was not affected to any extent by sulfate when selenite was the source of selenium in culture solution (*33; 43; 55; 80*, pp. 150, 151).

The selenium in *A. bisulcatus* extract is in organic form and contains no selenate. The accumulation of selenium from organic selenium and selenite was not regulated or influenced by the presence of sulfate in the culture solution but the accumulation from selenate was reduced (Fig. 28) (*80*, pp. 150, 151).

Cameron (*15*) in 1880 suggested that selenium may replace sulfur in the sulfur compounds and that the damage to plants is due to the substitution of selenium for sulfur in organic compounds.

Growth inhibition studies by Hurd-Karrer (*29*) with crop plants grown in soil and culture solution have demonstrated that the injury from selenate was a function of available sulfate concentration. Subsequent studies

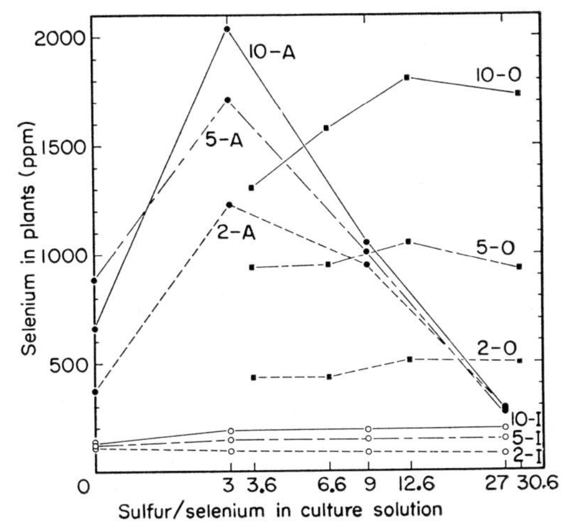

FIG. 28. Selenium accumulation by corn in relation to sulfur : selenium ratio (in ppm) in culture solution. (Log scale of abscissas except the zero.) Cultures received 2, 5, and 10 ppm of selenium as selenite (I), selenate (A), or organic selenium (O) from an *Astragalus* extract. Sulfur supplied as sulfate.

indicate that growth inhibition by selenium as selenate varied inversely with the concentration of sulfate within limits (*30–32, 34*).

Sulfate not only depressed the absorption of selenium and prevented growth reduction, but decreased the toxic effects of selenate. These structural analogs behave like metabolites and antimetabolites. According to Woolley (*86*), antimetabolites have not only structural resemblance but also biological properties which are antagonistic in action to that of the metabolite.

TOXIC EFFECTS OF SELENIUM ON PLANTS

There are striking differences between the selenium-accumulating plants and the nonaccumulators in the amount of selenium they may absorb without showing symptoms of injury. The indicator plants may contain several thousand parts per million of selenium without showing chlorosis, dwarfing, or other signs of poisoning. The ability of these plants to store large amounts of selenium is probably regulated by some mechanism whereby the absorbed selenium is detoxified. In contrast, a crop plant, such as wheat or corn, can accumulate only a few hundred parts per million (maximum probably 300 ppm) from inorganic selenium compounds without visible injury. The primary indication of the toxic effects of selenium is growth inhibition of the plants. Younger plants are more susceptible and growth inhibition is greater than in mature plants.

Small degrees of stimulation by dilute selenium solutions of some plants have been reported by various workers (*5, 33, 42, 63, 71*). The stimulation of growth of crop plants with low concentrations (0.001–0.05 ppm) of selenium was small in comparison with that observed in the indicator species of *Astragalus* (*74–76*).

Artificially selenized soils or studies in sand or culture solutions containing selenate or selenite indicated that with increased concentrations of selenium there was a corresponding decrease in growth (*28–30, 33, 43*). The inhibition of plant growth by selenites exceeds that of other inorganic selenium compounds.

Organic selenium (as *Astragalus bisulcatus* extract) produced less growth inhibition and toxicity to crop plants than inorganic selenium compounds (*3–5, 78, 79*).

Relative susceptibility of wheat plants grown in soils with different concentrations of selenium (as selenite) from the time of germination to 120 days was studied by Johnson and Whitehead (*36*). A typical S-shaped growth curve was obtained for each level of selenium when the dry plant weights were plotted against days of growth (Fig. 29).

Growth retardation produced by some selenium compounds in experimental studies was reduced or prevented by proteins, protein derivatives, amino acids, and sulfates as indicated by the studies of Trelease and coworkers (*77–79*) and Hurd-Karrer (*29, 32, 34*).

The effect of sulfur and sulfate on the toxic effects of selenate on plants was studied in detail by Hurd-Karrer (*28, 29*).

Concentrations of selenium as selenate as low as 0.1 ppm produced a slight detectable injury of wheat plants in culture solutions containing no sulfate (*28, 29*). No visible injury to the plants was observed when the proportion of sulfur (sulfate) to selenium (selenate) was 12:1 ppm or more. The point of minimum detectable injury lay between 9:1 and 11:1. When the ratio was 8:1 or less, the plants were chlorotic and stunted; when the ratio was as low as 2:1, growth was almost completely inhibited.

Using selenite instead of selenate, Martin (*43*) reported that sulfate had relatively little effect on the toxicity of selenium to wheat and buckwheat plants in soil or solution cultures. The toxicity of 1 ppm selenium could be counteracted by adding sulfate to the solution, but the toxicity of higher concentrations could not be inhibited. A sulfur:selenium ratio of 2.5:1 reduced toxicity nearly as much as a ratio of 40:1. Similar results were obtained by Hurd-Karrer (*33*) with wheat and by Martin and Trelease (*44*) with tobacco and soybeans. The selenite used in the experiments may have contained some selenate which would offer an explanation for some beneficial effects of sulfate.

Symptoms of Selenium Toxicity in Plants

Among the earlier workers, Awschalom (*1*) described the toxic effects of selenite on various kinds of higher plants as well as on several of the lower organisms. Levine (*42*) found that various selenium compounds,

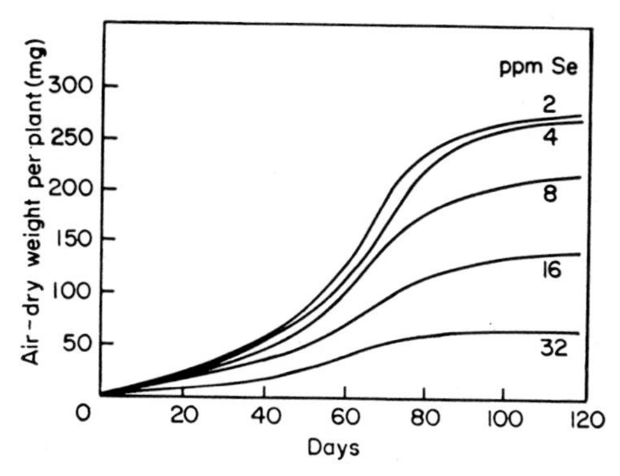

Fig. 29. The effect of selenite (2–32 ppm selenium) on growth of wheat plants (tops). (Johnson and Whitehead, *36*.)

when supplied in concentrations of 0.01 per cent or more, were injurious to seed germination and plant growth. The order of diminishing toxicity of the compounds tested was: selenious acid, selenic acid, selenite, selenate, and selenocyanate.

Selenium injury has not been observed in crop plants growing in natural seleniferous soils due to the lower selenium uptake by the plants under natural conditions. There are no outward signs of abnormalities in crop plants to indicate that they contain 10, 30, 60, or 120 ppm selenium.

The characteristic symptom of injury in soil, sand, or solution cultures in wheat plants by selenate is a snow-white chlorosis of the leaves (*29, 82*). The plants other than wheat that show chlorosis are sorgo, barley, and rye. When selenate is added to older plants, the white chlorosis appears only in newly emerging leaves and older leaves already formed merely turn yellow. A progressive diminution of chlorosis in successive leaves may be observed as the plants become older.

Leaves injured by selenite are likely to be darker green than normal, rather than chlorotic (*32, 33*). The older leaves later wither and turn brown. Higher concentrations of selenite (64 ppm selenium) produced white chlorosis and premature death of wheat plants (*43*).

The roots of wheat and corn plants poisoned by selenate are stunted but otherwise normal in appearance. Roots poisoned by selenite have a pinkish color. The main roots are thickened and the development of lateral roots is suppressed. On microscopic examination, tiny red granules were observed within the roots. Based on the appearance of the granules and solubility (in a mixture of hydrobromic acid and bromine) studies, it was indicated that the selenite was reduced to elemental selenium. These characteristics of selenite-injured roots have beeen reported by several investigators and are interpreted to be due to red colloidal selenium precipitated within the cells (*1, 33, 42, 72, 82*). In selenate-injured roots there are no red granules, and this is consistent with observations that selenates are not as readily reduced as selenites.

CHEMICAL FORMS OF SELENIUM IN THE PLANT

The similarity in the chemical properties of sulfur and selenium compounds has suggested the possibility that selenium may substitute for sulfur in plant metabolism (*10, 15, 42, 52, 57, 59, 60*). Although there is evidence to indicate that selenium substitutes for sulfur in metabolic pathways, the metabolism of these elements may not be identical. Studies by Painter and Franke (*59*) suggested some differences between selenium and sulfur metabolism: (1) many indicator plants may contain high concentrations of sulfate but no selenate; (2) S:Se ratios of different parts of the same plants are not constant in all cases; and (3) selenium in cereal proteins appears to follow sulfur in most cases but there are wide variations in S:Se ratios.

Organic and Inorganic Compounds

The proportions of organic and inorganic selenium compounds accumulated in plants depend on the species or the genera of the plants. Experimental studies indicate that the selenium compound(s) and the concentration of these compounds may influence the form of selenium that accumulates in the plants. Inorganic selenium in plants occurs almost entirely as selenate and only insignificant amounts of selenite or elemental selenium were found under natural conditions.

Early investigations showed that only organic selenium was present in *Astragalus bisulcatus* (*2, 5, 62*). Beath and Eppson (*8*) reported that many species of plants contained selenate as well as organic selenium.

Organic water-soluble selenium is present in a number of species of

TABLE 38
Organic Selenium in Indicator Plants

Plants	Total Se in plant (ppm)	Form of Se[a] Organic (%)	Water-soluble Se (%)
Astragalus preussii	1,770	100	89
A. bisulcatus	1,587	100	74
A. pectinatus	1,564	100	88
A. confertiflorus	1,372	100	47
A. osterhouti	1,308	100	81
A. pattersoni	1,155	100	90
A. sabulosus[b]	1,066	100	82
A. grayi	350	100	95
Stanleya pinnata	804	100	65
S. integrifolia[b]	695	100	89

[a] Tests for selenate and selenite were negative.
[b] Soil contained only selenite selenium.

Astragalus and *Stanleya* (Table 38) as well as in crop and forage plants (Table 39).

Organic selenium and selenate are present in a number of species of native plants (Table 40), but selenite is absent with the exception of one species. The species of plants (Table 40) show wide variation—from

TABLE 39
Organic Selenium in Cultivated Plants

	Total Se in plant (ppm)	Form of Se[a] Organic (%)	Water-soluble Se (%)
Wheat (young plants)	227	100	52
Alfalfa	147	100	57
Barley	35	100	31
Oats	31	100	29
Sweet clover (yellow)	21	100	48
Corn	13	100	54

[a] Tests for selenate and selenite were negative.

nearly all organic selenium to nearly all selenate. The results indicate that species belonging to a single genus tend to be consistent in their proportions of the two forms of selenium. It should be noted that species of section *Xylorhiza* of *Machaeranthera* (woody aster) and *Atriplex* (saltbush), which are responsible for serious losses of livestock, are predominantly accumulators of selenate rather than of organic selenium.

TABLE 40

Organic Selenium and Selenate in Native Plants

Plants (arranged in order of decreasing % organic Se)	Total Se in plant (ppm)	Forms of Se[a] Organic (%)	Forms of Se[a] Selenate (%)	Water-soluble Se (%)
Castilleja chromosa	1,812	95	5	57
Agropyron smithii (Wyo.)[1]	98	91	9	63
Agropyron smithii (Wyo.)[2]	41	85	15	51
Oryzopsis hymenoides (Utah)[3]	93	78	22	57
Comandra pallida[4]	140	74	26	41
Haplopappus fremontii[b]	680	70	30	79
Agropyron smithii (Utah)[3]	202	51	49	78
Gutierrezia sarothrae	120	50	50	67
Haplopappus engelmanii[b]	101	47	53	74
Castilleja angustifolia	250	46	54	84
Grindelia squarrosa	102	45	55	78
Haplopappus fremontii subsp. *wardii*[b]	932	42	58	67
Gutierrezia diversifolia	723	37	63	71
Aster commutatis	325	25	75	92
Machaeranthera venusta[c]	3,486	24	76	89
Machaeranthera glabriuscula[c]	1,431	23	77	91
Aster occidentalis	284	23	77	99
Atriplex canescens	477	19	81	84
Hymenoxys floribunda[2]	575	16	84	94
Machaeranthera ramosa	1,345	15	85	98
Atriplex confertifolia	1,734	10	90[5]	98
Aster caerulescens	560	9	91	98
Atriplex nuttallii	502	8	92	95

[a] Tests for selenite were negative except in the specimen referred to in the last footnote.

[b] Previously genus *Oonopsis*.

[c] Previously genus *Xylorhiza*.

NOTE: [1] Rooted in the Niobrara shale. [2] Rooted in tuffaceous soil. [3] Rooted in Salt Wash Member of Morrison Formation. [4] Attached to *Haplopappus fremontii* (previously genus *Oonopsis*), immediately following. [5] About 80% was selenate and 3% was selenite.

In sand or culture solution, the selenium compound supplied to the plant may influence the proportions of organic selenium and selenate selenium that accumulate in the stem and leaves. This was demonstrated in an experiment in which young corn plants were grown in sand cultures with selenite, selenate, or organic selenium (*Astragalus* extract). The results are given in Table 41 (*80*, p. 157). When selenite or *Astragalus* extract was supplied to the roots, only organic selenium accumulated in the tops. About 50 per cent of the selenate absorbed by the plants was converted into organic compounds and the remainder was unchanged selenate. No selenite could be detected in the tops of any of the plants, but it may have been present in the roots. When lower concentrations of selenate were added to the culture solution, a greater proportion was converted into organic form (Table 41, second test).

Shoots and roots of *Neptunia amplexicaulis* and wheat grown in nutrient solution with Se^{75}-selenite contained high concentrations of the selenite ion in the ethanol extract, while rye grass and white and red clovers retained only small amounts of selenite (*64*).

TABLE 41

Relation of the Form of Selenium Accumulated by Corn to the Form of Selenium Supplied in the Culture Solution

Form and amount of selenium supplied to plants	Selenium accumulated in tops				Ave. dry wt. of tops (gm)
	Total Se (ppm)	Forms of Se[a] Organic (%)	Forms of Se[a] Selenate (%)	Water-soluble Se (%)	
First test					
Selenite, 5 ppm	156	100	0	24	1.50
Selenite, 10 ppm	199	100	0	24	0.69
Selenate, 10 ppm[b]	1,054	48	52	64	1.18
Selenate, 10 ppm	1,362	46	54	67	.70
Organic, 1 ppm[c]	342	100	0	61	1.76
Organic, 2 ppm[c]	732	100	0	76	1.70
Second test					
Selenate, 1.1 ppm	111	95	5	52	1.61
Selenate, 3.3 ppm	515	56	44	62	1.23
Selenate, 10 ppm	1,367	41	59	71	0.31

[a] Tests for selenite were negative.
[b] This solution contained 76 ppm sulfur as sulfate; all other solutions, 51 ppm.
[c] From an extract of *Astragalus bisulcatus*.

It should be mentioned that the selenium compound supplied to the feeding roots of any seleniferous *Astragalus* and *Stanleya* plant does not influence the form of selenium that accumulates in the aerial parts of the plants. These plants convert the absorbed selenium into organic form.

Solubility of Selenium Compounds in Plants

About 75 per cent of the selenium in most samples of dried stems and leaves of *A. bisulcatus* and *A. pectinatus* (ground to 20–40 mesh) may be extracted by soaking the material for a few hours in water at 20° C or for a shorter period in hot water (*2, 3, 8, 78*). The water solubility of organic selenium in various species of *Astragalus* and *Stanleya* ranged from 47 to

95 per cent (Table 38). In the cultivated forages and grains, the water-soluble fraction varied from 29 to 57 per cent (Table 39).

Solubility of selenium compounds in leaves plus stems and excised roots of five species of plants grown in nutrient solution containing Se^{75}-selenite was studied by extractions with 80 per cent (v/v) boiling aqueous ethanol followed by extractions with boiling water (*64*). Boiling ethanol extracted about 90 per cent of Se^{75} from the young shoots of *Neptunia* and 60.3 per cent from the mature shoots. Shoots of red and white clovers contained more ethanol-extractable Se^{75} than rye grass or wheat, but the aqueous ethanol fraction in these plants was one third to one fifth that of the *Neptunia.* Higher percentages of Se^{75} remained in the residue of young *Neptunia* roots (22–31%) than in the shoots (3–6%). The proportion of Se^{75} in the residue of mature *Neptunia* roots (63%) was similar to that of other species of plants (45–77%).

The lability of chemical bonds of the selenium compounds in indicator plants has been noted by many investigators who have attempted to isolate the seleno-compounds. To prevent decomposition of seleno-compounds in *Stanleya bipinnata,* the use of nonpolar and polar solvents was investigated (*12*).

Stanleya bipinnata was transplanted from a seleniferous area and grown in the greenhouse in soil containing Se^{75}-selenite (*45*). The distribution of Se^{75}-compounds in various solvents by sequential extraction of macerated leaves was investigated. The sequence of extraction from nonpolar to more polar solvents showed differential distribution of the seleno-compounds (*12*). Skellysolve F and acetone extracted small amounts (only a fraction of a per cent); methanol (4 extractions) removed 14.9 per cent of the labeled seleno-compounds; ethyl ether, chloroform, ethyl acetate, and carbon disulfide extracted only trace amounts; phenol (2 extractions) contained 18.8 per cent; and pyridine removed 14.7 per cent of the Se^{75}-compound(s). The solubility of the Se^{75}-compounds in the above solvents suggests the presence of at least three groups of compounds in S. *bipinnata* leaves (*12*).

Sequential solvent extraction from more polar (water) to less polar solvents suggested the presence of at least six different compounds based on the solubility of Se^{75}-compound(s). Water extracted more than 50 per cent of Se^{75}-seleno-compounds from the macerated dry plants (*12*).

Although the differential extraction of seleno-compounds from dry and fresh plants was not fully investigated, preliminary studies indicated that there may be some changes in physical as well as in chemical characteristics of seleno-compounds in S. *bipinnata* during drying. Hot tetrachloroethylene extracted 17 per cent of Se^{75}-compound(s) from the fresh S. *bipinnata,* and only 3 per cent of the Se^{75} was extracted from the ground, dry plant (McColloch, personal communication). The relative solubility of seleno-compounds in fresh leaves of S. *bipinnata*, macerated in a Waring blendor with hot solvents, in decreasing order was: Skelly B, cyclohexane, carbon tetrachloride, benzene, butanol, and tetrachloroethylene. When fresh leaves were cut into hot butanol, 21 per cent was extracted by the solvent.

Sequential solvent extraction offers considerable promise for the separation of labile seleno-compound(s) from plants with diverse chemical properties. Solubility of seleno-compounds from fresh leaves by nonpolar organic solvents was used by McColloch *et al.* (*45*) for the crude separation of a seleniferous wax from S. *bipinnata*. Details of purification and identification will be presented subsequently in this chapter.

Selenium is present in the relatively insoluble gluten of wheat grain (*18*, *25*, *58*). About 50 per cent of selenium in the grain could be dissolved in water at room temperature (*5*). Seleno-compounds from gluten hydrolyzate were insoluble in chloroform, petroleum ether, alcohol, and benzene, but almost all the selenium passed into the butyl alcohol fraction when extracted from nearly neutral hydrolyzate (*25*, *57*).

Dialysis of Seleno-Compounds

Dialysis is a procedure widely used in protein chemistry for the removal of electrolytes, and for precipitation, fractionation, and crystallization of proteins.

Dialysis experiments have demonstrated that the selenium in aqueous extract of *A. bisulcatus* is present in small molecular weight, water-soluble compounds which diffuse readily through a cellophane membrane (*79*). An equilibrium of the soluble seleno-compounds was established throughout the cellophane bag and the external medium within 2 days at 5° C. These compounds were not reduced to elemental selenium by reagents which reduce inorganic selenites or selenates.

Seleniferous wheat proteins peptized by KCN did not diffuse through the cellophane bag. By similar treatment of elemental selenium, selenocyanide (the compound formed) readily passed through the membrane (*17*). These studies indicated that there was no elemental selenium or small molecular-weight seleno-compound present in the peptized wheat proteins.

Electrodialysis of acid or alkali-peptized seleniferous proteins removed only traces to small amounts of selenium from the proteins. The protein-bound selenium was more labile in alkaline than in acid solution (*18*). The decomposition of small amounts of seleniferous peptized protein by alkali suggests that this compound was selenocystine. Decomposition of cystine by alkali or alkaline hydrolysis is well known (*23*).

These and subsequent experiments have given presumptive evidence that the selenium in seleniferous grains and grasses is present as protein-bound amino acids.

Loss in Drying and Storage

Native seleniferous vegetation may lose considerable amounts of selenium from the time it is collected until it becomes air dry (*5*). The loss in drying can usually be held to a minimum (about 10%) if the material is dried quickly in a forced draft oven at 60°–70° C. After the plant material has been thoroughly dried, the subsequent loss in a closed container will be lower for a limited time. However, there is no evidence to indicate that selenium in farm crops volatilized while being air dried (*5*).

Cereal grains stored for several years decrease in their toxicity to livestock (*20*). Moxon and Rhian (*49*) reported that there was a decrease of selenium in some cereals in storage after 3 to 5 years. The loss of selenium amounted to about 40 per cent. Studies on the effect of temperature showed that the loss of selenium was much greater at higher temperatures. Seleniferous corn dextrinized at 160° C for 2 hours lost 27 per cent selenium, and a wheat sample lost 24 per cent.

Volatility with Steam

Steam distillation of seeds of *Astragalus bisulcatus* containing 4000 ppm selenium yielded 23 per cent in volatile forms (*8*). Addition of mercuric chloride precipitated one fourth of the selenium in the distillate. About 95 per cent of the total selenium was extracted with hot water. The volatile selenium in *Astragalus preussii* and *Astragalus pattersoni* was 11 per cent. The volatile material contained no selenite or selenate. On electrodialysis it was reduced to elemental selenium at the cathode. The composition of the volatile forms of selenium (at least two being indicated) is not known. On fractionation of aqueous extract of *Stanleya* there was a continuous loss of Se^{75} from the various fractions, suggesting the presence of a volatile selenium compound or decomposition to volatile selenium compound(s) (*12*).

Smaller amounts of volatile selenium were obtained by steam distillation from species of *Stanleya*, section *Xylorhiza* of *Machaeranthera* and secondary selenium absorbers (Beath, unpublished).

Selenium in Cereal Proteins

It is generally agreed that selenium in crop and forage plants is an integral part of the protein molecule and cannot be removed without hydrolysis of the proteins (*18, 25, 37, 38, 52, 57, 58, 60, 62, 64, 70, 83, 84*).

In presenting the data and methods used, the results of earlier investigators will be reviewed briefly. This will be followed by some recent studies using isotopes and chromatographic methods. It should be stated that no seleno-compound(s) free of sulfur analog(s) were isolated from seleniferous proteins or indicators.

Earlier studies indicated that selenium from the cereals could not be extracted with various solvents, effective for inorganic selenium or for elemental selenium, and could be liberated only by the action of strong bases or strong oxidizing agents (*25*, *58*).

The fact that selenium was not removed by solvents effective for inorganic or elemental selenium is in itself a presumptive evidence of the presence of nitrogenous selenium compounds in cereals. After hydrolysis of proteins by acids, considerable amounts of selenium were present in the hydrolyzate (*25*, *57*, *58*, *60*). Numerous attempts were made to obtain the major portion of the selenium bound in the proteins without decomposition of the selenium compounds.

Hydrolyses of proteins were carried out with various concentrations of HCl and H_2SO_4 (*25*, *57*, *58*). The humin formed when seleniferous proteins were hydrolyzed always contained selenium. Acid hydrolysis of selenocystine with 20 per cent HCl or 33 per cent H_2SO_4 slowly decomposed the compound with deposition of elemental selenium (*62*), suggesting that some of the selenium in humin may have been elemental selenium (*58*). The selenium compounds in the proteins were less stable than sulfur to acid hydrolysis since the S:Se ratios in humin were lower than in the protein or hydrolyzate (*58*, *60*). Westfall and Smith (*83*) cleaved more selenium than sulfur from seleniferous proteins by strong oxidizing agents. The selenium in the humin was increased by the use of stronger acids or by the addition of carbohydrates during hydrolysis (*58*).

Hydrolysis of seleniferous wheat proteins by concentrated hydriodic acid and repeated ether extractions removed the selenium from the hydrolyzate (*58*). Hydriodic acid cleaves ethers and, when used to hydrolyze proteins, cleaves the methiol group of methionine to form an α-amino γ-thio lactone (*62*). This compound is soluble in ether. The cleavage of selenium by acid and extraction with ether suggested the presence of a seleno-analog of methionine in the proteins.

That selenium was present in the gluten of seleniferous wheat was recognized by early investigators (*25*, *57*, *59*). The method of isolation and identification of amino acids from the protein hydrolyzates was used for separation of the hydrolytic products of gluten by Horn *et al.* (*25*). There was no selenium present in the dicarboxylic amino acid fraction and little, if any, in the fraction containing arginine, histidine, and lysine. By fractional crystallization of the monoamino acids, the selenium was concentrated in the leucine fraction which also contained some valine and phenylalanine. This mixture contained about 2 per cent of the selenium. McConnell and Wabnitz (*46*) reported a fraction from rat liver protein hydrolyzate concentrated in the area adjacent to leucines.

Painter and Franke (*57*) found considerable amounts of selenium in the phosphotungstic acid precipitate of protein hydrolyzates. $HgCl_2$, an amino acid precipitant, was effective in removing the selenium from the hydrolyzates. Copper salts partially precipitated some selenium compounds, but silver salts which precipitate histidine and arginine removed only trace amounts of selenium. The fractions that contained methionine and cystine also contained selenium, although not in the same S : Se ratio. When the selenium-containing precipitates of mercury and copper salts were decomposed with hydrogen sulfide, much of the selenium was precipitated with the metallic sulfide.

Some selenium was cleaved when seleniferous proteins were hydrolyzed in alkaline solutions (*60*). "Labile" selenium and "labile" sulfur compounds were rapidly decomposed by alkaline solutions (*61*). If hydrolysis was carried out in the presence of alkaline plumbite, a high percentage of sulfur precipitated out as PbS which also removed a greater percentage of selenium.

Studies on the cleavage of diselenides in alkaline solution indicate that cleavage is similar to that of disulfides (*61*). Inorganic selenide and some selenites precipitate out in the presence of plumbite. There was considerable evidence to indicate that some inorganic selenide was formed when seleniferous proteins were hydrolyzed in alkaline solution, but inorganic selenite was not detected (*60*).

The selenium and cystine contents of partially hydrolyzed gluten were studied by Jones *et al.* (*38*). Gluten was prepared from seleniferous wheat and digested for 3 hours with pepsin. Four fractions of partial hydrolysis products of the protein were separated. The fraction representing 11.5 per cent in weight of the gluten contained 58 per cent of the total selenium and 10.5 per cent of the total cystine. By removing the dicarboxylic amino acids from the fraction, the selenium and cystine could be concentrated in this small partially hydrolyzed gluten fraction.

The relationships between the amounts of selenium, sulfur, and nitrogen in isolated cereal proteins were investigated by Painter and Franke (*59*). The variations in the N:Se ratios were greater than the variations in the S:Se ratios. The N:Se and N:S ratios in gliadin, glutenin, zein, and gluten were higher than in the whole cereal grain which may have been due to the nonprotein selenium or sulfur. Sulfur was detected as sulfate but there was no selenate present. However, the deposition of selenium in cereal proteins followed that of sulfur in most cases. There were some variations in the S:Se ratios, possibly due to the differential cleavage of sulfur as well as the selenium compounds by the reagents used.

RECENT STUDIES

These studies utilized paper and column chromatograms and paper electrophoresis for separation of the seleniferous plant proteins. Smith (*70*) separated the seleniferous corn proteins and gluten hydrolyzate by paper chromatography. The highest concentration of selenium was localized at areas of the selenocystine and selenomethionine, and some unknown seleno-compounds were present in other areas of the paper.

Wheat and corn grown in the greenhouse in soil containing varying amounts of Se^{75} (selenate) were used for the identification of seleno-compounds in the proteins (*37*). The protein hydrolyzates were separated on a starch column. The activity was associated with several compounds of unknown identity, but no seleno-substituted amino acids were detected in protein hydrolyzates.

Whitehead *et al.* (*84*) studied the cytoplasmic proteins of leaf and seed proteins (glutenin and gliadin) of plants grown in soil containing S^{35} (sulfate) and Se^{75} (as selenate or selenite). The protein hydrolyzates were separated by starch and resin column chromatograms. By the above methods, S^{35}-methionine and S^{35}-cystine were isolated but no seleno-substituted amino acids in leaf or wheat proteins were detected.

The decomposition of selenocystine during acid hydrolysis has been noted (*62, 64*), and although selenomethionine is more stable, its decomposition during protein hydrolysis by acids has been reported (*9*). Whitehead *et al.* (*84*) failed to indicate the amount of Se^{75} present in the grain or leaf proteins before acid hydrolysis. The loss may have occurred during hydrolysis or after the hydrolyzate was added on the columns. The negative results may have been due to low specific activity of the proteins and losses incurred by the methods used. Peterson and Butler (*64*) noted that only 8 per cent of Se^{75} plant ethanol extracts was eluted from Dowex 50 column by 1 to 6 *N* HCl and if elution was continued with 0.01 to 1 *N* NH_4OH, an additional 17 per cent of the activity was eluted.

The characteristic differences in the biosynthesis of Se^{75}-seleno-amino acids in five species of plants were investigated in great detail by Peterson and Butler (*64*). The bulk of Se^{75}-selenite incorporated into the crop plants was bound to the proteins by peptide links. The protein preparations underwent partial denaturation during storage at 2° C. If the denatured leaf protein was digested with trypsin and chymotrypsin, 95 per cent of the radioactive compounds was liberated. Ethanol extracts of the plants contained considerable amounts of radioactivity.

The percentage distribution of the principal compounds and unknown substances in fractions of alcohol extracts in the different species of plants is shown in Table 42. The extracts were separated by resin, electrophoresis, and paper chromatograms. The distribution of radioactivity in

TABLE 42

Percentage Distribution of Se^{75}-Labeled Compounds Present in the 80% Ethanol Extracts of Five Plant Species[a]

Compound number[b]	Compound	*Neptunia*		Wheat		Red clover		White clover		Rye grass	
		Shoot	Root	Shoot	Root	Shoot	Root	Shoot	Root	Shoot	Root
1	Immobile	14	18	10	5	Trace	4.4	Trace	5.3	Trace	4.9
2	Selenocystine	—	—	—	—	17	41.5	16	41.1	13	2.5
3	Unknown (selenoglutathione ?)	—	—	—	—	—	18.3	—	20.5	—	4.8
4	Se-methylselenomethionine selenonium salt (?)	—	—	—	—	—	2.4	—	2.4	—	5.9
5	Selenocysteic acid	—	—	—	—	40	10.2	20	7.6	10	6.0
6	Selenocysteine seleninic acid (?)	—	—	—	—	Trace	Trace	Trace	Trace	—	6.8
7	Selenite ion	27	23	90	93	8	4.4	11	7.7	12	38.8
8	Unknown	—	—	—	—	—	3.0	—	5.7	—	—
9	Selenomethionine selenoxide	—	—	—	—	10	5.0	14	Trace	Trace	Trace
10–11	Unknowns	—	—	—	—	—	Trace	—	Trace	—	1.3
12	Selenomethionine	—	—	—	—	18	4.7	17	4.6	15	1.3
13	Unknown	—	—	—	—	4	Trace	5	Trace	Trace	Trace
14	Unknown	—	—	—	—	3	6.1	17	5.1	50	3.1
15–19	Unknowns	—	—	—	—	—	—	—	—		24.6
20	Unknowns (3)	—	—	—	2	—	—	—	—	—	—
21	Unknown streaks	59	59	—	—	—	—	—	—	—	—

[a] Peterson and Butler (*64*).

[b] Indicates the location and identification of the compounds on the paper.

the areas was determined by scanning the chromatograms and electrophoretic strips. Radioautographs of one- and two-dimensional chromatograms on samples of high activity were prepared.

It is interesting to note that in the ethanol extract of wheat, the selenium was predominantly unchanged selenite, while other crop plants contained a multitude of seleno-compounds. There was greater diversity in the number of seleno-compounds in the alcoholic extract of the roots than in the shoots. The biosynthetic processes in red and white clovers were almost identical.

The enzymic digestions of the residue (after ethanol and water extractions) of roots and shoots of wheat, clovers, and rye grass released from 50 to 92 per cent of the radioactivity present in the denatured plant tissues. The percentage of Se^{75} liberated by enzymic hydrolysis in the rye grass roots was lower than in other tissues. Bromine water extracted 20 per cent of the Se^{75} from these root proteins indicating the presence of elemental selenium. The compounds liberated by enzymic hydrolysis were separated by electrophoresis and paper chromatograms and they behaved identically with selenomethionine, selenomethionine selenoxide, and selenocystine. In wheat protein a peak was observed which differed from the other seleno-amino acids in the hydrolyzates. This was similar to the decomposition product of selenocystine (*64*).

Selenium Compounds in Indicator Plants

A crystalline amino acid containing selenium and sulfur was isolated from *Astragalus pectinatus* by Horn and Jones (*27*). The air-dried plant material contained from 1500 to 2000 ppm of selenium of which about 80 per cent was extractable with hot water. Direct fractionation, various methods of precipitation, and other procedures yielded only syrupy and indefinite products. Mercuric acetate gave a precipitate that contained nearly all of the selenium, but was difficult to dissolve or purify without decomposition of the organic component(s).

A procedure adapted was based on a method of amino acid separation and pyridine precipitation. A semicrystalline precipitate was formed with addition of pyridine. A large amount of the selenium was removed from the aqueous extract of the *Astragalus* by the charcoal used for clarification; a considerable amount remained in the solution after precipitation with pyridine; other losses occurred during subsequent purifications.

The semicrystalline precipitate was recrystallized several times in dilute ammonium hydroxide; thick lustrous rectangular prisms separated. The compound isolated contained no water of crystallization and it decomposed at 263° to 265° C (uncorrected). It was slightly soluble in water, insoluble in alcohol, and the common organic solvents, but readily soluble in dilute ammonium hydroxide and hydrochloric acid. The presence of other constituents of *Astragalus*, such as asparagine, greatly modified its solubility. Boiling with 20 per cent sodium hydroxide produced no apparent decomposition. At no time during the isolation was there evidence of any inorganic selenium. The compound gave a strong ninhydrin reaction indicating the presence of an amine (*26*).

The percentage composition of the crystalline substance corresponded to the empirical formula $C_{21}H_{42}N_6Se_2SO_{12}$, indicating a mixture of selenium and sulfur compounds. Substitution of selenium for sulfur in the formula $C_7H_{14}N_2O_4Se$ suggested that there were probably two isomorphic compounds–$C_7H_{14}N_2O_4Se$ (selenocystathionine) and $C_7H_{14}N_2O_4S$ (cystathionine)–in the ratio of 2 : 1, respectively. Such an assumption is in agreement with the following formula:

$$\begin{array}{c} HOOC{-}\underset{\displaystyle NH_2}{\underset{|}{C}H}{-}CH_2{-}\underset{(S)}{Se}{-}CH_2{-}CH_2{-}\underset{\displaystyle NH_2}{\underset{|}{C}H}{-}COOH \end{array}$$

This seleno-amino acid isolated from *Astragalus* was a free amino acid since the procedure used was not drastic enough to break the protein bonds or peptide links.

Recently two additional amino acids have been isolated and identified from an extract of *A. bisulcatus* by Trelease *et al.* (*81*). The air-dried, ground plants contained 1000–3000 ppm selenium. A 10 per cent water extract was prepared with isopropyl alcohol added as preservative. The neutral amino acids were separated from the other components by the use of Amberlite resins (IR-4B, buffered IRC 50 and IR 120 in acid form). This fraction contained about 80 per cent of the selenium. The neutral amino acids were absorbed on Dowex 50x4 (200–400 mesh) and eluted with 0.01 M NH_3 resulting in the partial separation into a sulfur and a selenium fraction. The sulfur fraction contained no selenium but the selenium fraction did contain some sulfur. These fractions were treated separately to isolate the S- and Se-amino acids. By fractionation of the S-amino acids on filter paper columns and elution with solvent mixtures containing various amounts of ethanol, butanol, acetone, water, and formic acid, a crystalline sulfur amino acid identical with that of synthetic S-methylcysteine ($C_4H_9O_2NS$) was isolated from the *A. bisulcatus.* By the same procedure the seleno-amino acid fraction was separated and a mixture of Se-methylselenocysteine was isolated. The substitution of selenium for sulfur in S-methylcysteine may occur in biological systems.

$$CH_3{-}\underset{(S)}{Se}{-}CH_2{-}\underset{\displaystyle NH_2}{\underset{|}{C}}HCOOH$$

The infrared spectrum of the crystalline selenium compound was stated to be close to but not exactly the same as that of the pure synthetic

Se-methylselenocysteine indicating a mixture of compounds (*81*). The R_f value of the seleno-compound in two solvents used was almost identical with the sulfur analog. The R_f value differed from that of methionine and selenomethionine, cystine, homocystine, lanthionine, cystathionine, djenkolic acid, methionine sulfoxide, and S-methylcysteine sulfoxide.

Even partial separation of sulfur and selenium compounds was not accomplished by other investigators. It is regrettable that only fragmentary details are given in the procedures used. It would be quite valuable to other investigators to obtain more detailed information on the method of isolation and separation of selenium and sulfur compounds.

S-Methyl-L-cysteine has been isolated from beans (*Phaseolus vulgaris*) by Thompson *et al.* (*73*). It has been suggested that this amino acid is the precursor of S-methyl-L-cysteine sulfoxide and they are metabolically interconvertible. In the *Astragalus* no S-methylcysteine sulfoxide was detected, suggesting that in this plant these amino acids are not metabolically interconvertible.

A few studies on the separation of seleno-compounds in other species of indicator plants were carried out. The ethanol extract of *Neptunia amplexicaulis* contained a high concentration of unidentified Se^{75} complexes (Table 42). Approximately 25 per cent of the radioactivity in roots and shoots was present as selenite ion (*64*). There was little radioactivity present in the denatured proteins of the shoots. Only a small proportion of the radioactivity in the denatured *Neptunia* root tissues was released by enzymic digestion suggesting that in this indicator plant, as in other indicators, selenium does not combine with the proteins of the plants. The major part of the Se^{75} in root residue was soluble in bromine water indicating the presence of elemental selenium. Smith (*70*) was unable to detect any selenium in the acid hydrolyzate of *A. bisulcatus* seeds. In water extracts of *A. bisulcatus* tops, selenium was in organic combination but the distribution of the compounds on paper chromatograms had no relation to selenocystine or selenomethionine. Acid extracts (2 *N* HCl) showed different localizations of spots than the water extract. There were ninhydrin-positive areas on the paper in water and acid extracts, but the compounds were not identified.

A labile seleniferous wax preparation was isolated from *Stanleya bipinnata* leaves by McColloch *et al.* (*45*). The wax preparation was obtained by rinsing the fresh leaves with Skelly F. The labile selenium was lost from the wax when dissolved in chlorinated solvents, CS_2, and alcohols. Considerable amounts of selenium volatilized after pelleting in KBr for infrared spectrum studies. The loss of Se^{75} from CS_2 solutions ruled out metallic selenium since elemental selenium is stable in this solvent.

The infrared spectrum in KBr pellets of a crude preparation showed a prominent doublet at 13.75 and 13.95, suggesting that the samples contained long hydrocarbon chains whose transition point was above room temperature. The spectrum indicated the presence of prominent acid and ester carbonyl absorption peaks.

The urea clathrate of the Se^{75}-wax indicated that selenium was chemically bound in the wax and was not present in the sterol fractions. Fractionation of the seleniferous wax on silica gel gave confirmatory evidence that selenium was part of the vegetable wax.

The infrared studies of the fractions separated by silica gel column indicated the spectrum of a hydrocarbon wax with prominent ester carbonyl absorption at 5.74 and only slight free-acid carbonyl absorption at 5.84. This fraction contained most of the radioactivity in the purified wax. According to Renson and Dragnet (65), 5.84 is also the location of the displaced ester carbonyl of seleno-esters. This would suggest that at least some of the selenium in the wax was present as

$$\text{R–C–}\overset{\displaystyle /\!\!/ \text{O}}{\text{Se}}\text{–R}$$

The high molecular weight, waxy material isolated from the crude wax preparation was recrystallized 5 times to nearly constant count. The residual crude wax fraction which contained the lower molecular weight compounds also contained a large portion of the radioactivity.

The data suggest that in the *Stanleya* leaf, some of the selenium is intimately associated with the waxes of these plants. If selenium could be conclusively proven to be a part of the wax molecules in *Stanleya* and other indicator plants, it would indicate different biochemical pathways for selenium and sulfur in these plants.

The chemical studies presented further evidence that alkali disease, produced by selenium in grains and grasses, and blind staggers, caused by selenium in indicator plants, are the manifestations of the toxic effects of the different seleno-compounds present in plants.

References

1. Awschalom, M. 1921. Datos sobre la influencia del selenio en la vegetación cuando sustituye el ion súlfurico en el líquido nutritivo de Knop. *Rev. Fac. Agron. La Plata* **14**:122–162.
2. Beath, O. A., J. H. Draize and C. S. Gilbert. 1934. Plants poisonous to livestock. *Wyoming Agr. Expt. Sta. Bull. No.* **200**:1–84.
3. Beath, O. A., H. F. Eppson and C. S. Gilbert. 1935. Selenium and other toxic minerals in soils and vegetation. *Wyoming Agr. Expt. Sta. Bull. No.* **206**:1–55. (See other publications by same authors in Chapter II.)
4. Beath, O. A. 1937. The occurrence of selenium and seleniferous vegetation in Wyoming. II. Seleniferous vegetation. *Wyoming Agr. Expt. Sta. Bull. No.* **221**: 29–64.

5. Beath, O. A., H. F. Eppson and C. S. Gilbert. 1937. Selenium distribution in and seasonal variation of type vegetation occurring on seleniferous soils. *Am. J. Pharm. Assoc.* **26**:394–405.
6. Beath, O. A., C. S. Gilbert and H. F. Eppson. 1939. The use of indicator plants in locating seleniferous areas in western United States. II. Correlation studies by states. *Am. J. Botany* **26**:296–315.
7. Beath, O. A., C. S. Gilbert and H. F. Eppson. 1941. The use of indicator plants in locating seleniferous areas in western United States. IV. Progress report. *Am. J. Botany* **28**:887–900.
8. Beath, O. A. and H. F. Eppson. 1947. The form of selenium in some vegetation. *Wyoming Agr. Expt. Sta. Bull. No.* **278**:1–15.
9. Blau, M. 1961. Biosynthesis of (^{75}Se) selenomethionine and (^{75}Se) selenocystine. *Biochim. et Biophys. Acta* **49**:389–390.
10. Brenner, W. 1916. Züchtungsversuche einiger in Schlamm lebenden Bakterien auf selenhaltigem Nährboden. *Jahrb. Wiss. Botanik.* **57**:95–127.
11. Brooks, S. C. 1937. Selective accumulation with reference to ion exchange by the protoplasm. *Trans. Faraday Soc.* **33**:1002–1006.
12. Brown, S. K. 1963. A study of seleniferous compounds of *Stanleya bipinnata* (Desert Prince's Plume). M. S. Thesis. 44 pp. University of Wyoming, Laramie, Wyoming.
13. Byers, H. G. 1935. Selenium occurrence in certain soils in the United States, with a discussion of related topics. *U. S. Dept. Agr. Tech. Bull. No.* **482**:1–47. (See other publications by this author in Chapter II.)
14. Byers, H. G. 1936. Selenium occurrence in certain soils in the United States with a discussion of related topics. Second report. *U. S. Dept. Agr. Tech. Bull. No.* **530**:1–78.
15. Cameron, C. A. 1880. Preliminary note on the absorption of selenium by plants. *Proc. Roy. Dublin Soc. Sci.* **2**:231–233.
16. Cannon, H. L. 1960. The development of botanical methods of prospecting for uranium on the Colorado Plateau. *U. S. Geol. Survey Bull.* **1085–A**:1–49.
17. Franke, K. W. and E. P. Painter. 1935. Selenium in proteins from toxic foodstuffs. IV. The effect of feeding toxic proteins, toxic protein hydrolysates, and toxic protein hydrolysates from which the selenium has been removed. *J. Nutrition* **10**:599–611.
18. Franke, K. W. and E. P. Painter. 1936. Selenium in proteins from toxic foodstuffs. I. Remarks on the occurrence and nature of the selenium present in a number of foodstuffs or their derived products. *Cereal Chem.* **13**:67–70.
19. Franke, K. W. and E. P. Painter. 1937. Effect of sulfur additions on seleniferous soils. Binding of selenium by soil. *Ind. Eng. Chem.* **29**:591–595.
20. Franke, K. W. and E. P. Painter. 1938. A study of the toxicity and selenium content of seleniferous diets, with statistical consideration. *Cereal Chem.* **15**:1–24.
21. Ganje, T. J. and E. I. Whitehead. 1958. Selenium uptake by plants as affected by the forms of selenium in the soil. *Proc. South Dakota Acad. Sci.* **37**:85–88.
22. Gile, P. L., H. W. Lakin and H. G. Byers. 1938. Effect of different soil colloids and whole soils on the toxicity of sodium selenate to millet. *J. Agr. Res.* **57**:1–20.
23. Greenberg, D. M. 1951. "Amino Acids and Proteins," pp. 61, 100. Thomas, Springfield, Illinois.
24. Harrison, B. F. and R. F. Nelson. 1957. Preliminary investigation of the role of selenium in *Stanleya pinnata. Utah Acad. Sci. Proc.* **34**:159.
25. Horn, M. J., E. M. Nelson and D. B. Jones. 1936. Toxic wheat grown on soils containing selenium. *Cereal Chem.* **13**:126–139.

26. Horn, M. J. and D. B. Jones. 1940. Isolation of a crystalline selenium-containing organic compound from plant material. *J. Am. Chem. Soc.* **62**:234.
27. Horn, M. J. and D. B. Jones. 1941. Isolation from *Astragalus pectinatus* of a crystalline amino acid complex containing selenium and sulfur. *J. Biol. Chem.* **139**:649–660.
28. Hurd-Karrer, A. M. 1933. Inhibition of selenium injury to wheat plants by sulfur. *Science* **78**:560.
29. Hurd-Karrer, A. M. 1934. Selenium injury to wheat plants and its inhibition by sulfur. *J. Agr. Res.* **49**:343–357.
30. Hurd-Karrer, A. M. 1935. Factors affecting the absorption of selenium from soils by plants. *J. Agr. Res.* **50**:413–427.
31. Hurd-Karrer, A. M. and M. H. Kennedy. 1936. Inhibiting effect of sulfur in selenized soil on toxicity of wheat to rats. *J. Agr. Res.* **52**:933–942.
32. Hurd-Karrer, A. M. 1937. Selenium absorption by crop plants as related to their sulphur requirement. *J. Agr. Res.* **54**:601–608.
33. Hurd-Karrer, A. M. 1937. Comparative toxicity of selenates and selenites to wheat. *Am. J. Botany* **24**:720–728.
34. Hurd-Karrer, A. M. 1938. Relation of sulphate to selenium absorption by plants. *Am. J. Botany* **25**:666–675.
35. Jacobson, L. and R. Overstreet. 1947. A study of the mechanism of ion absorption by plant roots using radioactive elements. *Am. J. Botany* **34**:415–420.
36. Johnson, R. R. and E. I. Whitehead. 1951. Growth and selenium content of wheat plants as related to the selenite selenium content of soil. *Proc. South Dakota Acad. Sci.* **30**:130–136.
37. Johnson, R. R. and E. I. Whitehead. 1952. Studies with selenium 75. I. Selenium uptake by wheat plants as determined by measurements of radioactivity and A.O.A.C. method of selenium analysis. *Proc. South Dakota Acad. Sci.* **31**:194–198.
38. Jones, D. B., M. J. Horn and C. E. F. Gersdorff. 1937. The selenium and cystine contents of some partial hydrolysis products of gluten from toxic wheat. *Cereal Chem.* **14**:130–134.
39. Lakin, H. W., H. G. Byers and K. T. Williams. 1938. "Nontoxic" seleniferous soils. *Ind. Eng. Chem.* **30**:599–600.
40. Lakin, H. W. and H. G. Byers. 1941. Selenium in wheat and wheat products. *Cereal Chem.* **18**:73–78.
41. Leggett, J. E. and E. Epstein. 1956. Kinetics of sulfate absorption by barley roots. *Plant Physiol.* **31**:222–226.
42. Levine, V. E. 1925. The effect of selenium compounds upon growth and germination in plants. *Am. J. Botany* **12**:82–90.
43. Martin, A. L. 1936. Toxicity of selenium to plants and animals. *Am. J. Botany* **23**:471–483.
44. Martin, A. L. and S. F. Trelease. 1938. Absorption of selenium by tobacco and soybeans in sand cultures. *Am. J. Botany* **25**:380–385.
45. McColloch, R. J., J. W. Hamilton and S. K. Brown. 1963. An apparent seleniferous leaf wax from *Stanleya bipinnata*. *Biochem. Biophys. Res. Comm.* **11**:7–13.
46. McConnell, K. P. and C. H. Wabnitz. 1957. Studies on the fixation of radioselenium in proteins. *J. Biol. Chem.* **226**:765–766.
47. Miller, J. T. and H. G. Byers. 1937. Selenium in plants in relation to its occurrence in soils. *J. Agr. Res.* **55**:59–68.
48. Moxon, A. L. 1937. Alkali disease or selenium poisoning. *South Dakota Agr. Expt. Sta. Bull. No.* **311**:1–91.

49. Moxon, A. L. and M. Rhian. 1938. Loss of selenium by various grains during storage. *Proc. South Dakota Acad. Sci.* **18**:20–22.
50. Moxon, A. L., O. E. Olson, E. I. Whitehead, R. J. Hilmoe and S. N. White. 1943. Selenium distribution in milled seleniferous wheats. *Cereal Chem.* **20**: 376–380.
51. Moxon, A. L., O. E. Olson and W. V. Searight. 1950. Selenium in rocks, soils and plants. *South Dakota Agr. Expt. Sta. Revised Tech. Bull. No.* **2**:1–94.
52. Nelson, E. M., A. M. Hurd-Karrer and W. O. Robinson. 1933. Selenium as an insecticide. *Science* **78**:124.
53. Olson, O. E., D. F. Jornlin and A. L. Moxon. 1942. The selenium content of vegetation and the mapping of seleniferous soils. *Am. J. Soc. Agron.* **34**:607–615.
54. Olson, O. E., D. F. Jornlin and A. L. Moxon. 1942. Field studies on methods of determining availability of selenium to plants. *Soil Sci.* **53**:365–368.
55. Olson, O. E., E. I. Whitehead and A. L. Moxon. 1942. Occurrence of soluble selenium in soils and its availability to plants. *Soil Sci.* **54**:47–53.
56. Overstreet, R. and T. C. Boyer. 1940. The nature of absorption of radioactive isotopes by living tissues as illustrated by experiments with barley plants. *Proc. Natl. Acad. Sci. U. S.* **26**:16.
57. Painter, E. P. and K. W. Franke. 1935. Selenium in proteins from toxic foodstuffs. III. The removal of selenium from toxic protein hydrolysates. *J. Biol. Chem.* **111**:643–651.
58. Painter, E. P. and K. W. Franke. 1936. Selenium in proteins from toxic foodstuffs. II. The effect of acid hydrolysis. *Cereal Chem.* **13**:172–179.
59. Painter, E. P. and K. W. Franke. 1940. On the relationship of selenium to sulfur and nitrogen deposition in cereals. *Am. J. Botany* **27**:336–339.
60. Painter, E. P. and K. W. Franke. 1940. The decomposition of seleniferous proteins in alkaline solutions. *J. Biol. Chem.* **134**:557–566.
61. Painter, E. P., K. W. Franke and R. A. Gortner. 1940. Organic selenium compounds: their decomposition in alkaline solutions and other properties related to the behavior of selenium compounds in cereals. *J. Org. Chem.* **5**:579–589.
62. Painter, E. P. 1941. The chemistry and toxicity of selenium compounds with special reference to the selenium problem. *Chem. Rev.* **28**:179–213.
63. Perkins, A. T. and H. H. King. 1938. Selenium and Tenmarq wheat. *J. Am. Soc. Agron.* **30**:664–667.
64. Peterson, P. J. and G. W. Butler. 1962. The uptake and assimilation of selenite by higher plants. *Australian J. Biol. Sci.* **15**:126–146.
65. Renson, M. and Dragnet, C. 1962. Préparation des sélénol-esters et discussion de la position de leur bande C=O en infra-rouge. *Bull. Soc. Chim. Belg.* **71**: 260–275.
66. Robinson, W. O. 1933. Determination of selenium in wheat and soils. *J. Assoc. Offic. Agr. Chem.* **16**:423–424.
67. Rosenfeld, I. and F. Wirtz. 1962. Part I. The respiratory enzyme systems in *Astragalus racemosus* leaves. *Wyoming Agr. Expt. Sta. Bull. No.* **385**:5–19.
68. Rosenfeld, I. and H. F. Eppson. 1962. Part II. Translocation of radioactive selenium in *Astragalus bisulcatus*. *Wyoming Agr. Expt. Sta. Bull. No.* **385**:21–25.
69. Rosenfeld, I. 1962. Part III. Absorption and exchange of Se^{75} by *Astragalus preussii* root seedlings. *Wyoming Agr. Expt. Sta. Bull. No.* **385**:31–42.
70. Smith, A. L. 1949. Separation of the selenium compounds in seleniferous plant protein hydrolysates by paper partition chromatography. Master's Thesis, 33 pp. South Dakota Coll. Agr., Brookings, South Dakota.
71. Stanford, G. W. and O. E. Olson. 1939. The effect of low selenium concentrations upon the growth of grain. *Proc. South Dakota Acad. Sci.* **19**:25–31.

72. Stoklasa, J. 1922. Über die Einwirkung des Selens auf den Bau- und Betriebsstoffwechsel der Pflanze bei Anwesenheit der Radioaktivität der Luft und des Bodens. *Biochem. Z.* **130**:604–643.
73. Thompson, J. F., C. J. Morris and R. M. Zacharius. 1956. Isolation of (—)S-methyl-L-cysteine from beans (*Phaseolus vulgaris*). *Nature* **178**:593.
74. Trelease, S. F. and H. M. Trelease. 1938. Selenium as a stimulating and possibly essential element for certain plants. *Science* **87**:70–71.
75. Trelease, S. F. and H. M. Trelease. 1938. Selenium as a stimulating and possibly essential element for indicator plants. *Am. J. Botany* **25**:372–380.
76. Trelease, S. F. and H. M. Trelease. 1939. Physiological differentiation in *Astragalus* with reference to selenium. *Am. J. Botany* **26**:530–535.
77. Trelease, S. F., S. S. Greenfield and A. A. Di Somma. 1942. Absorption of selenium by corn from *Astragalus* extracts and solutions containing proteins. *Science* **96**:234–235.
78. Trelease, S. F. and A. A. Di Somma. 1944. Selenium accumulation by corn as influenced by plant extracts. *Am. J. Botany* **31**:544–550.
79. Trelease, S. F. and S. S. Greenfield. 1944. Influence of plant extracts, proteins and amino acids on the accumulation of selenium in plants. *Am. J. Botany* **31**: 630–638.
80. Trelease, S. F. and O. A. Beath. 1949. "Selenium," 292 pp. The Champlain Printers, Burlington, Vermont. (Published by the authors.)
81. Trelease, S. F., A. A. Di Somma and A. L. Jacobs. 1960. Seleno-amino acids found in *Astragalus bisulcatus*. *Science* **132**:3427.
82. Turina, B. 1922. Vergleichende Versuche über die Einwirkung der Selen-, Schwefel- und Tellursalze auf die Pflanzen. *Biochem. Z.* **129**:507–533.
83. Westfall, B. B. and M. I. Smith. 1939. Experiments on the separation of selenium from its combination with proteins in grain. *Cereal Chem.* **16**:231–237.
84. Whitehead, E. I., C. M. Hendrick and F. M. Moyer. 1955. Studies with selenium 75. II. Comparison of selenium and sulfur metabolism in wheat. *Proc. South Dakota Acad. Sci.* **34**:52–57.
85. Williams, K. T., H. W. Lakin and H. G. Byers. 1941. Selenium occurrence in certain soils in the United States, with a discussion of related topics. Fifth Report. *U. S. Dept. Agr. Tech. Bull. No.* **758**:1–69.
86. Woolley, D. W. 1952. "A Study of Antimetabolites," 269 pp. Wiley, New York; Chapman and Hall, London.

CHAPTER V

SELENIUM POISONING IN ANIMALS

Elements which occur in group VIA in the periodic table resemble one another in many ways. The most striking similarities in this group are shown by sulfur, selenium, and tellurium. Selenium and sulfur are closely related crystallochemically and geochemically, but there is a vast difference in their physiological actions. Sulfur may be present in living cells in comparatively high concentrations; selenium is toxic in low levels. The toxicity of selenium is comparable to that of arsenic. Selenium is among the few elements known to be absorbed by food and forage plants in sufficient amounts to create toxicity hazards to animals.

Recent studies indicate that selenium is an important dietary element for mammals as well as for birds. The lack of trace amounts of selenium in the diet can produce various disease syndromes. Therefore, the physiological effect of selenium must be considered on the basis of whether the disease syndrome is produced by an excess or a lack of selenium in the diet.

LIVESTOCK

Throughout vast grazing areas of the western United States the fatal alkali disease in livestock has been recognized since 1856. Another form of poisoning commonly referred to as blind staggers has been observed in Wyoming since 1920. Selenium was not associated with livestock poisoning until 1933.

Most of the highly seleniferous indicator plants are rather unpalatable to livestock. It is commonly believed by cattlemen that range animals avoid the highly seleniferous forages, some of which possess a telltale garlicky odor. Horses are very particular in their choice of food; they usually select grasses and avoid the weedy type of forage that is most seleniferous. Cattle show less discrimination than horses. Sheep actually tend to seek the coarser forage. The woody asters (*Machaeranthera* spp.) are especially dangerous to sheep because they grow close together and occupy much of the ground. Were it not for their bitter taste during their period of active growth, woody asters would cause much more serious losses.

Where normal grazing conditions prevail, livestock avoid forage containing enough selenium to give it an offensive odor (*12*). In some areas even the native grasses associated with a vetch (*Astragalus bisulcatus*) are distasteful to grazing animals. Late in the season when the grasses and selenium indicator plants wither, some of their selenium content is lost and the danger of acute toxicity by the plants is reduced.

Forage plants that are moderately seleniferous or withered plants that lack the highly offensive odor are more dangerous because they are eaten freely. Winter fat (*Eurotia lanata*) and saltbushes (*Atriplex canescens* and *Atriplex nuttallii*), which are very palatable and normally free of selenium, become sufficiently toxic in some areas to cause severe losses. Unlike most weeds they remain succulent during the winter months and so, when seleniferous, they are dangerous throughout the year.

Mention should be made here of loco disease, although a discussion of this type of plant poisoning is outside the scope of the present work. Loco disease is caused by organic poisons, and its toxic effects are not related to selenium. A representative loco weed is *Oxytropis sericea* Nutt. This plant usually grows on soils derived from granites, sandstones, and volcanic ash. It sometimes occurs on seleniferous soil, but rarely absorbs more than traces of selenium. When consumed daily in moderate amounts, it produces loco disease in cattle in approximately 50 days (*11*). Other important loco weeds—also usually selenium free—are *Astragalus mollissimus* of the Northern Plains and the closely related *Astragalus earlei* of Texas. Although the symptoms of loco disease are different from those of selenium poisoning, the two types of poisoning sometimes occur in the same general localities and frequently cattlemen are unable to differentiate between this disease and selenium poisoning.

Seleniferous plants can produce either acute or chronic poisoning in livestock. The chronic poisoning occurs in two forms, one known as blind staggers and the other as alkali disease. Each type is discussed below the appropriate heading.

ACUTE SELENIUM POISONING

Acute selenium poisoning results from the consumption, usually in a single feeding, of a sufficient quantity of highly seleniferous weeds which produces very severe symptoms. In many cases death follows within a few hours.

Causative Agents

Native seleniferous plants distributed over the ranges of many of the western states are responsible for the acute poisoning of sheep and cattle, and sometimes of hogs and horses. These plants include many species of *Astragalus, Stanleya,* section *Oonopsis* of *Haplopappus* and section *Xylorhiza* of *Machaeranthera.* The toxic nature of *Astragalus bisulcatus* was recognized by feeding 285 gm to a sheep. The animal died within 30 minutes. Many other species are now known to be able to produce acute selenium poisoning in animals.

Field Observations

The largest single loss due to seleniferous plants, observed by Beath *et al.* (*8*), occurred in the vicinity of Elk Mountain, Wyoming, where approximately 340 mature sheep died within 24 hours after consuming *Astragalus bisulcatus.* Acute selenium poisoning in cattle as well as in other livestock due to this vetch has been observed in other parts of Wyoming (*8*).

Experimental Observations

Acute selenium poisoning was produced in sheep by forced feeding with *Machaeranthera glabriuscula** (Nutt.) Cronq. and Keck (*14*). Plant material containing 400–800 ppm selenium was fatal to mature sheep when fed in amounts ranging from 8 to 16 gm per kilogram of body weight. The lethal dose was roughly proportional to the selenium content of the plants. *Astragalus grayi, Astragalus pectinatus,* and *Astragalus bisulcatus* were found to be comparable in toxicity to *M. glabriuscula* of equivalent selenium content.

Dudley (*46*) reported that 550 mg of sodium selenite killed a hog weighing 28 kg in 3 days; that 600 mg of the same compound killed a calf weighing 30 kg in 6 hours; and that plant material containing 678 mg of selenium killed a sheep weighing 61 kg in 20 hours. Miller and Williams (*166*) stated that the minimum lethal dose of selenium (administered orally as selenite) for horses and mules was about 3.3 mg per kilogram of body weight, for cattle about 11 mg, and for swine about 15 mg. More recent investigations indicate that the minimum lethal dose for cattle is not over 3 mg selenium per kilogram of body weight. Orstadius (*195*) in studying the toxicity of a single subcutaneous dose of selenite in pigs reported that 2 and 1.2 mg selenium per kilogram of body weight caused death in 4 hours and 5 days, respectively. The latter acute toxic dose is more in agreement with the opinion of other investigators than the dose given by Miller and Williams (*166*) for swine. Farmers on seleniferous areas are of the opinion that among farm animals hogs are the most susceptible to selenium poisoning (*181*).

Symptoms

At the onset of acute poisoning, the movement and posture of the animal become abnormal (*11*). The animal is likely to walk a short distance with an uncertain gait and then stop and assume a characteristic stance,

* Formerly known as *Xylorhiza parryi* (Gray) Greene.

with head lowered and ears drooped. Dark, watery diarrhea usually develops. The temperature is elevated to 103°–105° F. The pulse is rapid and weak, 90 to 300. Respiration is labored, with mucous rales, and there may be bloody froth from the air passages. Bloating is usually pronounced and is accompanied by abdominal pain. Urine excretion is greatly increased. The mucous membranes are pale or bluish in color. The pupils are dilated. Before death there is complete prostration and apparent lethargy. Death is due to respiratory failure. The duration of the illness varies from a few hours to several days, depending upon the toxicity of the plant ingested. In the pig, emesis, diarrhea, apathy, and paresis develop with administration of a toxic dose of selenium (*195*).

Distribution of Selenium

Selenium is transmitted by the circulatory system to all organs of the body. In cases of acute poisoning the highest concentrations are found in the liver, blood, kidney, spleen, and brain. The muscles, hide, hair, and bones usually contain only traces. Dudley (*46*) reported 4–25 ppm in the liver, kidney, and spleen, and 7–27 ppm in blood. The results of many analyses performed by Beath and co-workers lie within the range reported by Dudley. On the average, the blood contains 5–15 ppm; liver 22 ppm; kidney 10 ppm; spleen 8 ppm; and heart 4 ppm. In mules and horses the selenium content of the stomach, kidney, and liver was higher than that of the other tissues examined (*166*).

Elimination of selenium in acute poisoning takes place in the urine; smaller quantities are excreted in the feces, breath, perspiration, and bile. The urine may contain 0.1–20 ppm and bile 1–6 ppm selenium (*46, 166*).

Gross Pathology

Postmortem examination of the organs shows the following pathologic changes (*42, 217*).

Heart—petechial hemorrhages of the endocardium. Lungs—acute congestion and diffuse hemorrhages. Rumen—fermentation producing a frothy mass and some flatus. Omasum—congestion, hemorrhages, and desquamation of epithelium of the mucous folds. Intestines—hemorrhagic enteritis and occasionally colitis and proctitis. Liver—passive congestion, hemorrhages, parenchymatous degeneration with focal necrosis. Gall bladder—enlargement, occasionally twice normal size. Pancreas—moderately acute congestion. Kidney—parenchymatous degeneration, hemorrhages with nephritis. Bladder—usually full of urine and showing some cystitis. Spleen—acute congestion.

Microscopic Pathology

The cells of the parenchymatous organs indicate an acute toxic reaction (*217*). The endocardium shows acute congestion, focal necrosis, and hemorrhages; the pericardium exhibits petechial hemorrhages. The lungs reveal hemorrhages in the alveoli and occasionally in the interstitial tissue. The mucosa and submucosa of the stomachs and intestine manifest edema, hemorrhages, and necrosis. There is desquamation of the epithelium. Damage in the liver consists chiefly of hemorrhage and necrosis. Some sections of the liver exhibit cell disintegration, while other sections may show coagulative necrosis. Fatty degeneration may also be present. The nuclei of the liver cells show various phases of fragmentation or disintegration. The capillaries of the lobules are dilated and congested. The kidney shows parenchymatous degeneration. The convoluted and collecting tubules exhibit the most marked injury. The epithelial cells are cast off in the lumen and extensive tubular hemorrhages are present. Other organs—pancreas, gall bladder, spleen, and lymph node—show congestion and hemorrhage.

Treatment

No treatment is known for counteracting the toxic effects of large amounts of selenium. Death usually occurs before the disease can be diagnosed.

CHRONIC SELENIUM POISONING

The manifestations of the disease syndrome described as chronic selenosis in livestock depend on the chemical characteristics of selenium. The discussion of chronic selenosis in livestock will be divided into three groups: (1) blind staggers, caused by organic selenium compounds, with or without small amounts of selenate, which are readily extractable with water from native selenium indicator plants; (2) alkali disease, produced in livestock having consumed plants or grain in which selenium is bound in the proteins and is relatively insoluble in water; and (3) chronic selenosis, produced experimentally by the administration of selenate or selenite to livestock.

Selenium from different sources produces different clinical and pathological syndromes because of the differences in the form of selenium present in the plants. The order of toxicity of the same amounts of selenium from different sources is as follows: wheat > corn > barley > selenite > selenate. The relative toxicity of indicator plants could not be included in the above classification owing to the lack of homogeneity of the selenocompounds in these plants.

Some of the characteristic manifestations of chronic selenosis as well as the form of selenium that induces the disease are summarized in Table 43.

CHRONIC POISONING OF THE BLIND-STAGGERS TYPE

The blind-staggers type of chronic selenosis appears in cattle and sheep when they consume moderately toxic amounts of seleniferous weeds over

TABLE 43

Manifestations of Chronic Selenosis and Associated Syndromes Produced by Different Chemical Forms of Selenium

	Alkali disease[a]	Blind staggers[a]	Experimental selenosis[a]
Sources of selenium	Seleniferous grains and grasses	Selenium indicator plants: *Astragalus*, *Machaeranthera*,[c] *Haplopappus*,[d] and *Stanleya*	Salts of selenate and selenite
Effects of selenium on food intake	Rarely affected	Decreased—followed by anorexia	Decreased—followed by anorexia
Visible signs of the disease	Lameness, loss of vitality, elongated hoofs, loss of hair from mane and tail	Emaciation. Neuromuscular involvement in 3 stages in cattle. Sheep, neuromuscular involvement not well defined	Emaciation. Some neuromuscular involvement not well defined (cattle)
Reproduction	Rarely affected	Cattle: impaired Sheep: malformations	Not studied
Selenium accumulation[b]	Cattle: hoofs 5–8 ppm; hair 5–10 ppm Horses: hoofs 11.0 ppm; hair 11–45 ppm Other tissues: lower than blind staggers	Cattle: hair variable Sheep: wool undetermined Other tissues: higher than in alkali disease	Cattle: hair 2.7–9.5 ppm; horn 0.25 ppm. Other tissues: similar to blind staggers
Characteristic gross pathology	Liver: atrophy and cirrhosis; kidney: chronic nephritis; gall bladder: rarely enlarged; heart: soft and flabby; intestinal tract: rarely involved	Liver: necrosis with cirrhosis; kidney: subacute and chronic nephritis; gall bladder: generally enlarged; heart: soft and flabby; intestinal tract: impacted with irritation	Liver: necrosis with occasional cirrhosis; kidney: acute nephritis; intestinal tract: ulceration and gangrene

[a] Data taken from various sections dealing with chronic selenosis.
[b] During selenium intake.
[c] Section *Xylorhiza*.
[d] Section *Oonopsis*.

a considerable period of time. The poisoning often terminates in a sudden collapse, followed by death (*9, 38, 42*). In a technical sense, the term blind staggers, commonly used by stockmen, is misleading because afflicted animals may not become blind and they do not necessarily stagger.

Causative Agents

Native range weeds, such as *Astragalus bisulcatus* and *Machaeranthera glabriuscula*, containing a moderate or high concentration of water-soluble selenium are responsible for the poisoning. The selenium content of the plants, and hence their toxicity, varies widely according to the stage of growth and type of soil. The severity of the toxicity depends upon the species of selenium indicator plants ingested (*9*). The presence of other toxic substances accompanying the selenium may also produce different manifestations of the disease. *Astragalus bisulcatus* contains little toxic material other than selenium. All selenium indicator plants when fed experimentally to sheep or cattle produce chronic selenosis. A high percentage of selenium in section *Oonopsis* of *Haplopappus* and section *Xylorhiza* of *Machaeranthera* is inorganic, and in experimental as well as under field conditions the tissue damage and symptoms appear to be similar to those observed with inorganic selenium compounds. Section *Oonopsis* of *Haplopappus*, a selenium accumulator, rarely produces poisoning in livestock owing to its unpalatability. However, it is a dangerous contaminant of the soil due to its high soluble selenium content. *Stanleya* under both experimental and field conditions produces blind staggers in cattle and probably in sheep.

Experimental Observations

Blind staggers in cattle has been produced by forced feeding with seleniferous weeds (Beath, unpublished data). The pathological changes are similar to those in range cases, but the sudden breakdown that is characteristic of severe cases in range cattle has not been observed. Steers were fed green seleniferous *Astragalus pectinatus* supplying daily doses of 2.2 mg of selenium per kilogram of body weight. After receiving 6–16 doses, the animals developed blind staggers. The disease developed in a steer after being fed *A. bisulcatus* in 7 daily doses, each supplying 3.4 mg of selenium per kilogram of body weight. Lambs that were fed *Machaeranthera glabriuscula* containing 800 ppm of selenium developed the characteristic symptoms. Lambs that were fed seleniferous *Atriplex canescens* for 3 weeks lost considerable weight and became nearly blind.

Symptoms

In cattle, blind staggers shows three stages as indicated in Fig. 30 (*9*). In the early stage of poisoning the animal wanders, frequently in circles,

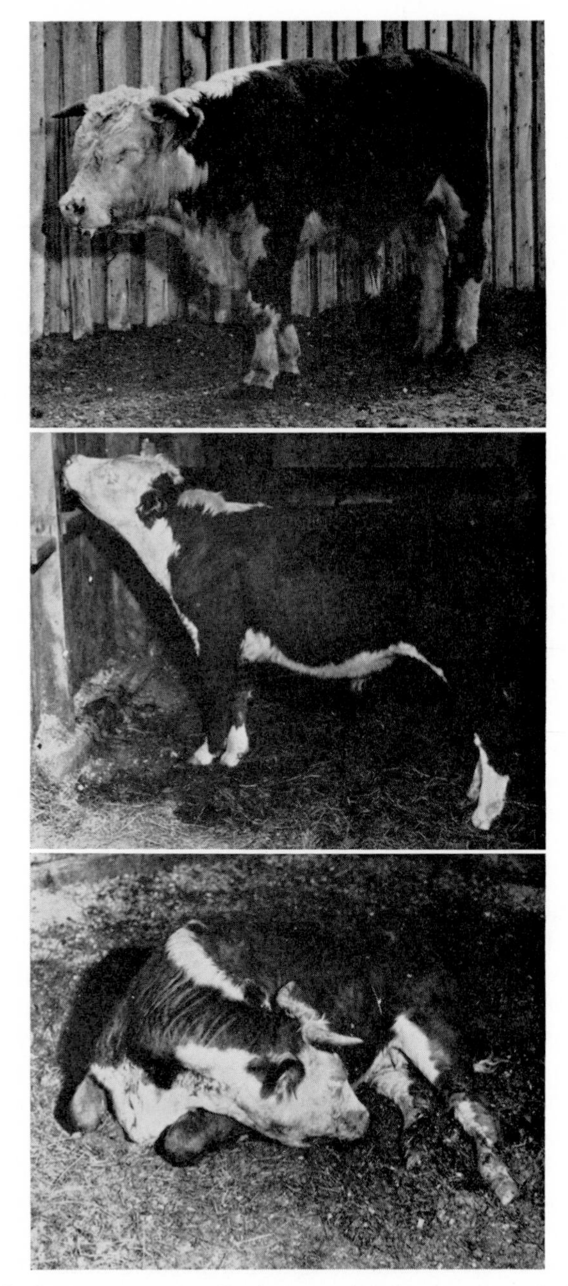

FIG. 30. Blind staggers in cattle showing the three stages of the disease in increasing severity from top to bottom. Note salivation and closure of eyes in all stages, and emaciation and paralysis in the final stage (Beath).

disregards objects in its path, and stumbles over them or walks into them. In this stage, the body temperature and respiration are normal. The animal shows little desire to eat or drink. It may give evidence of some impairment of vision.

In the second stage there is an increase in the manifestations of the first stage of the disease. In addition to that, the front legs seem to become weak and unable to support the animal. The animal loses desire to eat or drink, although the tongue and muscles concerned in swallowing do not exhibit paralysis.

The third or last stage prior to death is a paralytic stage. The tongue and the mechanism of swallowing become partially or totally paralyzed. The animal is nearly blind. Respiration becomes labored and accelerated. There is evidence of great abdominal pain, which may have been marked even in the second stage. The pain causes constant grating of the teeth and salivation. The body temperature is subnormal. The eyelids are swollen and inflamed, and the cornea is distinctly cloudy. The mucous membrane of the mouth is pale. In most cases the third stage appears suddenly and is fatal within a few hours. The immediate cause of death is respiratory failure. A gradual loss of weight always accompanies the disease and at the final stage the animal may appear emaciated.

Recovery may occur in the first or second stages, but if the third stage is reached the disease is usually fatal. Mature animals that recover do not become vigorous, and younger animals remain stunted.

The action of the poison may be delayed so that several weeks or months may elapse before the attack occurs (*10*). Cattle may show no outward sign of poisoning, but suddenly severe symptoms develop and death follows within a few days. This has been known to occur after cattle have been shipped to a feed-lot and are being fattened for the market. Diagnosis would be difficult by one not familiar with this type of delayed poisoning.

In sheep, chronic selenium poisoning is not as readily diagnosed as in cattle. The three stages are not clearly differentiated. The pathology, however, is the same as that in cattle.

Factors Influencing the Poisoning

A high-protein diet was found by Rosenfeld and Beath (*215*) to afford more protection against *Atriplex canescens* and selenite poisoning in sheep than a low-protein diet. The toxic dose with the high-protein diet was 20 mg given daily for 25 days, while that with the low-protein diet was 15 mg given for 6 days. The lethal dose with the high-protein diet was 30 mg for 30 days, and with the low-protein diet 20 mg for 13 days. Recovery from poisoning, as indicated by food intake, was slower with the low-protein diet. The selenium content of the blood reached a higher level in the animals on the low-protein diet, but the elevated level was of shorter duration. It is evident that the protein content of the diet has a marked influence on the toxicity of selenium. The effects of other factors remain to be investigated.

Distribution of Selenium

Selenium is distributed by the circulatory system, and accumulation in the different tissues tends to be similar in acute and chronic cases. The concentration in the blood, however, is much greater in acute than in chronic poisoning. In general, in acute cases it may reach 25 ppm, and in chronic poisoning it is usually much lower—1.5 to 4 ppm in blind staggers or 1 to 2 ppm in alkali disease. There may be some reports which show some variations from the above figures.

There is a considerable amount of data available on the selenium content of tissues of mammals and birds. Varying concentrations have been found in every tissue analyzed. In all species certain tissues consistently contain high concentrations of selenium. The liver and kidney usually contain large amounts while the brain has only traces. When results are calculated on the basis of whole organs or tissues, the muscles and bones contain high total amounts of selenium due to the large mass of these tissues which exist in the body.

Accumulation in the tissues depends not only upon the quantity but also upon the form of selenium ingested by the animals. Smith *et al.* (*246*) found that in laboratory animals, organic selenium was accumulated in higher quantities and was retained longer in the tissues than inorganic selenium. The same difference would probably be found in some tissues of livestock.

The distribution of selenium in tissues was studied by Dudley (*46*). In chronic poisoning of hogs and horses the blood contained 0.2–5 ppm, while in acute poisoning of hogs, calves, and sheep it had 7–27 ppm. The organs that contained the most were the kidney and liver, with 4–25 ppm in both chronic and acute cases. The spleen in chronic cases contained but a trace to 1.5 ppm, whereas in acute cases it had 4–20 ppm. The hoofs of animals with chronic poisoning contained 8–20 ppm, but those of animals acutely poisoned were free of selenium.

The selenium content of tissues in the terminal stages of blind staggers is directly related to the duration of life of the animal. If death occurs soon after the disease develops, all tissues contain high concentrations of selenium. If the disease is prolonged, the selenium content of tissues is considerably lower, the kidney containing between 2.0 and 5.0 ppm; liver 1–8 ppm; and blood 1.5–4 ppm selenium (authors' unpublished results, 1960).

The distribution of selenium in the tissues of sheep fed seleniferous

Atriplex canescens and later selenite was reported by Rosenfeld and Beath (*214*). The selenium content of the tissues was found to be proportional to the amount ingested. Variation in protein, within the range used, did not affect the distribution and concentration of selenium in the tissues. Large amounts were present in liver, kidney, spleen, heart, lung, and stomach; muscle and brain had small amounts; and fat was free of selenium. The blood contained 1.3–3.1 ppm selenium.

Retention and Excretion

Selenium in the urine has been reported to range from 0.1 to 8 ppm (*47, 167*). The excretion of selenium by sheep that received graded doses for 44 and 116 days was investigated by Rosenfeld and Beath (*214*). In the earlier stages of the selenium administration the excretion of selenium in the urine was low. After 30 days about 35 per cent of the daily intake was eliminated. As selenium feeding was continued, the elimination decreased and at the time of death the urine contained only 8–15 per cent of the daily intake. The decreased elimination was apparently due to kidney injury. In sheep that received 360–860 mg in 44 days and were then put on a nonseleniferous diet, the selenium previously stored was gradually excreted; 50 days after intake ceased, the urine was free of selenium or contained only trace amounts. Sixty-four days after feeding was stopped, the tissues contained only small amounts: the liver and kidney showed 1.1–1.9 ppm and all other organs showed less than 1.0 ppm.

Effects of Selenium on the Chemical Composition of Tissues

In animals that died of selenium poisoning, Rosenfeld and Beath (*216*) observed decreases in vitamin A and ascorbic acid. There was a decrease in blood protein and an increase in nonprotein nitrogen. When selenium feeding was discontinued before injury was severe, there was a slow but gradual increase in the blood protein and a decrease of nonprotein nitrogen.

Gradual depletion of protein and sulfur in the liver was associated with the poisoning in sheep (*216*). Even 64 days after discontinuing selenium feeding, the liver had 10 per cent less than the normal nitrogen content. Protein depletion of the liver during selenium feeding and protein replacement after its discontinuance took place gradually. The heart in some cases also showed depletion of protein. But the kidney, lung, and spleen showed no changes in nitrogen, protein, and sulfur. Vitamin A and ascorbic acid decreased in the livers of animals that died.

Wool and blood from 28 ewes grazed on a seleniferous range were analyzed for selenium. The wool designated as staple tip contained a greater amount of selenium than the part designated as staple base. Sulfur content of wool ranged from 3.0 to 3.4 per cent. As the selenium content increased, there was a corresponding decrease in the sulfur content of the wool (*129*).

Gross Pathology

The gross pathology of blind staggers was described by Draize and Beath (*42*) and by Rosenfeld and Beath (*217*) as follows. The heart is soft and flabby. The pericardial sac contains an abnormal amount of fluid. The epicardium shows numerous petechial hemorrhages. Fat tends to be deposited at the apex of the heart. There is some necrosis of the endocardium, leading to hemorrhages. The necrosis extends into the myocardium and is most pronounced around the blood vessels. There are patches of fibrous tissue scattered throughout the myocardium. The lungs are congested, with focal hemorrhages and areas of diffuse fibroses. Generalized edema is present, usually with most fluid in the posterior inferior regions of the lung. The smooth muscles exhibit atony. Dilation of the gastrointestinal tract, gall bladder, urinary bladder, and blood vessels occurs. Congestion of the blood vessels is observed throughout the viscera, mesentery, and peritoneum. Impaction of the rumen is a constant finding; dilation is occasionally observed. Stasis is evident in the omasum. The bases of papillae along the longitudinal folds of the omasum show irritation and hemorrhage. There may be some desquamation of the epithelium of the omasum, but this is rare in the rumen or the reticulum. The abomasum and the upper part of the small intestine reveal varying degrees of irritation and congestion of the blood vessels; in severe cases many petechial hemorrhages are noted and ulceration may be present. The large intestine, as a rule, is relatively free from irritation. There is a tendency to ascites, but distention of the abdomen, when observed, is due to distended stomachs rather than to an abnormal amount of serous fluid. The liver, although approximately normal in size, is acutely congested, and early in the poisoning it contains regions of focal necrosis surrounded by hemorrhages. There are areas of fibrous tissue which, on contraction, form pits on the surface of the organ. The liver shows the effects of both a chronic and a superimposed acute poisoning. The gall bladder may be enlarged to twice its normal size, and its mucosa shows degenerative changes. The blood vessels are congested and the bile is viscous. The pancreas in many cases exhibits congestion and is swollen, soft and red in color owing to hemorrhages. Acute hemorrhagic pancreatitis may be present. The medullary portion of the kidney is congested and hemorrhagic. Renal calculi are not uncommon. When they occur, obstruction of the ureters produces hydronephrosis. There may be atrophy of the affected kidney and compensatory hypertrophy of the other kidney. The testicles are soft, flabby, and acutely congested. In young females the ovaries are small and the corpus luteum is absent; in adults the ovaries are small, firm, and congested. The spleen presents a variable picture of fibrosis and congestion; it may be greatly enlarged or atrophic. The lymph nodes are enlarged, edematous, and altered by gelatinous degeneration. The brain is anemic, moist, and abnormally soft. The meninges show acute congestion. Distinction between gray and white matter may be absent. Moisture exudes readily from a cut surface. The sulci are narrowed. In less severe cases only acute congestion is present. The ends of the long bones exhibit erosion in approximately two thirds of the cases.

Microscopic Pathology

The following description is based upon the reports of Draize and Beath (*42*) and Rosenfeld and Beath (*217*). A serofibrinous exudate is observed around the coronary vessels of the heart. Numerous hemorrhages are present in the endocardium, myocardium, and pericardium. The myocardium exhibits regions of lymphocytic infiltration, fibrosis, and cellular atrophy. The lungs are congested. There is thickening of the alveolar wall, an increase in the interstitial tissue, and increased fibrosis around the blood vessels and bronchi. Focal hemorrhages and edema are present in the alveoli. The gastrointestinal tract, omasum, and abomasum indicate severe injury. Acute inflammation is evident at the base of the longitudinal folds of the omasum, and some desquamation of the epithelium occurs. Necrosis and hemorrhages are present in the omasum and abomasum. In rare cases the rumen and the reticulum may be slightly inflamed. The duodenum shows hemorrhages and acute inflammation. The ileum and the large intestines, however, are seldom affected. The liver exhibits parenchymatous degeneration. The cells are swollen and granular and in some regions they have disintegrated, producing wide sinuses and dilation of the central vein. Fatty metamorphosis is marked, and large areas of necrosis occur with distinct or confluent hemorrhages. In the portal area there are zones of bile duct and fibrocytic proliferation, lymphocytic infiltration, and replacement fibrosis. The mucosa of the gall bladder shows atrophy or edematous thickening. The cells of the mucosa and submucosa are edematous and vacuolated. The pancreas may exhibit only acute congestion with varying degrees of hemorrhage. In many cases, however, an acute hemorrhagic pancreatitis is present, and necrosis completely obliterates the normal histologic structure. The most severe injury of the kidney occurs in the proximal convoluted tubules of the medulla. Parenchymatous degeneration and desquamation of the epithelial cells are evident. Severe intertubular hemorrhages may be present. The convoluted tubules may show hyaline degeneration. An early glomerulonephritis is apparent. Regions of fibrosis are present in the medullary portion and around the blood vessels. The sex glands usually show congestion, atrophy of the seminiferous tubules in the male, large numbers of atretic follicles and complete absence of mature follicles in the female. In younger females the number of follicles is greatly decreased. The spleen appears congested with a heavy deposition of hemosiderin, or in cases of fibrosis its normal structure is obliterated. The lymph nodes show edema and some fibrosis and the normal architecture of the tissue may be destroyed. In the brain the interstitial lesions are vascular dilation, occasional hemorrhages, and edema. The meninges are congested but rarely have hemorrhages.

The pathology of blind staggers indicates that there is superimposed upon a chronic process an acute reaction which may be due to ingestion of extremely toxic plants or to sudden liberation of selenium stored in various organs because of some stress or secondary damage to the organs.

Treatment

Successful treatment of blind staggers in cattle may be difficult because the animal frequently shows no abnormality before the sudden development of severe symptoms. In less severe cases, Beath (*12*) found that some relief may be afforded by drenching with copious quantities of warm water and by injecting strychnine hypodermically. Two or three injections with strychnine sulfate may be given 2 or 3 hours apart. The dose should be small—one-tenth to one-fifteenth grain is satisfactory for an animal weighing between six hundred and eight hundred pounds. After a day or two, additional help can be given by drenching with a tonic containing iron and quinine sulfates and nux vomica. At no time during the initial stages of the illness is it advisable to administer laxatives. The general stasis of the third stomach cannot be overburdened with irritants if a reasonable recovery is to be expected.

Prostigmine was used by Rosenfeld and Beath (unpublished results) in treating blind staggers in 8 cows and 2 calves. The initial treatment of 4 ml prostigmine methyl sulfate (1:2000) given intramuscularly was followed by 60 mg prostigmine bromide in lukewarm water by drenching. Treatment was continued for 3 days, and each day the dose was decreased by 20 mg. Animals were given symptomatic treatment to prevent dehydration and starvation. Eight cows and one of the two calves responded favorably to this treatment. Application of the 5 per cent prostigmine bromide to the eyes also had beneficial effects in cases of visual disturbance.

Proposed Experimentation

Much more detailed information is needed on the effects resulting from the ingestion of seleniferous vegetation by sheep, cattle, hogs, and horses. Many unexplained conditions enter into the problem. It is not yet possible to state with any degree of accuracy what constitutes the minimum toxic dose of selenium in each of its forms for the different kinds of livestock.

No investigator has reported upon the cause of the final collapse in blind staggers. Further study is required on the effects of selenium on the tissues, blood constituents, and vitamins. There has been a tendency in feeding experiments to omit important factors which are present under range and farm conditions.

CHRONIC POISONING OF THE ALKALI-DISEASE TYPE

The type of chronic selenium poisoning known as alkali disease is characterized by loss of hair and deformation and sloughing of the hoofs in cattle, hogs, and horses that have consumed moderately seleniferous grains and forage grasses over a period of several weeks or months (*69, 134, 137, 172, 199*). Manifestations of this disease differ from blind staggers in that the animals affected (horses or cattle) only occasionally show the emaciation characteristic of blind staggers. The term alkali disease came into usage among the early settlers who erroneously believed the ailment to be due to alkali or mineral salts in the water or soil (*199*). The alkali disease due to selenium poisoning is clearly distinct from the disturbance termed alkali poisoning by Miller (*164*), which is caused by drinking water that is unusually high in salts. Selenium poisoning is also distinct from the so-called alkali disease of livestock in Pecos Valley, New Mexico and Texas, described by Marsh and Roe (*140*), which is caused by poisonous plants that do not contain selenium.

Causative Agents

Corn, wheat, barley, oats, grasses, and hay containing 10–30 ppm selenium are known to cause alkali disease. The selenium compound(s) in these feeds are bound in the proteins (*172*), therefore, differ in their chemical characteristic(s) from the selenium compounds present in indicator plants which produce blind staggers. The amount of selenium present in these plants is related to the availability of soluble selenium in the soil. Knott *et al.* (*123*) reported that a native plant of Queensland, *Morinda reticulata,* was a selenium accumulator and produced alkali disease in horses. Their studies on the chemical characteristics of selenium compound(s) in the plant indicate that only about 15 per cent of the selenium was in water-soluble form. This suggests that the chemical nature of the selenium compound(s) in *Morinda reticulata* is more closely related to the grain type selenium compound(s). The selenium must be bound in the proteins before the syndrome of alkali disease develops in animals (*172*).

Experimental Observations

Alkali disease was produced experimentally with seleniferous barley hay grown in soil that had a heavy stand of *Astragalus bisulcatus* (*11*). Barley straw and grain were fed to calves and were found to be toxic. At the end of 6 weeks the animals lacked normal coordination of movement, and their joints became stiff. In 4 months, the hoofs of the animals were badly affected and started to slough. At no time did the animals lack an appetite. One animal was killed and autopsied. Gross and microscopic pathology were identical with those of typical alkali disease. The other animal was kept under observation for a year. The hoofs sloughed 3 times during the winter and early spring. At the end of the year she appeared normal and was bred. The progeny seemed normal at birth.

Alkali disease in hogs was produced under experimental conditions by Evans and co-workers in 1925 and the results were reported by Moxon (*172*). Wheat from affected farms produced alkali disease in 14 days. The hair of the hogs began to fall out and within a short time most of them became hairless; on selenium-free feed, they recovered rapidly and grew new coats of hair. Corn also produced alkali disease in hogs. Extraction of corn with water, alcohol, and ether did not remove the toxic substance. Residues after extraction produced alkali disease in one hog within 10 days and in others in about 3 weeks. The extract did not cause the disease.

Corn containing 10 ppm selenium was fed to 2 hogs by Beath (unpublished results, 1932). One showed distinct loss of hair within 26 days, especially along the back from the shoulders to the hips and the other developed symptoms somewhat later. Lesions appeared on the hoofs and dewclaws of all feet. New growth of hoofs took place, pushing the old hoofs forward and producing sledrunner profiles. Alkali disease was produced in 2 hogs by Schoening (*234*) by feeding corn containing 10 ppm of selenium. Corn containing 5 ppm, however, did not cause the disease.

Symptoms

The general symptoms of alkali disease include lack of vitality, anemia, stiffness of joints, lameness, roughened coat, loss of long hair, and hoof lesions and deformities.

In horses, the first symptom is the loss of hair from the mane and tail. For this reason, the disease has been called bob-tailed disease in some localities. Loss of hair is followed by soreness of the feet. A circular break appears on the wall of the hoof below the coronary band. In a mild case the crack may remain shallow. As new growth of the hoof continues in the region of the coronary band, the break in the wall of the hoof moves downward. In severe cases the crack is so deep that the upper part of the old wall becomes separated from the new growth. As the new hoof develops, the old hoof is gradually pushed down and is finally sloughed. While the horse is shedding its hoofs and growing new ones, the animal is lame and in severe pain. Unless water and feed are given, it may die of thirst or starvation. Death may occur within 2 months after a horse has been placed on a seleniferous pasture. The various degrees of hoof injury are indicated in Fig. 31.

In cattle the early symptoms are occasional emaciation, lameness, and loss of long hair from the switch. In severe cases, the hoofs become involved in much the same way as those of horses. Tenderness of the feet and lameness impede the movements of the animal. Owing to the soreness

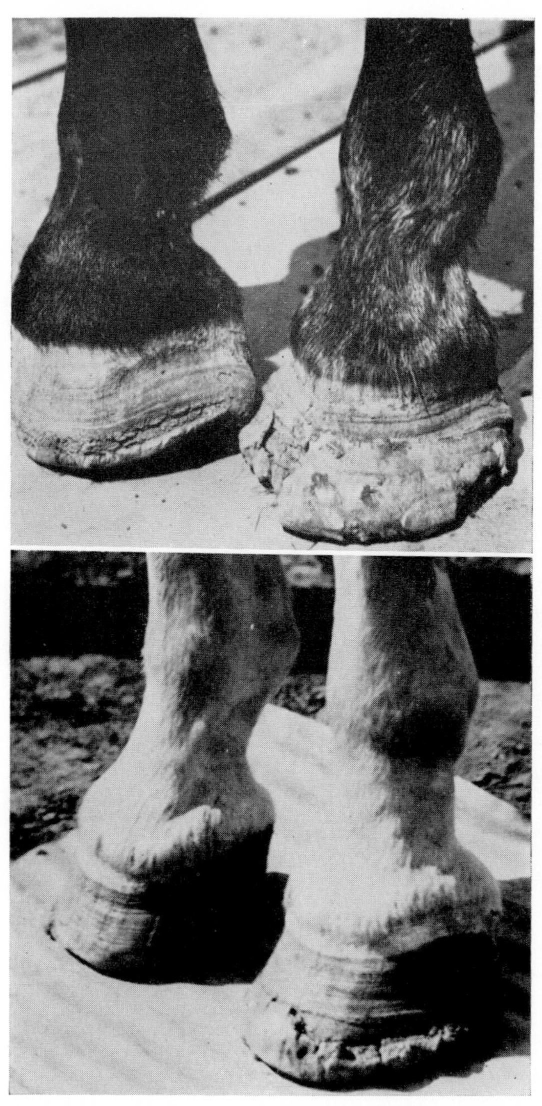

FIG. 31. Alkali disease in horses showing various degrees of hoof damage. Note the marked separation of the coronary band at the upper right hoof. (By courtesy of O. E. Olson.)

of feet, cattle often assume a kneeling position while grazing. The older part of the hoof, partially separated from the foot, usually does not come off completely but remains attached to the new growth. The ragged hoofs are often 8 or 10 inches in length and are turned upward at the ends. The deformed hoofs are sometimes called frozen feet by farmers. The horns may show distinct circular ridges comparable to those of the hoofs (Fig. 32).

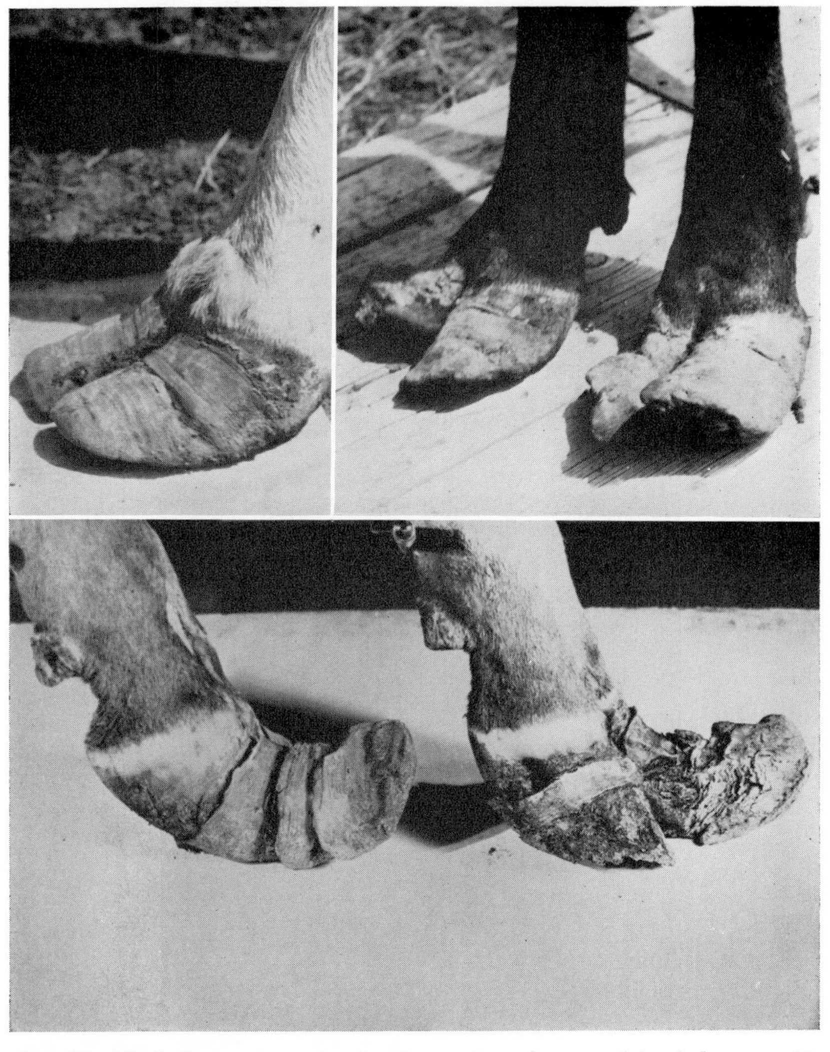

FIG. 32. Alkali disease in cattle showing various degrees of hoof damage. (By courtesy of O. E. Olson.)

In swine the symptoms include loss of hair from the body, retarded growth, emaciation, lameness, and hoof lesions and deformities followed often by the shedding of the hoofs.

Factors Influencing the Poisoning

Effects of the administration of bromobenzene to steers grazed on seleniferous vegetation for 5 months were reported by Moxon *et al.* (*180*). Bromobenzene appears to aid in the urinary excretion of selenium. It is possible that selenocystine and selenomethionine are conjugated with bromobenzene and excreted as the selenium analog of mercapturic acid. Although use of bromobenzene or naphthalene increased urinary excretion of selenium in cattle with alkali disease, it had no effect on the rate of recovery from selenium toxicity. Both compounds are toxic on prolonged administration; therefore, it is doubtful that they will prove to be of any therapeutic value in alkali disease (*40*).

Beneficial effects of arsenic in cases of chronic selenium poisoning were reported by Moxon and co-workers in numerous experiments with small animals, which are discussed in a subsequent section of this chapter. A few experiments with livestock have been reported by Moxon (*181*). Steers grazing on a seleniferous range for 2 years, supplied with 25 ppm of arsenic in the salt, made better gains and sold at slightly better prices than untreated animals (*184*). In grazing studies on a seleniferous range, the feeding of 550 mg of arsanilic acid per day to steers showed no significant difference in severity of selenium damage or the rate of gain when compared with the untreated animals according to Minyard *et al.* (*168*). They concluded that until a practical method can be devised for a controlled arsanilic acid administration to cattle while on pasture, the use of the arsenic compounds for counteracting selenium intoxication could not be recommended.

Distribution of Selenium

Experimental evidence in livestock indicates that selenium is excreted in urine, feces, bile, and milk, and that considerable amounts may be eliminated through the respiratory tract and sweat glands. There are no reports on the fecal excretion of selenium in alkali disease. Moxon (*172*) stated that suckling pigs and nursing calves get enough selenium from the milk of their affected mothers to develop alkali disease. He gives no definite results, but states that milk of alkali-diseased cows contains considerable quantities of selenium. Dudley and Byers (*45*) reported that in cows and pigs selenium in milk varied from 0.02 to 3.0 ppm, and in urine from 0.1 to 5.0 ppm. They did not designate the source of the material or the severity of the disease in the animals. Similar observations by

Smith and Westfall (*244*) showed the selenium content of milk to be between 0.16 and 1.27 ppm. The selenium content of urine in alkalied colts and horses was 33, 100, 125, and 170 μg per cent (*242*).

Alkali disease differs from acute selenium poisoning and blind staggers in showing lower selenium levels in all tissues except the hoofs, which contain higher concentrations. Moxon *et al.* (*184*) treated alkali-diseased steers with 25 ppm arsenic. The organs contained the following amounts of selenium (the results are the averages of 4 lots in each of the 2 groups): Group I—blood 1.7 ppm; kidney 2.2 ppm; liver 1.2 ppm; spleen 0.6 ppm; and meat (muscle) 0.9 ppm. Group II—blood 2.05 ppm; kidney 3.95 ppm; liver 5.6 ppm; spleen 2.49 ppm; and meat (muscle) 3.03 ppm. They suggested that arsenic slightly decreased the selenium content of tissues and reduced the incidence of symptoms.

Selenium concentration in hoofs was 8 and 5 ppm, and in bone 2.5 and 1.0 ppm in horses and cattle, respectively (*46*).

The rate at which the selenium content of tissues decreases in alkali disease in livestock and especially in cattle is almost unknown. The work at Reed Substation in South Dakota (*40*) indicates that if cattle are transferred from a seleniferous to a nonseleniferous area, the blood selenium level drops in about 60 days to 0–1 ppm; and in about 6 months the selenium content of hair decreases to between 0 and 5 ppm. Experiments were also carried out on the correlation of selenium content of blood and hair with the manifestations of the disease in cattle. Blood and hair samples were analyzed several times during the year. There seemed to be a seasonal variation as to selenium content in both blood and hair. The selenium content increased during the grazing season and decreased during the feeding period at which time the hay feed contained less selenium than the growing pasture. The results of these studies can be summarized as follows: blood values over 2 ppm indicate that damage by selenium is very likely to occur, of 1–2 ppm indicate possible poisoning, and of less than 1 ppm indicate no toxic effects. No correlation was found between the selenium content of hair and the occurrence of symptoms. Throughout the year over 95 per cent of the hair samples contained more than 10 ppm selenium. Some but not all of the animals developed symptoms of selenium poisoning. Hair analyses can indicate only the probability of the appearance of symptoms, but not the actual occurrence. As a general conclusion, it can be stated that when hair contains less than 5 ppm selenium, no symptoms or damage can be expected; between 5 and 10 ppm, occasional symptoms of the disease may occur; and above 10 ppm, alkali disease is prevalent.

Knott *et al.* (*123*) reported that by feeding *Morinda reticulata* to horses in North Queensland, they were able to produce "change hoof disease" in the animals. Symptoms of this disease were identical with those of alkali disease. The selenium content in the various tissues is indicated in Table 44.

TABLE 44
Distribution of Selenium in Tissues in Alkali Disease[a]

Tissue	Selenium (ppm)
Left lobe liver	8.6
Middle lobe liver	9.8
Left kidney	8.2
Right kidney	8.2
Spleen	2.0
Lung	0.8
Muscle (psoas)	2.9
Muscle (semitendenosis)	1.6
Blood	4.1
Left front hoof	11.4
Body hair grown during feeding	11.2
Mane hair grown during feeding	19.4
Tail hair grown during feeding	45.4

[a] Knott *et al.* (*123*).

Gross Pathology

Several investigators have described the gross pathology of alkali disease in livestock (*42, 69, 172, 217, 234*). The lesions of alkali disease represent more chronic, progressive degenerations than those of blind staggers. The heart and liver exhibit the most severe injury. The heart is soft, flabby, and atrophied. There are petechial hemorrhages on the epicardium, although they are less prominent than in blind staggers. The lungs show focal fibrosis, early congestion, and some edema. The gastrointestinal tract may be normal or may show some injury. The liver is usually cirrhotic and atrophied. Its consistency is firm because of the development of fibrous tissue. In less severe cases the surface of the liver is granular owing to focal fibrosis; in advanced cases the surface has a characteristic nodular appearance. Discoloration of the liver varies with the degree of injury. Islands of apparently normal tissue are intertwined with strands that show yellowish-green and brownish discolorations resulting from deposition of fat, iron pigments, and staining by the bile. The gall bladder is rarely enlarged. Its surface is opaque and usually lacks the normal bluish color. The wall is thickened and fibrous and the cavity is reduced. The kidney is more seriously affected than in blind staggers. It may be shrunken and scarred or may contain calculi that obstruct the excretion of urine. Fibrous scars produce depressions in the surface, or there may be a more diffuse fibrosis present which gives the surface a coarsely granular appearance. The spleen is atrophic and dull brownish-yellow in color. The capsule is thickened and wrinkled, and a cut surface shows marked fibrosis. The hoofs are deformed as in typical cases of alkali disease. Erosion of the ends of the long bones is almost always present. In severe cases the bone marrow is gelatinous.

Microscopic Pathology

Histologically, alkali disease differs from blind staggers in that it lacks an acute reaction and shows more chronic types of degenerative changes (*42, 217*). The muscle-fiber cells of the heart are small, and at each pole of the nucleus there is an accumulation of yellow pigment. Focal or diffuse fibrosis is present in the myocardium. The lung is congested and some of the acini are filled with albuminous fluid. The walls of the alveoli are thickened and show fibroblastic proliferation and replacement fibrosis. The bronchi and blood vessels exhibit fibrosis. The gastrointestinal tract is normal or occasionally shows degeneration of the surface epithelium and round-cell infiltration of the mucosa and submucosa. The liver has the most marked changes. In less advanced cases the lesions are focal in distribution. Fibroblastic proliferation gives rise to connective tissue containing large numbers of bile ducts. There may be dim preservation of the lobular outline of the liver, indicating an earlier cirrhotic stage. In cirrhosis, the liver cells are separated by broad bands of fibrous tissue containing many bile ducts. The new ducts sometimes appear as solid cords. The normal lobular arrangement is destroyed. The nodules are composed largely of new cells that are irregular in size and arrangement. The bands of connective tissue between the islands of liver cells may be cellular or fibrous. Cells characteristic of chronic inflammations are present in large numbers. The gall bladder exhibits chronic inflammation with round-cell infiltration. Granulation tissue and fibrous tissue produce thickening of the wall. In hydronephrosis, the kidney shows marked atrophy of the tubules but fairly normal glomeruli. In some cases, fibrosis of the glomeruli occurs and the renal parenchyma is replaced by fibrous tissue. Even in advanced stages of hydronephrosis some normal glomeruli and tubules are present and probably continue to excrete urine. A scarred and shrunken kidney shows fibrosis, sclerosis of the glomeruli, and obliteration of many of the tubules. In the spleen, dilation of the sinuses and thickening of the fibrous framework extends through the reticulum and finally involves the main trabeculae. Masses of intracellular and extracellular hemosiderin are present. A high incidence of anemia in alkali disease has been reported (*183*), and the hemoglobin content of the blood can be used to detect early stages of the poisoning. In severe cases the hemoglobin may be as low as 7 gm per cent.

Treatment

The only certain therapeutic measure is to discontinue the feeding of seleniferous grain and forage or to remove the animals to a place where the disease does not occur. Grazing animals should be allowed as much free range as possible so that they may have an opportunity to avoid the toxic vegetation.

CHRONIC SELENIUM POISONING BY INORGANIC SELENIUM

Experimental chronic selenosis by inorganic selenium (sodium or potassium salts of selenate or selenite) was produced in livestock primarily to prove conclusively that the toxic factor in vegetation was selenium.

Experimental Observations

Sodium selenite was administered orally to 2 yearling heifers over a period of several weeks (Draize and Beath, unpublished data). One animal that received 7.7 gm of selenium for 23 days became very weak and lacked body tone. The jaws as well as tongue became rigid and the swallowing mechanism was partially paralyzed. In the terminal stage of the disease the animal exhibited a complete lack of appetite. It showed no tendency to walk in circles; there was no evidence of impaired vision. Growth of horns, hoofs, and hair appeared normal. The other heifer received 2.8 gm of selenium divided in 14 daily doses. In general the symptoms were similar to those described above, plus extreme emaciation. The animal died after 37 days. The excreta gave evidence of severe inflammation of the gastrointestinal tract.

The toxicity of inorganic selenium in pigs and equines was investigated in order to compare the effects of inorganic selenium with that of selenium in plants and grain. Selenite was added to the grain ration to give 25–392 ppm of selenium. All animals died from 10 to 99 days after diet initiation and showed post-mortem lesions similar to those seen in alkali disease (*165*). This is the only report which suggests that some degree of alkali disease develops in pigs with the use of inorganic selenium. To study the effect of long-continued feeding of inorganic selenium on equines, 24 and 17.3 ppm selenium was added to the food for about 2 months. This was followed by 48 ppm, and finally the dose was increased to 96 ppm (*167*). The animals which received the highest level of selenium survived only 5 weeks. The others survived for 6½ to 17½ months.

Recently, Maag *et al.* (*136*) studied the effect of sodium selenite on cattle under typical feed-lot conditions. They reported that 2 doses of 0.5 mg selenium (as Na_2SeO_3) per pound of body weight depressed food intake, and the animals showed acute toxic symptoms. The reduction of selenium dose to 0.25 mg per pound of body weight resulted in the disappearance of all visible signs of acute toxicity. By varying the oral dose of selenium from 0.25 to 0.5 mg per pound of body weight 3 times a week, 2 animals died in 8 weeks and 4 died in 20 to 23 weeks. Although the authors stated that under their experimental conditions no typical symptoms of alkali disease or blind staggers developed in the cattle, some of the symptoms described by the authors resemble some stages of the blind-staggers type of poisoning. Since inorganic selenium was used by the investigators to produce chronic selenosis in cattle, typical alkali-disease or blind-staggers types of selenium poisoning could not be expected to develop.

Tucker (*263*) carried out a similar experiment in sheep with sodium selenate. He determined the oral subtoxic dose as well as the maximum level of selenium tolerated by ewes without death. He reported that 0.125 mg of sodium selenate per pound per day was tolerated by the animals for 84 days without any recognizable toxic effects. When the dose was increased to 0.25 mg per pound per day, all animals died in between 9 and 28 days. Sodium selenate at 0.5 mg per pound per day was fatal to all animals within 4–9 days.

Symptoms

Decrease in food consumption is the most pronounced symptom when inorganic salts of selenium are fed or injected to all species of experimental animals as well as livestock. Repeated administration of small doses of selenite to equines and pigs produced some lesions characteristic of alkali disease. In equines the most marked symptoms were emaciation, drowsiness, and loss of appetite immediately before death; in pigs there was loss of hair and separation of the hoof (*165, 167*). Peculiar trembling of the skeletal muscles, shivering during exercise, anorexia, and inability to rise were noted in cattle (*136*).

Distribution of Selenium

Selenium content of tissues of livestock receiving repeated doses of selenite or selenate was studied by various investigators. The selenium content of different tissues of pigs in chronic poisoning with selenite was reported by Miller and Schoening (*165*). The highest concentrations were in the kidney, hoof, and liver. Other organs contained variable amounts. The bile contained from traces to 6 ppm and the urine contained 0.1–3 ppm of selenium. In equines that had received long continued feeding of selenite, Miller and Williams (*167*) reported highest concentrations in the blood, liver, kidney, spleen, hair, and hoof.

There are only limited data available on the rate and pathway of selenium excretion by livestock. Excretion in urine and feces varies with the dose and duration of the experiment and the severity of selenium intoxication. Selenium in the urine has been reported to range from 0.2 to 8 ppm and in feces from 0.5 to 8 ppm (*47, 167*). Maag *et al.* (*136*), using sodium selenite, reported that 2–10 ppm of selenium was excreted in the urine and the excretion appeared to be related to the dose.

The availability of high specific activity radioactive selenium offers a method to investigate the pathways of elimination of selenium in livestock. These studies should include the rate of elimination with tracer doses as well as with the subacute, chronic type of selenium intoxication.

Present data suggest that different species of animals may show differences in the route of elimination (*24a*). Using tracer amounts of Se^{75}-selenite, Buescher *et al.* (*23*) studied the effect of dietary calcium on distribution and retention of selenium in swine. They reported that 71.5 per

TABLE 45
Rate of Se^{75} Excretion by Sheep[a]

Total Se^{75} given	Interval (hours)	Per cent of dose recovered		
		Urine	Feces	Bile
95 mc[b]	0–24	22.0 (24)[c]	8.8 (24)	5.5
	24–48	11.9 (14)	16.7 (14)	8.4
	48–72	4.5 (10)	8.8 (10)	
	72–96	2.5 (7)	3.5 (7)	

[a] Rosenfeld (*228*).
[b] Dose administered 4 mc 3 times per week. Duration of experiment 60 days.
[c] Numbers in parentheses indicate the number of determinations.

cent of the total Se^{75} excreted was via the feces. This is in contrast to the sheep in which the urinary excretion of Se^{75} exceeded the fecal excretion (*228*) (Table 45).

By means of tracer doses of radioactive selenium with a subacute dose of selenite, it was shown that the percentage of selenium excreted in the urine and feces (sheep) varied only slightly regardless of the dose given (*228*). The biological half-life of selenium in sheep appears to be between 24 and 48 hours. The maximum excretion of selenium in urine was within 24 hours, while in feces it was 48 hours after the administration of Se^{75}. This difference may be due to the complex gastrointestinal tract of sheep. Excretion of Se^{75} in bile was studied in sheep with biliary fistula. The results suggest that in bile, as in blood, there is a gradual accumulation of selenium with continued intake (*225*). In the preceding study, subtoxic doses of selenium were given. Similar experiments in chronic selenosis would be of considerable importance. Experiments with rats indicate that in subacute selenosis the selenium elimination by the urinary tract is greatly depressed and functional damage to the excretory organs is produced before any symptoms of selenosis have developed. The excretion of radioactive selenium by sheep fed red clover in which the Se^{75} was predominantly incorporated in protein(s) indicates that in 99 hours 53.7 per cent of the ingested selenium was excreted in the feces and only 2.0 per cent in the urine (*203a*). This experiment suggests that selenium when attached to protein(s) may follow a different pathway than inorganic selenium.

The distribution of selenium in tissues of selenium-treated steers indicates that the accumulation of selenium in the tissues varies with duration of the experiment. In animals that died in 8 weeks, the selenium content of tissues in descending order was on the average: liver 5.5 ppm; kidney 3.2 ppm; hair 2.7 ppm; spleen 1.05 ppm; horns 0.25 ppm; muscle 0.125 ppm. Animals that died between 20 and 23 weeks showed a considerable increase in tissue selenium. The most significant increase was in the hair, which contained 9.5–11.3 ppm. The selenium content of the liver increased to 7.5, 9.5, 11.3, and 12.3 ppm selenium. Two animals were slaughtered at the termination of the experiment; the selenium content of their liver and blood was lower than that of the animals which died of chronic selenosis. The selenium content of blood varied with the dose and duration of selenium administration. Two steers died before the blood level reached 3 ppm. The blood level of the remainder of the animals was between 4 and 5 ppm, at which stage the animals were inactive, developed anorexia, and died of selenium intoxication (*136*).

Tracer doses of radioactive selenium were used to study the distribution of selenium in the various tissues in swine and sheep. The effect of excessive dietary calcium on the distribution and retention of selenium was studied in swine after one dose of Se^{75} was administered. On the average, 73 per cent of whole blood Se^{75} was present in plasma. The relative concentrations of Se^{75} in the tissues were as follows: kidney > liver > spleen > small intestine wall > lung > large intestine wall > vertebra > rib > heart > femur > teeth > large intestine contents > skin > small intestine contents > muscle > bile > hair. The relative selenium content of whole organs was as follows: liver > lung > kidney > heart > spleen (*23*).

The oral administration of subtoxic doses of radioactive selenium to sheep 3 times per week for 2 months gradually increased the blood selenium level. At the termination of the experiment blood samples were taken 24, 48, and 72 hours after the final dose was given; the retention of Se^{75} in the blood was 9.2, 8.4, 7.2, and 6.3 per cent, respectively. At the beginning of the experiment over 80 per cent of the selenium in the blood was present in plasma, but as selenium administration continued there was a gradual increase of selenium in the red blood cells. At the termination of the experiment plasma selenium was only 10 per cent higher than that of the red blood cells. The distribution of selenium in sheep tissues was similar to that in swine except that the liver accumulated more selenium than any other single organ (*228*).

Factors Influencing the Poisoning

Arsenicals were tried to prevent or reduce the toxic effects of chronic selenosis in pigs and beef cattle by various investigators.

The addition of 5 ppm arsenic (Na_2HAsO_3) to water to prevent the toxic effects of 9 ppm selenium (as selenite) in pigs reduced the selenium deposition in liver, kidney, hair, and muscles about 30 per cent when compared with animals which received only selenium. Lungs of selenized animals contained 9.2 ppm (moisture-free basis), and lungs in arsenic-treated animals contained 1.2 ppm selenium. There was no significant difference in selenium content of pancreas, spleen, heart, and stomach between the arsenic-treated group and animals not receiving arsenic (*181*).

Hendrick *et al.* (*97*) have reported that organic arsenicals gave partial protection against selenium intoxication in rats. Wahlstrom *et al.* (*268*) using the same arsenic compounds, i.e., arsanilic acid and 3-nitro-4-hydroxyphenylarsonic acid, studied the effectiveness of these compounds against chronic selenosis in pigs. They reported excellent protection against 10 ppm selenium (as selenite) by these arsenicals at levels of 0.02 and 0.05 per cent. Arsanilic acid at 0.01 per cent and 3-nitro-4-hydroxyphenylarsonic acid at 0.0025 per cent gave good to excellent protection when added to the selenium ration. Wahlstrom *et al.* (*269–271*) in further studies investigated the effects of organic arsenicals, linseed meal, and chlortetracycline on chronic selenosis in pigs. Arsanilic acid at 0.01 per cent and 3-nitro-4-hydroxyphenylarsonic acid at 0.005 per cent added to the basal diet gave best protection when used in combination with linseed oil meal. Chlortetracycline did not counteract the effect of selenium toxicity. Minyard *et al.* (*168*) investigated the effectiveness of arsanilic acid in counteracting selenium poisoning in range beef cattle. They reported that addition of 0.01 per cent of arsanilic acid to a ration containing 12 ppm selenite selenium appeared to reduce slightly the symptoms of selenium poisoning. They concluded that at the present stage of research it is doubtful that the administration of arsenicals either as preventative or as treatment for chronic selenosis is of any practical value.

The conflicting results obtained by various investigators as to the effectiveness of arsenicals for treatment or as a preventative against the toxic effects of selenium would suggest that considerable caution should be exercised before arsenicals are added to the diet.

Gross Pathology

The gross pathology of chronic selenosis by inorganic selenium may show some changes resembling blind staggers and in some animals the changes are similar to alkali disease.

Pigs. Gross pathology in pigs shows similar but less severe changes than those observed in alkali disease. The dewclaws separated from the hoof leaving a raw area. The hair along the spinal column was denuded. Icterus was evident on the skin and sclera. Severe enteritis developed in all cases (*165*).

Equines. In equines the mucous membranes and conjuctiva were pale and icteric. There was some emphysema in the lungs. Fat around the heart was gelatinous in consistency; heart muscle, pale; endocardium, yellow and spotted with a few subendocardial hemorrhages. Liver appeared dark in color, was somewhat smaller than normal, and showed marked cirrhosis. The cut surface had a yellowish-brown color and there was a marked increase of connective tissue. The spleen was small in size. The pulp appeared dark and doughy, and showed increase in the connective tissue. The kidneys were dark brown in color, and capsules adhered to the parenchyma. The cortex showed hemorrhages, the medulla was congested, and the pelvis was filled with clear gelatinous urine. Peritoneum was icteric. The intestines showed some enteritis (*167*).

Steers. Severe gastrointestinal irritation varying from shallow ulceration of mucosa to gangrene was noted in steers (*136*).

Microscopic Pathology

Microscopically, the changes reported resembled some phases of pathological changes in blind staggers. In the kidney, cloudy swelling, nuclear degeneration, and limited fatty degeneration in the cytoplasm were observed. Desquamation of tubular epithelium and a large number of casts were present. A number of glomeruli showed various degrees of atrophy. In the liver there were focal necrosis, fatty infiltration, congestion, edema, cellular changes with cloudy swelling, and complete loss of cellular structure. In some cases there was well-marked proliferation of interlobular and intralobular interstitial tissue. In the skin some atrophic changes appeared in certain hair follicles (*165*).

Proposed Experimentation

The difference between the causative agent of alkali disease and that of blind staggers should be definitely established. The most obvious symptoms of alkali disease—loss of hair and deformation and sloughing of hoofs —are absent in blind staggers. The selenium compounds responsible for each type of disease should be isolated and used for the production of the disease under controlled conditions. Inorganic selenium should be removed from plants before they are used in experiments in order to determine to what extent inorganic selenium contributes to the manifestations of alkali disease and blind staggers.

Many of the experiments that have been carried out with laboratory animals should be repeated with cattle, sheep, hogs, and horses. It cannot be assumed that all of the results obtained with laboratory animals are directly applicable to livestock.

Methods of treatment for acute selenosis as well as blind staggers and alkali disease offer a challenge for future investigators.

Studies dealing with mammalian malformations in relation to the age of the embryo or fetus and its susceptibility to selenium would be of great value to basic as well as to applied research. Detailed investigations dealing with the effect of selenium on the reproductive organs of males and females offer unlimited opportunity to resolve the question of how extensive the economic loss is in seleniferous areas by decreased reproduction in livestock.

These suggested researches were not investigated in livestock up to the present time because they require the use of a large number of animals in order to obtain significant results. The use of livestock as experimental animals is hindered by the prohibitive cost of a single experiment.

LABORATORY ANIMALS

Studies on selenium poisoning in laboratory animals have been carried out with various inorganic and organic selenium compounds. The toxic effect depends upon the type of selenium compound administered, the species and sex of the laboratory animal used, the age of the animal, conditions of the test, caloric intake, and the criterion of toxicity employed. Among the common laboratory animals, the rat has been found to be the most resistant to selenium poisoning and the cat the least resistant (*243*). Early investigations of the action of selenium were concerned with its pharmacological relations to other poisons. The significance of selenium as a toxic agent assumed greater importance when it became an economic and possibly a public health problem. More recent studies include not only the toxic effects of selenium but metabolic and biochemical effects *in vivo* as well as *in vitro*. This chapter will include only studies in intact animals as these studies may be or are related to the metabolism of selenium in selenium intoxication. *In vitro* studies of biological systems will be discussed in Chapter X.

Selenium poisoning in laboratory animals may be acute, subacute, or chronic, depending on the dose and duration of selenium administration. In subsequent sections, acute, subacute, and chronic toxicity will be discussed.

ACUTE SELENIUM POISONING

Acute selenium poisoning in laboratory animals is produced by a toxic dose of a selenium compound, administered orally, subcutaneously, intraperitoneally, or intravenously. The salt commonly used is sodium selenite or selenate. A few other seleno-compounds have been tested as to their acute toxic effects.

Experimental Observations

The toxicity of selenium in different forms has been determined by Franke and Moxon (*74, 77*), Smith *et al.* (*243*), and several other investigators. There is some disagreement in reports on the minimum lethal dose for various animals (*74, 183, 197, 243*). The different results may have been due to species differences in susceptibility and age of the animals. Table 46 presents the minimum lethal dose of several selenium compounds. The results from different laboratories are not exactly comparable because the minimum lethal or fatal dose is not rigidly defined. The minimum lethal dose of sodium selenite, expressed in milligrams of selenium per kilogram of body weight, for different laboratory animals, is given by Moxon and Rhian (*183*) as follows: 3.0–5.7 for the rat, 0.9–1.5 for the rabbit, and about 2.0 for the dog. These values apply to subcutaneous, intraperitoneal, or intravenous injections. Smith *et al.* (*243*) reported the minimum lethal dose of selenium as sodium selenate or selenite in rabbits, rats, and cats as 1.5 to 3.0 mg per kg, regardless of the route of administration.

The relative toxicities of selenite and selenate to rats have been compared by several investigators. Results obtained by Franke and Moxon (*74*) using intraperitoneal injection indicated a minimum lethal dose of 3.5 mg of selenium per kilogram of body weight with selenite and 5.3 mg per kilogram with selenate. Their criterion was the smallest dose that would kill 75 per cent or more of the animals in less than 2 days. Smith *et al.* (*243*) reported the minimum lethal dose of selenite or selenate to be either 3 or 4 mg of selenium per kilogram depending upon whether 40–50 per cent mortality or 80–90 per cent was taken as the criterion. They found no appreciable difference between selenite and selenate in toxicity to rats; but the action of a lethal dose of selenate was usually more rapid and the rats seldom survived beyond 12 to 18 hours, while deaths from selenite have been delayed for several days. The acute toxicity of selenite administered by subcutaneous injection into dogs was studied by Anderson and Moxon (*2*). They reported that the minimum lethal dose was 1.5–2.0 mg of selenium per kilogram of body weight.

Selenium oxychloride ($SeOCl_2$) is an extremely toxic and vesicant compound (*49*). With an application of 83 mg of this compound to the

TABLE 46

Minimum Lethal Doses of Selenium Compounds

Selenium compound	Mode of administration	Experimental animals	Number of animals used	Mg Se/kg body weight	References
Na_2SeO_3	Intraperitoneal	Rat	155	3.25–3.5	74
Na_2SeO_4	Intraperitoneal	Rat	90	5.25–5.75	
Na_2SeO_3	Intravenous	Rat	45	3.0	243
Na_2SeO_4	Intravenous	Rat	37	3.0	
Na_2SeO_3	Intravenous	Rabbit	9	1.5	
Na_2SeO_4	Intravenous	Rabbit	16	2.0–2.5	
Colloidal selenium	Intravenous	Rat		6.0	188
Selenocystine	Intraperitoneal	Rat	18	4.0	182
Selenomethionine	Intraperitoneal	Rat	16	4.25	114

skin of rabbits, death occurred within 5 hours; with 4 mg the animals died in less than 24 hours. The acute toxic effects of hydrogen selenide (H_2Se) in guinea pigs with a single exposure of 10, 30, or 60 minutes to graded concentrations of the gas ranging from 0.002 to 0.57 mg per liter was investigated (*48*). All animals exposed to 0.02 mg per liter for 60 minutes died within 25 days; 93 per cent of those exposed to 0.043 mg per liter for 30 minutes died within 30 days; and all exposed to 0.57 mg per liter for 10 minutes died within 5 days. Decreasing the concentrations of hydrogen selenide, and increasing the time of exposure to 2, 4, or 8 hours produced death in 50 per cent of the animals (guinea pigs) within 8 hours (*50*).

Experimental studies based on the toxic effects of organic selenium compounds are limited. This limitation is due to the unavailabilty of seleno-organic compounds and to the toxicity hazards created during the preparation of these compounds. Some organic selenium compounds were tested as to their acute toxic effects (*114, 174, 178*). The minimum lethal dose for rats, by intraperitoneal injection, was 4 mg of selenium per kilogram of body weight for optically inactive *dl*-selenocystine; 20–25 mg for *n*-propylseleninic acid; 25–30 mg for β-seleninopropionic acid and β,β'-diselenodipropionic acid; and more than 40 mg for β-selenodipropionic acid; selenocystine appeared to be the most toxic among the above organic seleno-compounds. Subsequent experiments showed that the toxicity of the optically inactive *dl*-selenocystine was mainly due to *l*-selenocystine, since the latter was many times more toxic than *d*-selenocystine (*182*). The minimal fatal dose of selenomethionine by intraperitoneal injection in rats was 4.25 mg of selenium (as selenomethionine) per kilogram of body weight (*114*). LD_{50} of selenium compounds expressed as milligrams per kilogram of body weight by intraperitoneal injection were the following: methyl isoselenourea sulfate 3.0 ± 0.3; selenohomocystine 3.5 ± 0.4; *d*-, *l*-, *dl*-, or *meso*-selenocystine 4.0 ± 0.2; selenomethionine 4.5 ± 0.3; selenotetraglutathione 6.0 ± 0.3; β,β'-diselenodipropionic acid 25 to 30 ± 0.4. The symptoms of acute selenosis were produced with each compound except selenomethionine. Selenomethionine produced a comatose state in which the animal became hypersensitive to external stimuli (*120*).

Exposing rats, guinea pigs, and rabbits for 16 hours to an atmosphere containing approximately 30 mg selenium dust per cubic meter produced in the animals mild interstitial pneumonitis. Rats exposed to selenium fumes by vacuum evaporation developed acute toxicity. Hall *et al.* (*88*) suggested that the fumes may have contained some selenium dioxide. The acute toxic dose of selenic anhydride was 5 mg per kilogram of body weight when animals were exposed to air containing 0.09 mg selenium per liter of air (*55*).

Investigations on the acute toxic effects of dimethyl selenide indicate that this compound has a low degree of toxicity in rats and mice. The LD_{50} by intraperitoneal injection was 1.3 gm for mice and 1.6 gm selenium (as dimethyl selenide) for rats per kilogram of body weight (*150*). The low toxicity of dimethyl selenide would suggest that detoxification of selenium in the animal body proceeds from a highly toxic form to a less toxic compound which is eliminated through the respiratory tract. The LD_{50} of 6-selenopurine following an intraperitoneal injection in mice was 160 ± 37 mg per kilogram. The low degree of toxicity may be associated with the relative instability of the compound. About half of the selenopurine in an aqueous buffer solution decomposed within 6 hours (*143*).

Acute toxicity of elemental selenium has not been investigated in detail. The conclusion of the authors and of various other investigators is that elemental selenium is not toxic owing to its relative insolubility. While the over-all effects of selenium compounds on the animals appeared to be similar, they gave no indication of the mode of action. There is considerable evidence in *in vitro* studies that selenium compounds react with the sulfhydryl groups of various enzyme systems. At the present time no *in vivo* studies dealing with the effect of acute toxicity on sulfhydryl enzymes have been carried out. Results of studies *in vitro* and *in vivo* are not always interchangeable.

Symptoms

The classical description of acute poisoning in rabbits, cats, and dogs from sodium selenite or selenious acid is that of Czapek and Weil (*36*). The first symptoms appeared about 5 minutes after subcutaneous injection or 15 minutes after oral administration of the selenite. The breath had a garlicky odor and the animal showed signs of nervousness and fear, disclosed by loud crying. The state of excitation was more evident in rabbits than in dogs. In dogs, vomiting and diarrhea were pronounced. The further course of the intoxication was essentially the same in all 3 animals. The primary symptoms were followed by quietness and somnolence. Respiration was difficult. The reflexes decreased but the heart remained normal. The labored breathing was followed by opisthotonos, tetanic spasm in the muscles of the extremities, clonic spasm, and death. A marked symptom was the gradual fall in blood pressure, starting 15–30 minutes after injection of selenite and continuing until death. The symptoms described by Czapek and Weil are essentially the same as those reported by a number of other investigators (*2, 108, 170, 243*).

The median lethal dose of dimethyl selenide after a subcutaneous injection to mice and rats produced a state of hyperpnea for 2 to 3 hours with an overwhelming garliclike odor of the breath. Convulsions were observed in mice but not in rats. In most cases, death followed within a few hours, but a few animals lived until 36 hours (*150*).

Cardiovascular and respiratory effects of selenium were investigated by intravenous injections of sodium selenite in anesthetized dogs. Selenium at levels of 2.0 mg per kilogram decreased systemic blood pressure and peripheral resistance and produced electrocardiographic changes suggesting some cardiac damage (*95*). Intravenous injections of graded doses of sodium selenite and selenate produced respiratory stimulation with terminal apnea before death. Selenite-induced respiratory stimulation may have been noted by previous investigators, but the labored breathing and panting may have obscured or masked the respiratory stimulation (*96*).

Distribution and Excretion

The distribution of selenium in the tissues of rabbits after intravenous injections of 1 mg of selenium (as sodium selenite) per kilogram of body weight was investigated by Smith *et al.* (*246*). Five minutes after the injection, the selenium concentration in the kidney became higher than in the blood. During the first 6 hours the concentration in the liver and kidney increased while that in the blood fell rapidly. After 6 hours the selenium in the kidney and liver decreased rapidly, whereas the blood selenium decreased slowly. At the end of 48 hours the selenium reached a retention level, with little change during the next 24 hours. Excretion in the urine accounted for the fall in tissue selenium during the first 24 hours following its preliminary rise. About 43 per cent of the total selenium injected was recovered in the urine at the end of 48 hours. Relatively little selenium was found in the bile.

The application of 4 and 12 mg of selenium oxychloride to the skin of rabbits brought about a concentration of 2.0–4.3 ppm selenium in the liver and 0.6–2.2 ppm in the blood (*49*).

The distribution of radioselenium in various tissues of the rat was studied by McConnell (*144*) after a single subtoxic, subcutaneous injection of radioactive selenate. The highest concentrations were in the liver, kidney, muscle, total gastrointestinal tract, and blood. Lesser amounts were present in the lung, spleen, heart, and tumor (carcinosarcoma) (*256*). Traces appeared in the brain and testis. At the end of 24 hours neither skin, fur, teeth, nor long bones contained selenium (*144*).

Detailed data are given by Dolique and Giroux (*41*) on the distribution of selenium in the viscera of guinea pigs and rabbits injected with 1–6 mg of selenium (as selenite or selenate) per kilogram of body weight. The lung contained the highest concentration of selenium, followed by the liver. Other organs contained trace amounts of selenium. Studies on the distribution of selenium in the tissues of mice were carried out at intervals from 15 minutes to 48 hours. The blood concentration was highest at 15 minutes after subcutaneous injection, and 5.7 per cent of the dose was present in this tissue. As the blood level decreased, the liver and kidney values increased and reached the maximum at the end of the first hour (*94*).

Elimination of selenium through the kidney, the gastrointestinal tract, and the lung was investigated by McConnell (*144*). Selenium administered subcutaneously as selenate was excreted chiefly by way of the kidney, in a nonvolatile, ether-insoluble form. About 42 per cent of the original dose appeared in the urine, while only 3–6 per cent was found in the feces during the first 24 hours.

The excretion of selenium in the milk and bile was investigated by administering a single subcutaneous and intraperitoneal injection of sodium selenate containing radioselenium (*146, 149*). The administered selenium passed through the mammary gland into milk. Time excretion studies of selenium via bile in a bile fistula showed an initial rapid excretion followed by a prolonged slower rate. The feasibility of the formation of selenohemoglobin similar to sulfhemoglobin (*111*) has been postulated.

The elimination of selenium by the respiratory route was postulated by Hofmeister (*100*) on the basis of observations made on dogs injected with selenite. The gas exhaled by the animals had a garlicky odor. Hofmeister suggested that the volatile compound was dimethyl selenide. Subsequent studies to characterize the volatile compound(s) have been made by various investigators.

The effect of methionine and choline on the respiratory elimination of volatile selenium in animals injected with selenite was studied by Schultz and Lewis (*236*). When 2.5–3.5 mg of selenium per kilogram of body weight was injected subcutaneously into adult rats, 17–52 per cent was eliminated within 8 hours as volatile compound(s). The administration of methyl donors had no influence on the elimination of selenium via the lung. It is possible that the available methyl group is not the limiting factor in the respiratory elimination of the injected selenium. There is a metabolic limitation as to the amount of selenium that can be converted to volatile selenium within the animal body. The methylation of inorganic selenium compounds by certain molds has been well established (*29*).

The rate of respiratory excretion of radioselenium was investigated by McConnell (*145*). Rats receiving a subcutaneous injection of 3–4 mg selenium per kilogram (as selenate) exhaled 3–10 per cent of the original dose within 24 hours. Approximately 75 per cent of these amounts was exhaled during the first 6 hours.

The amount of volatile selenium exhaled by rats after a single injection of sodium selenite was investigated by using various absorption train sequences. Best recoveries were obtained with 6 per cent mercuric nitrate and saturated mercuric chloride. Within 24 hours over 30 per cent of the injected dose was recovered as volatile selenium (*202*). Petersen *et al.* (*202*) suggest mercuric nitrate as an absorbent for quantitative recovery studies owing to the apparent ease of subsequent analyses.

Dimethyl selenide injected subcutaneously into rats rapidly entered the circulatory system and 70.9–79.3 per cent was eliminated within 6 hours through the lung (*151*). At the same time the authors studied the selenium compound formed from sodium selenate (containing trace amounts of radioactive selenium) injected in rats, by collecting the respiratory gases in mercuric chloride. Specific activities of selenium mercuric chloride precipitate, after 2 crystallizations (4 experiments), had a mean variation of 2.4 per cent. They concluded that inorganic selenate was methylated in the animal and appeared in the respiratory gases as dimethyl selenide.

Sublethal amounts of sodium arsenite were reported to protect rats against acutely toxic doses of sodium selenite when both were injected at the same site (*109*). The authors investigated whether or not the reduction of selenium toxicity by arsenic was due to an increased exhalation of volatile selenium compound(s) by rats. Their results indicate that sodium arsenite markedly reduced the expiration of selenium. After sodium selenite injection, the rats eliminated 12.4–23.6 per cent of the injected dose through the respiratory tract. The simultaneous administration of 2.9–4 mg per kilogram arsenic with selenite reduced the elimination of selenium by respiration. At the end of 6 hours only 0.5–1.7 per cent of the injected dose was recovered as volatile selenium. These results pose an important question as to the reported *in vivo* mechanism of selenium detoxification or protection by arsenic. Arsenic appears to block an important site of selenium detoxication, that is, elimination via the lung, a natural defense mechanism of the animal body. If selenium elimination is not increased by arsenic then it is bound in the tissues in inactive form and thereby the tissues of arsenic-treated animals should contain higher concentrations of selenium than the nontreated animals; this is not the case in all studies reported with the use of arsenic and selenium. Arsenic had only a slight effect on increasing the urinary and fecal excretion of selenium when these compounds were added to the diet (*200*). Therefore, the effect of arsenic on selenium excretion through the lung, gastrointestinal tract, urinary tract and the deposition in the tissues offer no explanation of how arsenic acts against selenium intoxication.

Gross Pathology

Pathological data on acute selenium poisoning in laboratory animals are meager. Jones (*108*) described the liver as being soft and pliable, the right auricle of the heart distended and full of clot, and the splanchnic vessels enormously dilated. Toxic edema of lungs and parenchymatous organs was noted in rats exposed to high concentrations of selenic anhydride (*55*). Rats, guinea pigs, and rabbits exposed to selenium fumes gave no evidence of injury except in the lungs, which were hemorrhagic. Animals killed one month after exposure to the fumes had a mild interstitial pneumonitis (*88*). Descriptions of histological and cellular pathology were not fully investigated.

Treatment

The treatment of acute selenium poisoning with BAL was reported to be ineffective. Intramuscular injection of 0.8 mg per kilogram selenium (as selenite) to rabbits followed by intramuscular administration of 30 mg per kilogram of BAL (as a 3 per cent aqueous solution) increased the toxicity of selenium. The animals treated with BAL survived from 2 to 6 hours, while those of the control series which received the same amount of selenium lived several days (*21*).

The effective treatment of heavy metal poisoning by calcium disodium ethylenediaminetetraacetate ($CaNa_2EDTA$) suggested this compound for use in laboratory animals as a preventive in acute selenium intoxication. Intramuscular injection of 7.5, 10.0, and 12.5 mg sodium selenite per kilogram in rats had a survival ratio of 14 : 30, 9 : 30, and 3 : 30, respectively. The intraperitoneal injection of 0.5 gm per kilogram of $CaNa_2EDTA$ (as a 10 per cent solution) appeared to increase the tolerance against 7.5–10 mg of selenite per kilogram, provided the treatment was started 15 minutes after selenium injection. However when the selenite dose was increased to 12.5 mg per kilogram, treatment with $CaNa_2EDTA$ was not effective (*240*).

SUBACUTE AND CHRONIC SELENIUM POISONING

Subacute and chronic poisoning in laboratory animals may be produced by the administration of small repeated doses over a long period of time. The selenium may be mixed with the food or given orally or by intraperitoneal, intramuscular, or subcutaneous administration. The poisoning may be produced by using selenium compounds, seleniferous grains or plants, or artificially selenized crops grown in soils treated with selenium salts or with seleniferous plant extracts.

Experimental Observations

Toxicity of Naturally Seleniferous Cereals and Plants

Early experiments on the toxic effects of cereal grains and grasses in laboratory animals were carried out in an attempt to determine the toxic agents in these natural foodstuffs and to correlate these findings with observations on livestock. Large numbers of feeding experiments were conducted in experimental animals before the harmful effects of cereal grains and grasses were associated with selenium. Robinson (*212*) reported the occurrence of selenium in wheat and soil from affected areas; subsequently, the relation of toxic vegetation and soil was connected with selenium.

Studies on subacute and chronic toxicity of wheat, corn, and barley were carried out by various investigators (*66–68, 70–72, 101, 189, 191*).

In most studies with toxic cereal grains, rats were used as laboratory animals. Limited numbers of studies used cats and rabbits in addition to rats (*243, 245, 246, 248*). The above investigators were chiefly interested in obtaining information on chronic selenosis as it pertains to the population living in selenium-endemic regions and ingesting a variety of selenium-bearing foods.

There is considerable individual variation in susceptibility to the toxic effects of selenium. In subacute and chronic selenosis, when fractions of a minimal lethal dose are given, the effects of selenium are cumulative. Cumulative effects of individual doses may be produced by 16–50 per cent of the minimum lethal dose. These marked differences are due to individual variations in susceptibility and not to lack of absorption or excretion, as the same variations exist when selenium is injected intravenously. The comparative results of all studies indicate that individual variations must be related to some detoxification mechanism which functions with greater efficiency in some animals.

On repeated administration of chronic or subacute doses of selenium there is no progressive reduction in the toxic response produced in the animals. There is a continual increase in the manifestations of the disease which suggests that there is no altered susceptibility or acquired tolerance which would account for individual variations. The injection of the minimum lethal dose after repeated subacute and chronic doses produced almost 100 per cent fatality in the experimental animals (*243;* Rosenfeld, unpublished results). In addition to individual variations, there is a difference in susceptibility with age. Younger rats are more susceptible to the toxicant than older animals (*72, 233, 248*). Older animals fail to gain weight, and the life span of younger animals is greatly reduced. Small differences in age and weight of the animals have a greater effect on susceptibility than the possible differences in the toxicity of the compounds tested.

There is a sex difference in susceptibility to selenium poisoning. Female rats are more susceptible than males under identical experimental conditions (*78, 222, 252*).

The feeding of seleniferous grains in the diet for 10-, 20-, or 30-day periods indicates that the growth rate of rats was depressed, and tissue damage resulted even if the toxic diet was fed for the 10-day period. Normal growth is resumed when the rats are placed on selenium-free grains (*70*), but the damage to the organs is permanent (*219*). Alternate feeding of a diet containing toxic corn and an atoxic diet results in rhythmic gain and loss of weight and growth in rats. The food consumption decreased with the toxic diet and increased when diets were changed to the selenium-free diet (*71*).

It is a common belief that animals possess the ability to select foods most beneficial to them where the choice is offered. The tendency for range animals to avoid toxic vegetation has long been recognized (*122*, *183*). Rats are able to distinguish between various concentrations of the toxicant in the diets which differed only by small increments in selenium content (*76*).

In general, concentrations of less than 5 ppm selenium (as seleniferous grain) in diets prevented normal growth; 9 ppm of selenium resulted in death in young animals; 10 ppm in the diet in adult rats produced restriction in food intake. The effect of seleniferous diets depends on the concentration of selenium in the diet. Food which contains 40–50 ppm of selenium even when consumed in small amounts is more toxic than food which contains 5 ppm when the intake is 10–12 gm per day (*78*).

Toxicity of Artificially Selenized Plants

The uptake of selenium by plants and the methods of obtaining artificially selenized plants were discussed in the previous chapter. Buckwheat raised in soil containing sodium selenite and fed to experimental animals apparently was as toxic as inorganic selenite (*141*). The toxicity of wheat grown on artificially selenized soil was comparable with that of inorganic selenium (*189*). Treatment of the selenized soil (selenate) with sulfur or gypsum reduced the selenium accumulation in the wheat; the wheat was atoxic to experimental animals (*104*).

Green alfalfa grown in the greenhouse on Morrison shale overlying a bed of seleniferous *Astragalus* and *Stanleya* contained 192 ppm selenium (Beath and Rosenfeld, unpublished, 1946). Ten guinea pigs were fed the seleniferous green alfalfa so that the daily intake was about 1.2 mg of selenium per kilogram of body weight. Rapid loss of weight, anorexia, and emaciation developed in the animals. Some animals died after 4 days on this diet, while others survived up to 21 days.

Similarity between Inorganic Selenium and the Natural Toxicant

The toxic manifestations of inorganic selenium compounds and seleniferous grains are almost identical under similar experimental conditions (*4*, *64*, *72*, *77*, *78*, *82*, *83*, *169*, *189*, *219*, *223*, *233*, *248*, *255*).

Comparing the chronic toxic effect of seleniferous grain with that of inorganic selenium (Na_2SeO_3) in dogs, it appeared that the manifestations of selenium intoxication were similar to those observed in other laboratory animals. The addition of 7.2 ppm selenium as seleniferous grain to the basic diet or 10 ppm selenium (as selenite) was toxic to dogs (*209*). When selenium was increased in the diet to 20 ppm, the dogs refused to eat and died in a very short time. It appears that dogs are more susceptible to selenium poisoning than rats (*209*).

From an evaluation of the studies of various investigators, it may be concluded that chronic selenosis may be produced in various experimental animals when their diet or drinking water contains more than 7 ppm, but does not exceed 16 ppm of selenium. If the selenium intake is between 20 and 30 ppm, subacute selenosis develops in the animals. Calculating the selenium intake in water or in the diet, Smith and Lillie (*248*) concluded that the continuous daily intake of from 1.0–1.5 mg selenium per kilogram is dangerously toxic. Their results also suggested that the toxicity of sodium selenite is greater than the toxicity of wheat selenium. Intraperitoneal, oral, or subcutaneous administration of selenite or selenate produces chronic or subacute selenosis in rats when the administered dose is between 1.5 and 2.2 mg per kilogram body weight (*15, 219, 223*).

The Toxicity of Organic Selenium Compounds

The work of Painter and Franke (*196*) demonstrated that the selenium in cereals is in organic combination. A group of organic compounds were tested in order to determine whether some organic compounds of known structure would be comparable in their toxic effects with that of selenium in the cereal grains. The toxicity to rats of several organic selenium compounds in decreasing order was as follows: dibenzyldiselenide, β,β'-diselenodipropionic acid, β-seleninopropionic acid, *n*-propylseleninic acid, and β-selenodipropionic acid. Diselenodiacetic acid and selenodiacetic acid were more toxic than the compounds with chains containing three carbon atoms. None of the compounds tested were as toxic as inorganic selenium salts or naturally occurring selenium in cereals (*174*).

Aromatic selenium compounds when injected daily at sublethal levels appeared to be less toxic than the aliphatic compounds. *O,O′*-Dicarboxydiphenyldiselenide produced hematological changes similar to those reported with the ingestion of seleniferous wheat and inorganic selenium (*110*). The aromatic bis(4-acetaminophenyl)selenium dihydroxide (0.1%) when added to the diet was innocuous but goitrogenic and toxic when fed in larger amounts. The biological action was more in line with the sulfur and carbon analogs than with the selenium content. Aromatic selenium compounds without the amino group, like their carbon and sulfur analogs, were neither goitrogenic nor toxic when fed in relatively large amounts (*238*).

The lower toxicity of the organic seleno-compounds was not related to the instability of these compounds. The selenium ether which contains selenium in the most stable form was the least toxic (*174*). The chronic toxic effects of seleniferous wheat, selenocystine, and sodium selenite were compared by oral administration. *d*-Selenocystine was less toxic while *l*-selenocystine appeared to be the most toxic organic compound. The toxicity of *l*-selenocystine is comparable with that of seleniferous wheat (*182*). Selenopurine compounds had a low degree of toxicity in comparison with inorganic selenium compounds (*143*).

Symptoms

Subacute and chronic selenosis in rats is characterized by marked loss in body weight and anorexia followed by cachexia. Ascites and edema

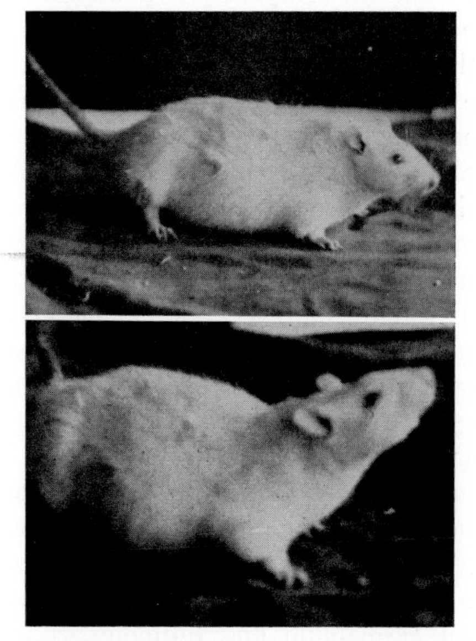

Fig. 33. Ascites and edema developed 2 months after the discontinuation of selenium and ascorbic acid administration. Rosenfeld and Beath (*219*).

may develop under identical conditions (*219*, *243*, *251*). Ascites and edema also may develop after the discontinuation of small chronic doses of selenium, provided the duration of administration was sufficient to produce damage to the liver. Figure 33 indicates the development of ascites and edema in rats 2 months after the termination of an experiment in which the rats received 0.15 mg of selenium per day with ascorbic acid for 3 weeks (*219*). The emaciated animals may assume a hunched posture; the fur is coarse and ruffled. Anemia may be present (*66*, *68*, *138*). In cats, the chief symptoms of chronic selenosis reported were intermittent anorexia, occasional vomiting, and decreased liver function. While anemia is readily developed in rabbits and rats, no hematological changes were observed in cats (*251*). As local irritants, selenium compounds may cause dermatitis and conjunctival and bronchial congestion (*80*).

Factors Influencing Subacute and Chronic Selenosis

Inorganic Compounds and Other Substances

The occurrence of numerous inorganic elements in the soil with selenium (*11, 25, 163*) and the influence of these elements on livestock poisoning by selenium prompted the study of the relative toxicity of numerous inorganic compounds and their effects on chronic selenosis.

The comparative toxicities of arsenic (Na_2HAsO_3), molybdenum [$(NH_4)_6Mo_7O_{24}$], tellurium (Na_2TeO_4), vanadium ($NaVO_3$), and selenium (Na_2SeO_3 and Na_2SeO_4) indicate that selenium was the most toxic when the salts of the elements were added to the diet at levels of 25 and 50 ppm (*77*). The toxicity of the elements was determined by their effects upon the hematopoietic system, growth, food consumption, and mortality of the animals (*77*). The combined toxicities of 11 ppm selenium (as seleniferous wheat) with vanadium, molybdenum, chromium, tungsten, fluorine, arsenic, cadmium, zinc, cobalt, uranium, and nickel given as water-soluble salts (5 ppm) in the drinking water indicate that with the exceptions of tungsten (Na_2WO_4) and arsenic (Na_2HAsO_3), the elements increased the mortality rate of rats. The addition of 5 ppm of arsenic in the drinking water prevented the toxic effects and symptoms of selenium poisoning. Tungsten reduced the mortality rate, but did not prevent liver damage in rats (*177*).

The interaction of copper and zinc studies in rats and their effects on chronic selenosis indicate that copper had no influence on the toxic effect of selenium while zinc enhanced the selenium effects. The interaction of the effects of these compounds was based on the growth rate of the animals (*228*). Gallium, germanium, and antimony are in the same position with arsenic in the periodic table. With the exception of gallium they all gave some protection against the toxicity of selenium in rats (*187*). Iron oxide fed at the 1 per cent level in diets containing 10 ppm of selenium did not protect rats against selenium poisoning (*127*).

Ascorbic acid and potassium iodide were ineffective, but beet pectin gave some protection against chronic selenosis (*219*).

The relationship between selenium toxicity and dietary energy source has been studied with rats. Rats on high fat diets were less affected by selenium than those on high carbohydrate diets (*247*). Ad libitum feeding of an isocaloric amount of carbohydrate (dextrose) and fat (lard) in the diet which contained 2.75 μg selenium per Calorie indicated that the diets which contained carbohydrate with low or moderate amounts of fat were inferior in preventing growth depression and possible liver damage than diets containing fat as the energy source (*213*).

Some protection in chronic selenosis was obtained in small young rats by the injection of small intermittent doses of ACTH (*203*). The most pronounced effect was in improved growth rate, modification of adrenal enlargement, and thymus involution. Characteristic liver damage was present.

The daily subcutaneous injection of 200 μg vitamin B_{12} did not prevent weight loss in rats but increased the weight gain after selenium feeding was discontinued (*211*). Menadione and α-tocopherol had no effect on selenium toxicity (*254*).

Arsenic

Early experiments on the protective effect of arsenic (Na_2HAsO_3) on chronic selenosis (*173*) produced by inorganic selenium or seleniferous grain were followed by experiments in which larger numbers of inorganic and organic arsenicals were tested in order to determine whether small amounts of arsenic compounds will prevent chronic selenosis. Arsenic sulfides (AsS_2 and AsS_3) failed to give any protection against selenium in the diet. Arsenite (Na_2HAsO_3) and arsenate (Na_2HAsO_4) were equally effective in preventing the toxic action of selenium in seleniferous wheat, sodium selenite, and selenocystine (*27, 44, 184, 186, 187, 209*).

Organic arsenicals, neoarsphenamine, sulfarsphenamine (*187*), calcium and sodium methyl arsonates (*98*) and arsanilic and 3-nitro-4-hydroxyphenylarsonic acids (*97*) have been found to give partial protection against chronic selenosis in rats. Arsanilic acid, *p*-hydroxyphenylarsonic acid, arsenomethane, As-1, 2-disulfide, triphenylarsine (15 ppm) in the diet gave 100 per cent protection against 10 ppm selenium (sodium selenite). Seven parts per million 3-nitro-4-hydroxyphenylarsonic acid was also effective. Dodecylamine-*p*-chlorophenylarsonate gave some protection (*128*).

The mechanisms by which arsenicals counteract the toxicity of selenium at the present time are unknown. The administration of arsenic compounds had no significant influence on the absorption, excretion, or tissue retention of selenium in the experimental animals whether inorganic or seleniferous grains were used as toxicant (*115, 186, 200*). The effect of arsenic is independent of the route of administration of either selenium or arsenic (*186*).

Sulfur

The injection of a mixture of sodium selenite and sodium sulfide in an atomic ratio of 1:0.4 was less toxic to dogs than the same amount of selenite injected separately or the same amount of independent intravenous injection of sulfide and selenite (*278*). The addition of 0.29, 0.58, and 0.87 per cent inorganic sulfate to the diet which contained 10 ppm (selenate or selenite) selenium alleviated from 20 to 40 per cent of the selenium-produced growth depression in rats, but it did not prevent liver damage (*92*).

Sulfate in the diets modified or partially alleviated chronic selenosis induced in rats by selenate but was less effective against selenite (*78b*) and had no effect on selenosis produced by seleniferous wheat (*92a*). Other sulfur compounds were less effective in preventing and modifying the toxic effects of selenite or selenate and were completely ineffective against seleniferous wheat.

Dietary Proteins

Increasing the protein content of the diet provided protection against selenium poisoning whether selenium was inorganic or organic as in toxic grains (*172, 247*). The protective action of dietary protein against selenium toxicity was indicated by the experiments of Smith (*247*). When the diet of rats contained only 10 per cent of protein, the continued ingestion of 10 ppm of wheat selenium produced high mortality, high incidence of anemia and effusions, and severe damage to the liver. But when the seleniferous diet contained 30 per cent of protein (the additional protein, in the form of casein, replacing an equivalent amount of starch), the animals grew at a normal rate and showed scarcely any pathological effects. It is evident that the toxicity of naturally occurring organic selenium is determined, within certain limits, by the ratio of protein to selenium in the diet rather than merely by the selenium content of the diet. A diet containing 10 ppm of selenium was highly toxic to rats if the protein content was 10,000 times as great as the selenium content. But this diet was scarcely toxic when the protein content was increased to more than 30,000 times the selenium content. This would suggest that the protection afforded by the protein depends on the protein-selenium ratio. The importance of the protein-selenium ratio was confirmed by the experiments of Lewis *et al.* (*132*). A diet with 30 per cent casein afforded significantly more protection than an equal caloric diet with 6 per cent casein against selenium intoxication (sodium selenite) at levels of 25–50 ppm selenium.

Lactalbumin, ovalbumin, wheat protein, dried brewer's yeast, and desiccated liver afforded considerable protection against chronic selenosis produced by inorganic selenium or seleniferous wheat. Gelatin and edestin were not as effective or gave only slight protection (*84, 252, 254*).

Linseed oil meal and several of its fractions protected rats against chronic selenosis (*89, 193, 235*). Linseed meal and crude casein at a level of 25 per cent alleviated growth depression and liver damage produced by 10 ppm of seleniferous wheat in the ration. Soybean oil meal showed little protection against chronic selenosis (*201*). Linseed oil meal appeared to protect rats against chronic selenosis produced by inorganic (selenite) selenium as well as against seleniferous corn. The protective principle could be extracted from linseed oil meal with 50 per cent aqueous alcohol. The ash of the active extract was not protective (*91*). Vitamin B_6 participates in a large number of metabolic reactions involving amino acids and is concerned with the enzymatic decarboxylation and transamination of the amino acids (*162*). Halverson and Hendrick (*90*) investigated the possible relation of linseed oil meal protection against selenium poisoning through inhibition of some reaction involving the selenium analog of methionine. There was a negative relation between the selenium-protective factor and the anti-vitamin B_6 principle of linseed oil meal.

Glucosamine gave partial protection according to Smith and Stohlman (*252*), but Olson *et al.* (*194*) reported it was effective only with methionine. Homocystine and creatine also gave slight protection against chronic selenosis produced with selenite. Cystine, which would not readily donate methyl groups in its intermediary metabolism seemed to be ineffective in counteracting the toxic effects of inorganic selenium (*132, 239, 252*).

Although the mechanism whereby proteins decrease the toxicity of selenium is a matter of conjecture, it seems to represent a true detoxification, since all the known manifestations—effusions, anemia, impairment of growth, and liver injury—are reduced equally. Perhaps an explanation may be found in the differential action of selenium compounds on enzymes concerned with metabolic processes (*247*).

The apparent discrepancies as to the *in vivo* effects of biologically active methyl groups of methionine, choline, and betaine on chronic selenosis may be due to the characteristics of the seleno-compounds used for producing chronic selenosis in experimental animals. The disease syndromes produced in livestock with seleniferous grains, weeds, or inorganic selenium compounds markedly differ from each other. Although this difference is not apparent when rats are used as experimental animals, it is possible that cellular and tissue responses to the different forms of the toxicant may not be identical even in experimental animals. When the results are evaluated on the basis of the chemical nature of the selenium compounds, there is some agreement as to the effect of methionine, choline, and betaine on chronic selenosis.

Supplementation of deficient diets with methionine, choline, or betaine, or the addition of these compounds to the diet provided considerable protection against chronic selenosis produced by the toxic action of selenate or selenite (*132, 148, 194, 223, 239, 254*).

The addition of methionine to seleniferous grain diets of rats had no beneficial effects on chronic selenosis (*113, 119, 194, 247*).

The addition of graded increments of casein to a low-protein diet supplemented with cystine and methionine indicated that the degree of protection against the toxicity of 15 ppm of selenium as selenite was related to the protein in the diet and not to its cystine or methionine content (*252*). Crude protein diet enhanced the respiratory elimination and decreased the tissue retention of selenium, while purified protein diet (extracted casein) reduced the volatile selenium formation about 50 per cent (*78a*).

The effect of the biologically active methyl group on chronic selenosis still needs further study. There is some experimental evidence at the present time to indicate that selenosis appears more rapidly in animals on protein diets low in methionine or choline and that the addition of these compounds to the diet will reduce the toxic effects of selenium if inorganic selenium is used as a toxicant. It is doubtful that selenium from seleniferous grains is converted in the intestinal tract of the animals to ionic selenium, which form of selenium is essential for methylation according to Challenger and co-workers (*28, 29*). They postulated that utilization of selenium by fungi proceeds by successive methylations and reducing steps, but biological detoxification of selenium by methylation *in vivo* in mammals must have its limitation. The administration of large amounts of selenium may produce enough damage to the cells to prevent cellular function and thereby interfere with or block transmethylation.

Bromobenzene

The administration of bromobenzene to rats and dogs fed a seleniferous diet increased the urinary selenium output (*179*). Westfall and Smith (*281*) were unable to confirm the above findings. Rabbits injected with bromobenzene 3 months after selenium intoxication showed an increase in selenium excretion (*256*), while other studies indicate that bromobenzene had no effect on the selenium excretion when selenious acid was given to rabbits (*232*).

2,3-Dimercaptopropanol (BAL)

The injection of 10 mg per kilogram of BAL per day had no effect on the subacute poisoning produced by the intramuscular injection of 0.3 mg selenium (selenite) per kilogram per day in rabbits. The BAL treatment increased the toxicity of selenium (*21*). The additive toxic effect of BAL on chronic selenosis was noted in rats by Belogorsky and Slaughter (*15*), but they reported that liver damage was absent in the BAL-treated animals. They suggested that SH groups furnished by BAL prevented liver damage by sodium selenite but did not reduce the total toxic action of selenite. The synergistic effect of selenium and BAL was observed in rats receiving selenium from seleniferous wheat. BAL did not block the beneficial effect of arsenic on selenium toxicity (*93*).

Absorption and Excretion

Selenium is absorbed rapidly and efficiently from the site of administration. Whether selenium is added to the diet or administered per os, or injected subcutaneously, intramuscularly, intraperitoneally, or intravenously, it enters the circulatory system and is distributed to the various tissues. The rate of absorption of selenium from natural seleniferous diets or diets with added inorganic selenium is comparable as determined by the toxic effects of the diets. Franke and Painter (*78*) reported a higher rate of absorption of selenium from cereals than from selenium compounds. As the selenium enters the circulatory system and is deposited in the various tissues the defense mechanism of the body probably takes over in an attempt to detoxify and eliminate the selenium. Selenium is excreted chiefly by the respiratory tract, urine, feces, and perspiration. Although a large percentage of the administered dose is eliminated from the body, it has cumulative effects and produces permanent injury of the tissues.

Selenium may be eliminated by the respiratory tract in chronic as well as in acute selenosis. This mode of elimination was discussed in detail in the section on Acute Selenium Poisoning. Studies dealing with the respiratory elimination of selenium in chronic selenosis were not investigated, but indirect evidence indicates that in chronic selenosis the detoxification mechanism by respiration is more active than when an atoxic dose of selenium is given. Balance studies on selenium recovery in chronic selenosis in rats produced by 1.4 mg selenium (selenite) given intragastrically indicate that from 50 to 70 per cent of the administered dose could not be accounted for by fecal or urinary excretion or by deposition in the tissues (*200*); therefore, the remainder must have been eliminated by the respiratory tract.

Subacute selenosis produced in rats by the oral administration of 2.5 mg of selenium per kilogram (Na_2SeO_3) added to a tracer dose of $Na_2Se^{75}O_3$ indicates that urinary and fecal excretion and total tissue retention were over 60 per cent; about 40 per cent of the total dose was eliminated by the respiratory system. Animals which received tracer doses of $Na_2Se^{75}O_3$ containing 7.5 μg of selenium eliminated up to 27 per cent of the dose by the respiratory tract in 90 days (*228*).

The urinary and fecal excretion of selenium in chronic selenosis in different species of animals has been reported by various investigators (*1, 83, 169, 172, 182, 189, 200, 226, 232, 245, 256*).

When inorganic selenium compounds are injected or given orally, the selenium is rapidly excreted by cats and rabbits (*245*) and rats (*83*). Most of the selenium was eliminated 2 weeks after the administration was discontinued; however, small amounts may be excreted for several months. Rats which received radioactive selenite continued to excrete (urine and feces) small amounts of selenium for up to 155 days (*226*). Naturally occurring organic selenium compounds were retained longer and the percentage of selenium excretion in the urine was less (40%) than with inorganic selenium (50–80%). The fecal excretion on the average was about 20 per cent in both groups (*82, 245, 246*). A comparison of the urinary and fecal excretion of rats receiving organic or inorganic selenium from seleniferous wheat, selenocystine, and sodium selenite showed no significant difference in the amount of excreted selenium. The total selenium excretion was 55–65 per cent of the ingested dose (*182*).

The rate of selenium elimination by the gastrointestinal and urinary tract depends on whether a subtoxic or toxic dose of selenium is given to the animals. The urinary excretion of selenium was higher with tracer doses of Se^{75} ($H_2Se^{75}O_3$) than when toxic doses were used. In the male rats which received intragastrically 2.5 mg selenium (Na_2SeO_3) per kilogram with a tracer dose of Se^{75}, the urinary elimination was reduced about one half and the maximum fecal excretion was at the end of 48 hours. The biological half life with a subtoxic dose of selenium was less than 24 hours, and with a toxic dose it was 48 hours (*228*).

The depressed urinary excretion of Se^{75} in the toxic group may have been due to damage to the kidney, and the longer retention of Se^{75} in the gastrointestinal tract was due to interference with the normal motility of the organ. At the termination of the experiment (10 days) the total Se^{75} excreted in the urine was 17 per cent by the toxic group and 41 per cent by the tracer group. The total fecal excretion of Se^{75} by the toxic group was approximately the same as that of the tracer group, around 30 per cent (*228*). The lowered urinary and fecal excretions in chronic selenosis produced by Na_2SeO_3 are evident from the data of Peterson *et al.* (*200*). Decrease in urinary and fecal excretion of selenium at the terminal stages of chronic selenosis in rabbits has been observed by Tajiri (*255*).

Discrepancies in the results on the rate of elimination may be due to the difference in the damage to the excretory organs. The kidney damage is more severe and occurs more rapidly than the damage to the intestinal tract. The elimination of selenium in the pancreatic juice was studied by a tracer dose of $Na_2Se^{75}O_4$. A small amount of selenium was eliminated by way of the external secretion of the pancreas (*152*).

Elimination of selenium by the sweat glands occurs in all species of animals. Over 50 per cent of selenium from wool and rat fur can be removed by repeated washings with 0.1 per cent detergent in lukewarm water (Rosenfeld, unpublished results).

Studies for whole-body turnover or total excretion of selenium over a prolonged period of time indicate that selenium is involved in the metabolism of the animal. The rate-limiting processes are the renal clearance of 2 chemically different forms of selenium and the smaller rate constant is the rate of release of selenium from the tissues (*20*).

Distribution and Retention

The distribution and retention of selenium in chronic and subacute selenosis depend on the daily dose, route of administration, experimental animals used, and the form of selenium administered to produce the toxicity. Detailed studies on the distribution of selenium in the tissues in chronic selenosis have been reported by various investigators (*1, 172, 189, 209, 245*). All results indicate that the highest concentration of selenium is

TABLE 47
Selenium Retained in the Tissues[a]

Tissue	From organic Se (ppm)	From inorganic Se (ppm)	Ratio
Liver	9.90	1.40	7.0
Kidney	4.60	1.35	3.4
Heart	3.00	0.80	3.8
Muscle	2.90	0.10	29.0
Lung	2.50	0.40	6.3
Bone	1.50	0.20	7.5
Skin	1.50	0.10	15.0
Brain	1.50	Trace	—
Blood	1.60	0.70	2.3
Hair	4.00	—	—

[a] Smith *et al.* (*246*).

present in the liver or kidney, regardless of the experimental animals used. The spleen, pancreas, and lung showed more variations as to selenium content. The heart, muscle, blood, brain, and other tissues always contained variable amounts of selenium depending on the experiment. The accumulation of selenium in the hair of an animal chronically poisoned with naturally occurring organic selenium was found to be a good index of the length of time that the animal had been ingesting selenium and of the amount of selenium it had stored in vital tissues and organs (*280*).

Retention of selenium in tissues of rabbits or cats fed naturally occurring organic selenium was far greater than when sodium selenite was given. Table 47 shows this comparison (*246*). When an inorganic salt of selenium was fed to animals, the capacity of tissues to store selenium seemed to be less, for the concentration in the tissues was only gradually affected by the length of the feeding period. With the lengthening of the feeding period during which organic selenium in grain was fed to animals, the tissues showed a progressive increase in storage and retention of selenium (*246*). When albino rats were used as experimental animals the selenium content of the various tissues showed only slight differences depending on whether seleniferous wheat, selenocystine, or sodium selenite was used as a toxicant (*182*).

The distribution after intravenous injection of diselenide-diacetic acid (CH_2–COOH–Se–Se–CH_2–COOH), diselenide-mercury diacetic acid, diselenide-dibutyric acid, and diselenide-mercury-dibutyric acid in tumor-bearing mice has been studied by Gusberg *et al.* (*86*). In the diseleno-diacetic and dibutyric acid groups the distribution differed from that of inorganic selenium. The lungs, kidneys, spleen, and liver accumulated the highest concentrations. The higher concentration of selenium in the lung may be due to the intravenous injection of the above compounds and the retention of a greater percentage of selenium by the pulmonary capillary. The addition of mercury to the organic seleno-compounds increased the selenium deposition in all tissues. The kidney retained almost 10 times more selenium than the liver.

The greater sensitivity to the toxic effect of selenium by young animals may be due to the apparently increased retention of selenium in their body tissues over the adults, although the liver storage in both groups was roughly comparable when seleniferous wheat was given as a toxicant. On transferring the animals (rats) to a selenium-free diet there was a rapid fall in the concentration of selenium, especially in the livers (*1*).

Alleviation of selenium poisoning by arsenic was reported in experimental animals (*1, 44, 173, 177, 209*). Investigations on the effect of arsenic on the retention and distribution of selenium in the tissues indicate that there are no significant variations in the tissue deposition of selenium when arsenic is included in the selenium diet (*115, 200, 209*).

The distribution of radioactive selenium in the intracellular particulate matter of rat liver cells at 24 hours after injection indicates that about one half to one third of the total Se^{75} activity expressed as the percentage of the homogenate was in the soluble and mitochondrial fractions, respectively, with smaller amounts in the microsomal and nuclear fractions (*158*). The incorporation of selenium into rat ribosome is dependent upon the supply of ATP and the soluble fraction of the cell (*161b*).

The time interval studies on the distribution of selenium in intracellular particulate matter of rat liver indicate that at each time interval from 15 minutes to 3 weeks the distribution of selenium in decreasing order was: soluble fraction, mitochondrial, microsomal, and nuclear fractions (*229*). The peak of intracellular fractions was reached at 6 hours, then leveled off to a plateau, followed by a second peak in about a week. Thereafter, the selenium content of all fractions decreased (*229*).

The distribution of Se^{75}-selenomethionine in dogs 2 hours after intravenous, subcutaneous, or oral administration indicates that the selenomethionine distribution in the tissues in decreasing order was liver > blood > pancreas > kidney > spleen. The pancreas specificity for selenomethionine may be related to the synthesis of the pancreatic enzymes and a substitution of the seleno-amino acid for its sulfur analog in the metabolic processes (*18*). Localization of Se^{75} in pancreas and metabolism of selenium in this organ may be of considerable importance. Selenium may play a functional part in the endocrine glands (*108a*).

The major salivary glands and saliva contain a relatively high concentration of selenium within minutes after intracardiac injection of radioactive selenium (*31*). The selenium uptake by the salivary glands and teeth depends upon the concentration of selenium in "freely diffusible fraction" in the blood and upon the volume of blood flowing through the organ per unit time (*32*).

The Systemic and Biochemical Changes in Tissues

The systemic changes associated with the chronic effects of selenium which are evidenced by emaciation, growth inhibition, decreased fertility, malformations, and pathological damage to the tissues are relatively greater than the detectable biochemical changes.

Only a limited number of metabolic studies were carried out where the degree of disease and the manifestation of toxic damage were defined and biochemical changes were correlated with the disease. Biochemical responses and the consequent action of toxin may show considerable variations under different experimental conditions. Some of these variables were discussed in the section on Experimental Observations. Therefore, some discrepancies in the biochemical changes reported by various investigators may be due to inherent differences in experimental design.

Damage to the gastric mucosa and hepatic injury have been described in chronic selenosis in livestock (*42, 217*), as well as in experimental animals receiving naturally occurring food selenium or inorganic selenium in the diets (*243*). Likewise, a high incidence of gastrointestinal disorders in man exposed to food selenium in endemic areas was reported (*244*). Studies dealing with gastric and hepatic functions indicate that continued ingestion of selenium (as seleniferous grain or sodium selenite) may be associated with a deficiency of gastric acidity, although in no sense an essential part in the picture of chronic or subacute selenium poisoning (*249*). The lowered liver function as measured by the bilirubin, rose bengal, or hippuric acid tests in chronic selenosis in rabbits and cats was observed, but structural or pathological changes were insignificant in these animals (*250*). An irreversible increase in prothrombin time due to liver injury and reduced vitamin K absorption due to intestinal mucosa damage were reported in chronic selenosis in rabbits (*58, 61*). Selenium impaired utilization of carotene given orally or intravenously. The storage of vitamin A was reduced, but the storage of carotene was not affected (*17*). There appears to be an interaction of vitamins E and A in detoxification of certain chemicals in rats as well as in livestock. Vitamin A depletion in blood and liver in chronic selenosis may be far more complex than the liver damage associated with the disease (*216*). Loss of liver capacity to dispose of bile pigment in chronic selenosis was indicated by an increase of blood bilirubin. The possible relation of jaundice in humans chronically exposed to selenite was suggested (*62*).

There is considerable contradiction on the effect of acute selenosis on carbohydrate metabolism (*57, 108, 126, 131, 198, 208, 287*).

In chronic selenosis there may be an increase or decrease in the blood glucose and liver glycogen, depending on the nutritional state of the animal. The conclusions of many investigators that glucose and its derivatives are natural defense mechanisms of the body against the toxic effect of selenium has not been substantiated by experimental evidence up to the present time. The variations in liver glycogen and blood glucose which were observed in chronic selenosis may be secondary effects related to the decreased food intake (*208*). Therefore, the direct effect of selenium on carbohydrate metabolism *in vivo* still needs clarification before its significance can be properly evaluated.

The decrease of tissue ascorbic acid and glutathione in chronic and acute selenosis has been confirmed by various investigators (*2, 59, 60, 116, 117, 125, 219, 253*). The decreased ascorbic acid may be a contributing factor to the vascular damage observed in selenosis. Although a number of investigators postulated that the decreased ascorbic acid in the tissues may be due to the utilization of ascorbic acid in the reduction of selenium, at the present time there is no evidence that there is a direct *in vivo* interaction between selenium compounds and ascorbic acid. Increased ascorbic acid intake had no effect on chronic selenosis (*219, 254*). The inclusion of cystine in a low-protein diet prevented the decrease of liver and kidney ascorbic acid and glutathione levels (*117*).

Changes in blood electrolytes in experimental chronic selenosis in rabbits showed a marked to moderate decrease in magnesium, phosphorus, and potassium; a marked increase in calcium; and no change in chloride, sulfate, or sodium (*34, 267*). Rhian and Moxon (*209*) observed no changes in the blood electrolytes in chronic selenosis in dogs. Inconsistent results were obtained on electrolytes and other components of the blood following intravenous injection of selenite to dogs (*96a*).

The enzymatic reaction between adenosine triphosphate (ATP) and selenate has been reported by Wilson and Bandurski (*285*). This reaction is similar to the sulfate activation reaction described by Bernstein and

McGilvery (*16*) and others (*39, 99*). Addition of selenate to the crude enzyme fraction resulted in an increased liberation of inorganic phosphate (P_i) similar to that of sulfate.

In vivo metabolic study of phosphorus metabolism as determined by P^{32} uptake in rats with chronic selenosis indicated that enzymatic reactions involving ATP and selenium take place in the intact animal (*221, 228*). The tissues which can carry out this reaction in the intact animal are the liver, kidney, and brain. In chronic selenosis the liver ATP decreased from 16.1 mg per cent to 6.7 mg per cent with an increase of P_i from 21.2 mg per cent to 29.1 mg per cent. The rate of formation of ATP as measured by the P^{32} uptake in rat liver in chronic selenosis indicates ATP formation was depressed. In normal rats the maximum uptake of P^{32} in ATP occurred between 30 and 60 minutes while in chronic selenosis the maximum was reached in 3 hours. The total P^{32} uptake in liver of chronic selenosis was lower than that of the normal rats, but the inorganic P^{32} in the liver of chronic selenosis always exceeded the P^{32} in normal liver (*228*).

Progressive anemia with constant decrease of hemoglobin values in mammals was reported by various investigators (*68, 138, 169, 209, 243, 255*). Whether seleniferous grain or inorganic selenium was fed or injected to rats, the hemoglobin level dropped and at the terminal stages of the disease the animals developed anemia. Blood smears showed achromia, anisocytosis, and polychromataphilic macrocytes (*72*). Bone-marrow hypoplasia, decrease of erythroid cells, and decrease in the number of mitotic figures in the erythroblasts were observed after repeated injections of sodium selenite in ducks (*210*). The mechanism of selenium action on the hematopoietic system of birds is assumed to be due to interference with the enzyme system in the formation of erythroblasts. Selenium effect on the hematopoietic system was counteracted by cysteine (*210*).

During poisoning with organic selenium, most of the selenium became firmly combined with the tissue proteins. Small doses of inorganic selenium also entered into combination with the proteins, especially those of the liver. But when relatively large doses of inorganic selenium were given, only a small part of the selenium formed protein combinations in the liver, while most of the selenium in the blood and kidney did not combine with proteins (*246*).

Selenium in the plasma proteins and liver proteins was present predominantly in the globulins (*279*). Digestion of the selenized liver with trypsin or pepsin released about 80 per cent of the selenium from its protein combination. Fractionation of protein-free filtrates of the digests of the liver indicated that the selenium compound was not associated with histone bases nor with cystine (*279*).

The apparent fixation or binding of trace amounts of selenium in the plasma and hemoglobin of dog blood (*147*), dog serum proteins (*153, 160*), dog leucocytes (*155*), serum lipoproteins (*161a*), and fibrinogen, urokinase and fibrinase (*27b*) was demonstrated by the use of radioactive selenium. The fixation of selenium by the various proteins would suggest that the binding is nonspecific, but there is a quantitative difference since different tissue proteins bind different amounts of selenium. At the present time the mode of fixing, binding, or attaching selenium to various tissue proteins in monogastric animals is not known. There is a possibility that some biosyntheses by the intestinal bacterial flora of sulfur amino acid may take place in monogastric animals. The utilization of inorganic sulfur compounds by bacteria and the rumen bacteria flora, and the substitution of selenium for sulfur by bacteria and the bacterial flora of the rumen have been well substantiated.

The biological syntheses of selenium analogs of sulfur amino acids have been reported (*35*): cystine and methionine in the dog liver protein (*154*); incorporation of Se^{75} in the cystine-rich protein keratin of dog hair (*159*); the synthesis of selenocystine and selenomethionine by bacterial flora in the rumen of sheep and deposition of the seleno-compounds in wool protein (*225, 226*); and selenotaurcholic acid in sheep bile (*225*).

The effect of chronic selenosis on the sulfur-containing amino acids in liver indicate that there is a significant decrease of methionine in the liver in chronic selenosis. This decrease was not associated with restricted food intake and subsequent starvation. *In vitro* studies suggested that the factors responsible for the decrease in methionine are the oxidation of sulfhydryl groups and probably methyl capture by "active" seleno-compounds. Both reactions may occur simultaneously *in vivo* and may serve as a detoxification mechanism in the animals (*224, 227*).

After subcutaneous injection of a trace amount of selenium as $H_2Se^{75}O_3$, rapid incorporation of selenium in cytochrome c was observed (*156*). The crystallized muscle protein, myosin (isolated after a subcutaneous injection of a subtoxic dose of Se^{75} into rabbits), contained 10–15 per cent of the whole muscle Se^{75} activity (*161*).

The urinary selenium seemed to consist of a relatively labile organic compound. It was nonvolatile and was not recoverable quantitatively by simple distillation with a bromine-hydrobromic acid and sulfuric acid mixture (*246*). In animals poisoned with organic selenium, relatively little organic selenium was present in the urine. The fractionation of urinary selenium in chronic selenium poisoning (produced by seleniferous wheat) in rabbits indicated that most of it was associated with the neutral and ethereal sulfur, and the mobilization from the tissues by administration of various agents including bromobenzene was not markedly effective (*281*). However, in animals acutely poisoned by intravenous injections of inorganic selenium, as much as 50 per cent of the urinary selenium was inorganic (*246*). In poisoning with inorganic selenium by oral administration, some inorganic selenium can usually be detected in the urine.

In chronic selenosis there was a drop in the combined sulfur, a rise in the free sulfur and no change in the total or the neutral sulfur in the urine (*60, 63*). The greater part of selenium excreted in the urine after intravenous injection of selenium to rats and rabbits was in inorganic form. Only a small part was soluble in alcohol and acetone. Methionine, cysteine, and choline had no effect on the urinary excretion (*169*). The relative and total quantity of ascorbic acid in the urine decreased in chronic selenosis (*59*).

Studies on the biosynthetic processes involving selenium in the formation of selenium analogs of sulfur compounds indicate that after subcutaneous administration of $H_2Se^{75}O_3$ and feeding of bromobenzene to dogs the mercapturic acid isolated from the urine contained radioactive selenium (*157*).

Enzyme systems which are affected by selenium are sulfhydryl enzymes. Only limited experimental studies have been carried out on the *in vivo* inhibition of enzyme systems. There is considerable discrepancy in the reported results. Decreased serum phosphatase and alkali reserve (*4*) and slight increase of serum phosphatase (*209*) were reported in chronic selenosis. Chronic selenosis has been shown to lower the liver succinic dehydrogenase levels *in vivo* and inclusion of arsenic in the selenium diet restored the enzyme values to normal after a short period of depression (*118*). Decreased cholinestrase activity in rabbits was reported in chronic selenosis (*255*).

More detailed studies on the effect of selenium on sulfhydryl enzymes *in vitro* will be presented in Chapter X.

Gross Pathology

The pathological changes depend upon the duration and dose of toxic substances. The pathology has been described by Franke (*66*), Munsell *et al.* (*189*), and Smith *et al.* (*243*). In early cases the most apparent feature is dilation of veins in the visceral region. The vena cava and right auricle are always enlarged. The lungs and liver are congested. The thymus shows degeneration. The reproductive organs are under developed and may have undergone degeneration. The stomach and intestinal tract show hemorrhages. The bladder is distended and filled with highly colored urine. The conditions just described represent a subacute type of poisoning. In the truly chronic cases the outstanding pathology occurs in the liver. The liver is hard, nodular, and shrunken in size, showing nodular cirrhosis (Fig. 34). Varying degrees of atrophy and necrosis are present. The heart and spleen are enlarged. Jaundice may or may not be present. The thymus and gonads show atrophy. The lymph nodes are en-

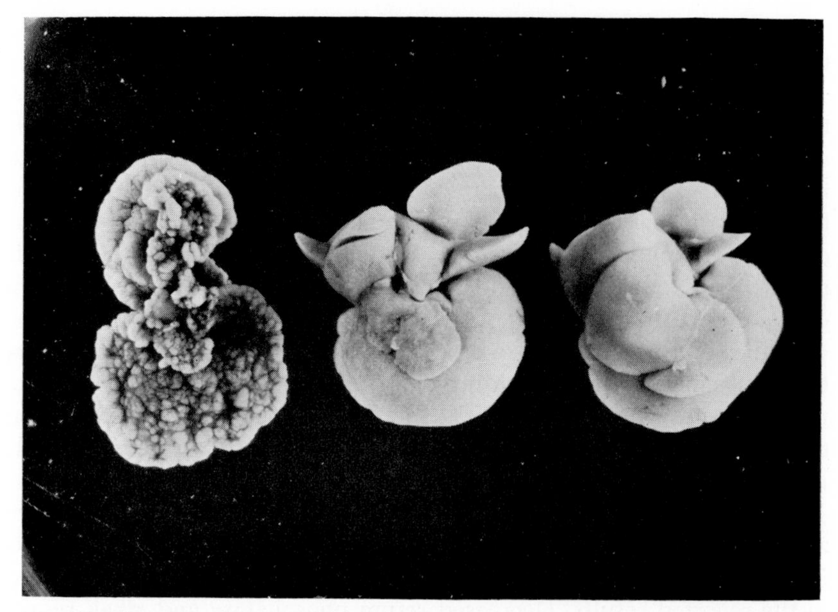

FIG. 34. Cirrhosis of liver (left). The external surface has a coarsely granular, hobnail appearance. Early cirrhosis (center) and normal liver (right). (By courtesy of O. E. Olson.)

larged and congested. Ascites and edema are common. In guinea pigs, poor subperiosteal ossification and hyperemia at the boundaries of primitive cartilage and hyperemia of parathyroid glands are present (*4*). Hypophyseal lesions in the anterior lobe were accompanied by changes in the genital organs (*266*).

MICROSCOPIC PATHOLOGY

The first description dealing with pathological changes related to chronic selenium poisoning was reported by Duhamel (*51*). The description of pathological changes produced in rabbits by the administration of colloidal selenium and selenious acid were toxic liver degeneration, kidney with subacute glomerulites, tubular degeneration and casts; the lung showed hemorrhagic exudate in the alveoli, dilated capillaries, and bronchial exudate. Histogenesis of hepatic cirrhosis in chronic selenosis was described by Lillie and Smith (*133*). Necrosis, hemorrhage, and fibrosis are the essential stages in the histogenesis of cirrhosis. The destructive process is continuous and develops finally into periportal cirrhosis. Telangiectasis with focal necrosis is frequently present in some stages of liver damage (*220*). The effect on the liver of the toxic agent that causes necrosis, fatty changes, and fibrosis, and the probable mechanism of liver damage were discussed by Drill (*43*). In the heart muscle there are varying degrees of degeneration of muscle fibers, with necrosis, lymphocytic infiltration, replacement fibrosis, and scarring. The stomach exhibits lymphocytic infiltration of the mucosa and submucosa. In the more advanced stages, it shows diffuse atrophy of the mucosa, necrosis, and circumscribed ulcers. In the kidney there is usually mild tubular degeneration with acute glomerular injury. Of the hematopoietic organs, the bone marrow has marked hypoplasia; myeloid metaplasia may be present in the liver and spleen (*133, 243*). Histological changes in the ovaries following intraperitoneal injection of selenite are described in great detail by Brusa and Oneto (*22*). When naturally occurring selenium was fed for 16 months to rats in addition to liver damage the lungs developed nodular fibrosis in several animals but no malignant changes were present (*121*). The application of Na_2SeO_3 in 5 per cent sulfonate on the epidermis of the rats caused keratinization in the deeper epidermal layers, with the disappearance of the basal cells. SeS_2 and Na_2SeO_4 were less effective substances in the keratinization of the rat epidermis (*24*).

Neoplasms and Selenium

Various investigators studied the carcinostatic and carcinogenic activity of selenium compounds. Tumor formation has been reported in chronic selenium poisoning. Eleven of 53 rats developed adenoma or low-grade carcinoma in cirrhotic livers, and 4 others showed advanced adenomatoid hyperplasia after having survived for 18 to 24 months. The incidence of spontaneous hepatic tumors in the same age group was less than one per cent (*191*). The development of multiple thyroid adenoma and adenomatous hyperplasia in liver of rats by the use of 0.05 to 0.01 per cent bis (4-acetaminophenyl) selenium dihydroxide within 10 weeks was reported by Seifter *et al.* (*237*). The goitrogenic action was apparent 4 to 5 days preceding the adenomas. Other organic and inorganic selenium compounds failed to produce similar changes. It was concluded that the *para*-amino group was essential for the goitrogenic action.

The possible additive effect between selenium and azo dyes has been studied by alternate feeding of *m′*-methyl-*p*-dimethylaminoazobenzene (*m′*-DAB) and sodium selenite (*33*). The incidences of tumors in the selenium and in the control (*m′*-DAB) groups of rats were 22 vs. 40 per cent in one series and 31 vs. 62 per cent in the second series, respectively. The injection of diselenides with or without the addition of mercury in the selenide compounds failed to have any selective inhibition of tumor growth (*86*).

Carcinostatic effects of inorganic and colloidal selenium were studied and conflicting results were reported by Von Wasserman *et al.* (*274*), Todd and Aldwinckle (*258*), and Todd (*259, 260*) and co-workers (*261*). In more recent studies organic seleno-compounds, which are analogs of physiologically active sulfur compounds, were investigated.

Selenocystine reduced the growth of transplanted tumor and produced a high percentage of tumor regression. Benzylselenocysteine had no significant effect on tumor growth (*275*). Selenocystine had rapid and striking effect on immature leucocytes of acute and chronic leukemia (*276*). Selenocystine was effective in patients refractory to other chemotherapeutic agents.

Regression of Yoshida ascites sarcoma in rats was produced by the concurrent injection of selenite with 4-methyl-benzeneselenonic acid, but either compound given separately showed no tumor-arresting effect (*54*). The tumor-inhibiting and antifungal activity of selenopurines, selenopyrimidines, selenosemicarbazones, and phenylselenourea has been studied by Mautner and co-workers (*107, 142, 143*). 6-Selenopurine, an analog of 6-mercaptopurine, inhibited the growth of mouse leukemia L-1210 (*142*). Methylating both seleno and mercapto compounds in the 6 positions lowered the antitumor activity of these compounds (*143*). 6-Selenopurine per se, but not its riboside or products of its decomposition, was found to be the active antitumor agent when tested in mice-bearing lymphoma L-1210 (*107*). Experiments on the effect of methionine on selenium incorporation into tissues of normal rats and rats with sarcoma-45 indicate that the incorporation of Se^{75} into the tissues of animals which had sarcoma was greater than in normal animals (*56*).

THE EFFECT OF SELENIUM ON REPRODUCTION AND CONGENITAL MALFORMATIONS

It is generally accepted that dietary, chemical, and physical factors may interfere with reproduction or embryonic development. The importance of selenium in reproduction, decreased fertility, and malformation was noted by many investigators in different species of animals. The economic loss due to the effect of selenium on reproduction in livestock is not known at the present time. Toxic and subtoxic amounts of selenium may interfere with fertility and reproduction in experimental animals.

The inhibitory effect of selenium on reproduction may be primary or secondary. The primary effect may be due to interference of selenium with the cellular oxidative processes during embryonic development. Selenium inhibits oxidative enzymes, and since embryonic tissue has critical oxygen requirements, fertility and reproduction may be reduced even in low-grade chronic selenosis. The secondary effect of chronic selenosis is emaciation. Conception cannot take place in these emaciated animals (Rosenfeld, unpublished data).

Reproduction in Mammals

The placental transmission of selenium to the fetus in chronic poisoning was demonstrated by experiments in rats and cats (*277*). Tests were made with both organic and inorganic selenium in the diet. The retention in the tissues of the newborn was higher with organic food selenium than when selenite selenium was added to the diet. When rats were fed seleniferous oats during the latter half of the gestation period, the young, which at birth were about 28 per cent of the mother's weight, had stored about 14 per cent of the mother's total selenium intake. In newborn cats the concentration of selenium was nearly the same as that in the kidney, heart, and other organs of the mother. No developmental malformations, such as were reported in chick embryos by selenium, were seen in the mammalian fetuses, even when the animals that were mated had been reared on seleniferous diets from the time of weaning.

Placental transmission of selenium ($Na_2Se^{75}O_3 + Na_2SeO_3$) was studied in two groups of pregnant rats. One group received radioactive selenium which contained 7.5 μg of selenium. The other group was injected with 2 mg of selenium per kilogram of body weight in addition to the Se^{75}. The distribution and placental transmission of selenium was determined in the placenta, amniotic fluid, and fetus after 7 days of selenium and radioactive selenium administration (approximately 18–20 days of pregnancy). These results indicate that the placental transmission was higher in the atoxic group than in the group which received the toxic dose. The placental tissue always contained more selenium than the uterus and amniotic fluid. The concentration of Se^{75} in the fetus was lower than in all other tissues connected with reproduction. This gave further evidence that repeated injections of toxic amounts of selenium interfere not only with the cellular metabolism but probably with cellular permeability (*228*).

Evidence of placental transmission of selenium in human beings was reported by Hadjimarkos *et al.* (*87*). Placental and fetal cord blood from normal patients in a nonseleniferous area contained 0.18 and 0.12 ppm selenium, respectively. They suggested that the placental transmission of selenium may be responsible for the higher selenium content in the primary teeth in comparison with that of the permanent teeth.

Franke and Potter (*72, 76*) reported that rats which received selenized wheat diets were unable to reproduce. Matings between males and females which were fed toxic diets were infertile. Matings in which one of the animals was normal were sometimes fertile but affected females were unable to rear their young. Munsell *et al.* (*189*) reported that selenium-containing diets of rats had a detrimental effect on growth and reproduction in direct proportion to the selenium intake. The effect of low concentrations of selenium on successive generations of rats was studied by Rosenfeld and Beath (*222*). They reported that the intake of 1.5 and 2.5 ppm selenium in water had no effect on the (1) reproduction of breeding rats, (2) number of young reared by mothers, or (3) reproduction of two successive generations of males and females. The second generation of selenized rats which received 2.5 ppm selenium had normal offspring, but the number of young reared by the mothers decreased about 50 per cent. The intake of 7.5 ppm selenium in water from 5 to 8 days before parturition had no effect on the young before birth but there was a decrease in the number of survivors with continued selenium

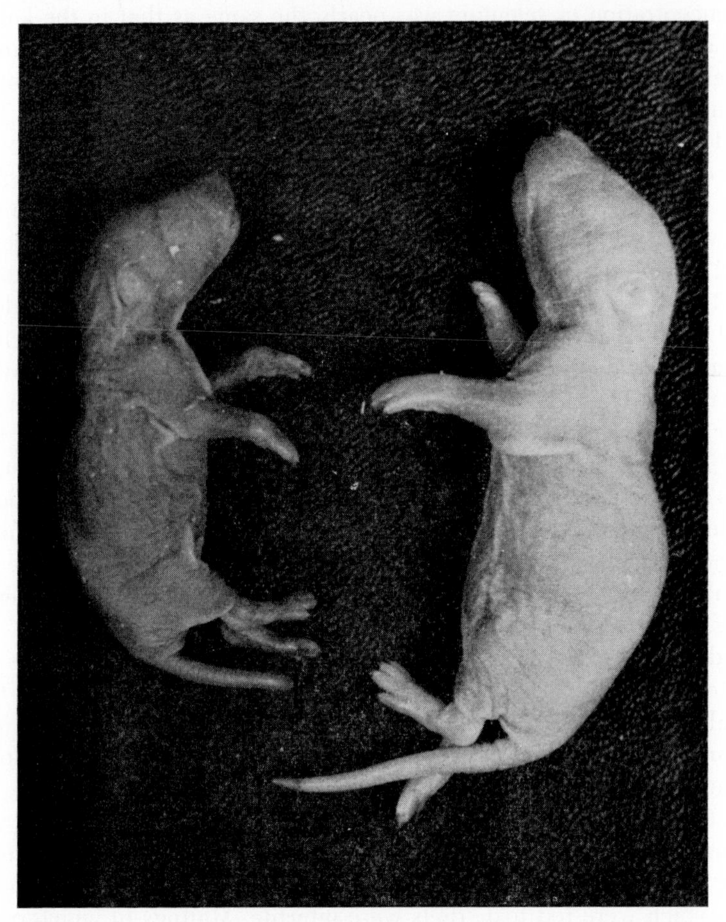

Fig. 35. Progeny of first generation of selenized males and females on left, compared with a normal newborn rat (Rosenfeld).

intake. Crossbreeding of selenized males and females with normal animals indicated that the fertility of the males was not affected but the females failed to conceive, or the few young born to selenized females were unable to suck and appeared emaciated at birth as indicated in Fig. 35.

Wahlstrom and Olson (*272*) conducted experiments to determine the effect of selenium on reproduction in swine and tested the value of arsanilic acid as a selenium-poisoning preventive. The addition of 10 ppm of selenite selenium to the diet lowered conception rate, increased the number of services required for conception, decreased the number of survivors, and significantly reduced the weights at the age of 56 days. The addition of arsanilic acid in selenium ration improved the percentage of animals born alive, increased the 56-day weight of animals, but had no effect on birth weight and number of pigs weaned per litter.

Congenital Malformation in Chicks

Detailed study of the sequence of events of the effect of selenium on 1- to 5-day-old chick embryos from eggs laid by selenium-fed hens indicated that there is a retarded development of the embryo in the presence of selenium (*85*). In early embryonic development the abnormalities showed a constant pattern of tissue necrosis. Necrosis appeared after 2½ to 3 days of incubation in the brain, spinal cord, eyes, and limb buds. As a result of the necrosis, structural alterations were present in the face, nasal pits, upper beak, and the caudal portion of the trunk-tail node. There was a marked retardation not only of growth but in differentiation of the directly or indirectly affected primordia (*85*). The primary effect of selenium on the cells is focal necrosis with regressive functions of the organs if selenium administration is continuous. There is no reason to consider that embryonic cells would not be affected in a similar manner.

Since the settlement of western South Dakota and northern Nebraska, residents of certain regions have found that eggs from the chickens on their farms did not hatch satisfactorily, either by natural or artificial incubation (*69, 199*). The causative agent was assumed to be the same as that of alkali disease in livestock. Chicks that hatched appeared greasy or wiry and never became fluffy. The affected chicks were weak and usually lived only a short time. If a large fraction of the eggs hatched, the mortality of the chicks was very high. It is remarkable that full-grown chickens or even young chicks hatched from eggs free of selenium are little affected by the toxic grains, except for some loss of feathers.

To ascertain the reason for the low hatchability, Franke and Tully (*73*) obtained eggs from an affected farm and incubated them in the usual manner. They found that most of the embryos were badly deformed. The failure of the eggs to hatch was therefore not due to infertility but resulted from deformities that prevented hatching. The deformed chicks showed many types of abnormalities (Fig. 36). Legs, toes, wings, beaks, or eyes were malformed, rudimentary, or entirely lacking. Disturbance in the normal process of bone and cartilage formation was evident. The abnormalities usually occurred on only one side of the embryo. Although malformations were frequent, there was no duplication of parts. Only 5 to 10 per cent of the eggs hatched, and 75 per cent of the eggs that failed to hatch on the twenty-first day contained deformed embryos. Chicks

FIG. 36. Malformations in chicks due to selenium poisoning. (By courtesy of O. E. Olson.)

from some of the eggs that hatched lived only a few hours. The selenium content of the deformed embryos varied between 6 and 18 ppm (*205*).

When healthy chicks were fed a ration containing 65 per cent of a toxic grain, their growth was distinctly inhibited. Egg production was delayed and reduced (*264*). When chicks received only 25 per cent of this grain, they made practically normal growth. The internal organs of chickens, however, showed no lesions like those observed in rats fed on toxic grain.

The chick embryo is extremely sensitive to selenium poisoning. Hatchability of eggs is reduced by concentrations of selenium in feeds that are too low to produce symptoms of poisoning in other farm animals. Poor hatchability of eggs on farms has therefore proved to be an aid in locating potentially seleniferous areas where alkali disease in cattle, hogs, and horses may occur.

By injecting selenite into the air cell of eggs before incubation, abnormalities of beaks, eyes, and legs were produced (*75*). This experiment provided evidence that the deformities resulting from toxic grains were due to selenium. The highest frequency of abnormalities resulted when the selenium dosage was about 0.7 mg per kilogram of egg yolk plus egg white, but amounts as low as 0.01 mg produced some abnormalities.

A single injection of 0.7 ppm of sodium selenite in 0.1 ml of 0.85 per cent sodium chloride solution into the air cells of eggs before incubation produced an average mortality of about 50 per cent of the developing chicks (*278*). About 25 per cent of the surviving embryos were malformed. When glutathione was injected with selenite to give a selenium : sulfur ratio of 1:2 or 1:5, the mortality was greatly reduced, and malformations in chicks were prevented. Sodium monosulfide gave similar protection. Sodium sulfite was not effective against the toxic action of selenite injected into the eggs. Arsenic at levels of 2.5 and 5 ppm in drinking water partially increased the hatchability of eggs from hens receiving a ration containing 10 ppm of selenium in wheat (*185*). Dietary arsenic compounds partially reduced the growth inhibition produced in chicks by selenite (10 ppm selenium) but increased the selenium content of muscle and liver (*27a*).

Chronic poisoning of laying hens with seleniferous grain had more severe effects on the progeny of genetically abnormal hens known as Creeper mutation than that of genetically normal hens, when both were bred to Leghorn cocks (*124*). In the Creeper progenies embryonic mortality was higher, and malformations were more extreme than in the genetically normal sibs. The inherited abnormalities exaggerated the developmental derangements caused by selenium.

Tolerance levels of selenium in rations for laying hens were investigated by Poley and Moxon (*206*). The hatchability of fertile eggs was not significantly reduced by a ration containing 2.5 ppm of selenium from toxic grain, and it was only slightly reduced by a ration containing 5 ppm; but it was reduced to zero by a ration containing 10 ppm. Chicks hatched from eggs of hens receiving 5 ppm had normal growth rate and mortality. A few chicks that hatched from eggs of hens receiving 10 ppm showed a high mortality rate, but the growth of the surviving chicks was not affected.

Moxon and Poley (*175*) studied the distribution of selenium in poultry meat and eggs from laying hens fed with seleniferous grain ration. Chemical analyses of meat and organs showed considerable variation, but the data indicate a correlation between selenium intake and selenium content of the tissues. Selenium content of ovaries and oviduct was higher than that of the liver and kidney; white and dark meat contained less selenium than all other organs. The eggs that were laid during the experiment contained the concentrations of selenium given in Table 48. Results were based on normal moisture content. If based on dry weight, the selenium content would be much higher in the egg white than in the yolk since whites contain 84.5 and yolks 53.5 per cent water.

A study of the rate of growth of chicks fed seleniferous grain was reported by Poley *et al.* (*207*). Chicks that received 2, 5, or 8 ppm of selenium in their starting rations grew as rapidly as those receiving no sele-

TABLE 48
Distribution of Selenium in Eggs[a]

Selenium in ration (ppm)	Selenium (ppm)	
	White	Yolk
2.5	1.8	1.7
5.0	3.0	2.7
10.0	6.4	3.9

[a] Moxon and Poley (*175*).

nium. But 10 ppm in the starting ration reduced the growth rate, and 14 ppm was markedly toxic, causing reduced growth and high mortality. Pullets from 8 to 24 weeks old grew as rapidly on diets containing 5–8 ppm as those that were selenium-free. These concentrations had no apparent ill effects on the health of the pullets. The authors recommended that starting and growing rations contain no more than 5 ppm of selenium. This would allow a margin of safety, since 8 ppm is the maximum concentration at which selenium may be fed without reducing the growth rate. In view of the present knowledge on the effect of small amounts of selenium on exudative diathesis in chicks, it is of considerable interest to note that 5 ppm of selenium had no deleterious effect on growth rate of chicks.

FIG. 37. Congenital malformation in lambs. Note the thickening of joints, malformed extremities, and the various abnormalities of the eyes.

MAMMALIAN MALFORMATIONS

Studies dealing with the effect of radiation on developing mammalian embryos indicate that abnormalities and malformations have a critical period at which time the embryos are sensitive to developmental damage (*230*). Therefore, selenium-induced malformations in mammals require more research in order to determine the critical period of embryonic susceptibility and the spectrum of the teratogenic dose which would permit maximum placental transmission, and survival of the embryo and development of the fetus. It appears that in the avian eggs these conditions are met, and malformed embryos develop in the presence of selenium.

Congenital alkali disease was reported by Smith *et al.* (*242*) in a 14-day-old colt born of a mare that developed symptoms of the disease dur-

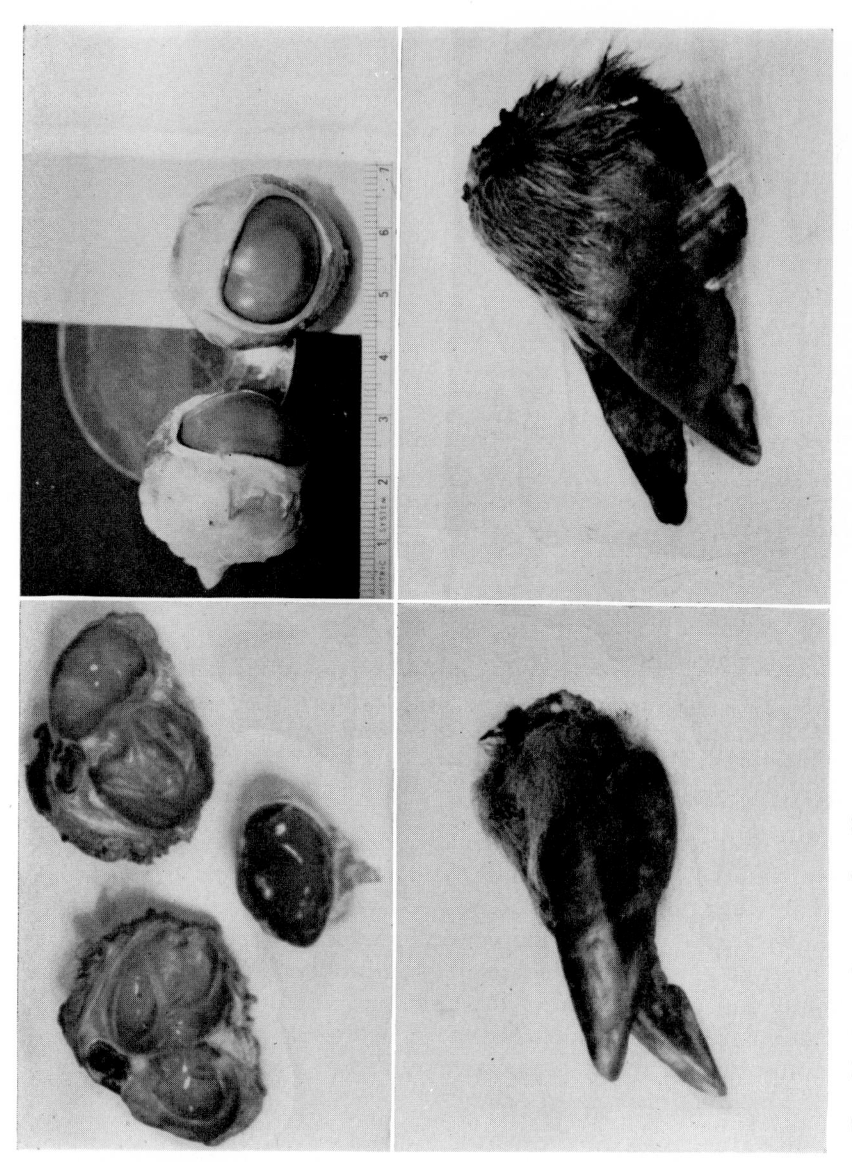

FIG. 38. Top: Congenital malformations of eyes of lambs on left showing multiple cysts, microphthalmia and displacement of visual area; normal eyes on the right. Bottom: Hoofs of the same animals.

ing gestation. The disease in the colt appeared to be similar to that in the adult animal.

Malformation in lambs that were the progeny of ewes which grazed on seleniferous ranges was reported by Beath *et al.* (*13*). The various organs showed pathological changes similar to those present in the blind-staggers type of poisoning. The eyes had cystic elevations that protruded through the lids. The joints of the extremities were thickened and nodular in appearance. Most of the young lambs were unable to stand and died soon after birth. The lambs that survived developed deformed legs, with thickening at the joints which impaired locomotion (Fig. 37).

Observations on 250 malformed lambs born to ewes that grazed on a seleniferous range were made by Rosenfeld and Beath (*218*). About 75 per cent of the malformed animals died at birth and 10 per cent died at ages between 3 and 5 months. The defective lambs that lived longer showed deformities of eyes and extremities and hypoplasia of the reproductive organs.

Gross and histological changes in the malformed eyes of 16 lambs were studied and reported in detail (*218*). The eyes presented various degrees of malformation. The abnormalities indicated that developmental arrest occurred rather early in gestation, and the capacity for differentiation was impaired or lost. The different stages of embryonic development attained by the eyes indicated that the injury did not occur in all animals at the same time. The eyes showed various degrees of deformity, microphthalmia, rudimentary development, microcornea, and colobomas of the various structures (Fig. 38). These changes represent incomplete and abnormal development in the eye of the young before birth. The histological picture of the defective eyes presented a bizarre structural arrangement, which evidently resulted from arrested growth, cellular proliferation, and lack of differentiation at certain developmental stages. Decreased vitamin A and ascorbic acid, shown to follow selenium ingestion (*216*), may have been a contributing factor to the malformations. The lens, vitreous humor, and retina were embryonic in character in some of the malformed eyes studied. The cystic cavities were connected with the eye by multiple sinuses that were lined with retinal epithelium. As the animals matured, the increase in eye size was due to the enlargement of the cysts. No relation existed between the age of the animals and the development of the eyes. The eyes showed no pathological changes indicating that the fluid in the cysts exerted no excessive pressure. The normal pressure in the various cavities was maintained through the sinuses and defects in the walls of the cysts and the sclera. This pressure equilibrium suggests that the fluid was not foreign in orgin, but was produced in the same manner as vitreous humor. The core of the papillary projections was composed of neural and fibrous tissue. The retinal epithelium formed an adenomatous arrangement within the eye.

The malformations observed in sheep apparently involved the same primordium by selenium as reported in chicks. If comparison of effective teratogenic dose of different agents can be made, the work of Wilson (*284*) would suggest that eye malformations can be produced with lower range of teratogenic agent and greater regularity than in other organs. Malformation of the feet ranked next to the eye in order of frequency. These observations are in agreement with gross malformations of the eyes, beaks, and extremities observed in chicks hatched from eggs in seleniferous areas, and also the malformations observed in the progenies of sheep grazed on seleniferous vegetation.

INSECTS AND MITES

During the past decade a great many insecticides have been introduced all over the world to increase yields, improve quality, facilitate storage of food, and control diseases. Some of the pesticides introduced earlier almost approach the limits of their effectiveness owing to their inherent toxicity to mammals and/or the resistance of the insects to the various insecticides (World Health Organization, 1956). An advantage of selenium compounds as pesticides is due to the inability of insects to develop tolerance to the toxic effect of selenium. At least up to the present time, no observations on the development of acquired resistance in selenium-sensitive strain insects or mites have been reported.

Hazards from Selenium Insecticides

Selenium compounds as insecticides also may create public health problems, and the Food and Drug Administration stipulates a nil residue in the harvested produce. The objections to the use of selenium as an insecticide are due to the extreme stability of selenium in the soil, contaminations of the soil by rendering it unsuitable for use for food crops, the high price of selenium insecticides, and its extreme toxicity to mammals as well as birds. At the present time selenium is no longer used as a pesticide; however, it is included in this chapter because insects may become a valuable source of research material for the study of many facets of selenium metabolism.

A wild strain of *Drosophilia melanogaster* appeared to respond to selenium in an interesting manner. The addition of 1–10 ppb of selenium to the culture gradually increased the number of flies hatched. An increase of selenium to 0.5 ppm caused a 3 per cent reduction and 3 ppm caused a 70 per cent reduction in the reproduction of the flies (Ellis, unpublished results).

A comprehensive review of selenium as an insecticide and its relation to health hazards has been published by Smith (*241*).

Although some insects are capable of completing their life cycles on food containing at least 70 times the concentration that is lethal for mammals, other insects are very sensitive to selenium.

Insects with Native Resistance

In view of the high toxicity of selenium to many insects, as well as to mammals and birds, it is surprising to find that the larvae of bruchids (beetles) and seed-chalcids (wasplike insects) were capable of consuming the seeds of one of the most poisonous of the range plants, *Astragalus bisulcatus* (*262*). Analysis of the seeds showed that they contained 1475 ppm of selenium. The bruchids were identified as *Acanthoscelides fraterculus* Horn, and the seed-chalcids as *Bruchophagus mexicanus* Ashmead (or a closely related species). Another wasplike insect, *Amblymerus bruchophagi*, was present as a parasite on the seed-chalcid. These insects seemed to be virtually immune to selenium poisoning, for they were capable of completing their life cycles on food containing about 70 times the concentration that is lethal for mammals. The developing bruchid larvae either absorbed relatively little selenium or they eliminated it effectively, perhaps through their respiration. Analysis of their bodies showed the presence of 67 ppm of selenium, most of which may have been in the alimentary canal.

Flies were reported by Byers *et al.* (*26*) to be living on a sample of *Astragalus pectinatus* containing 1800 ppm of selenium. Analysis showed that the flies contained 20 ppm, live weight. Fly larvae, thought to be of the same species, were found infesting the roots of *Astragalus racemosus*. The larvae showed a selenium content of 7.5 ppm, and they were inhabiting roots that contained 190 ppm. Another sample of the same larvae had a selenium content of 10 ppm while infesting roots containing 420 ppm. Grasshoppers that were collected on seleniferous plants contained as much as 20 ppm of selenium and exhibited no deleterious effects according to Moxon (*176*). Ten species of insects were found feeding on *A. pectinatus* and *A. bisulcatus* that presumably contained selenium (*65*). Blister beetles (*Lytta nuttalli*) showed no injury when they consumed seleniferous flowers of *A. bisulcatus* and *A. racemosus* (Beath, unpublished). The beetles were found to contain 21 ppm of selenium when they were collected on flowers of *A. racemosus* containing 2300 ppm.

Insects Sensitive to Selenium

Selenium was used about half a century ago in an effort to control disease and insects on plants, but the amounts used were phytotoxic and the results were not promising (*135*). The observations that aphids and red spiders did not attack wheat plants supplied with selenate in solution cultures or soils suggested the possible effectiveness of selenium as a pesticide (*105*). The aphids were sensitive to concentrations of selenium in the plant too low to visibly affect the plants.

Several investigators have reported experiments on the control of insects in greenhouses by the addition of selenium as selenate to the soil or culture solution. Leukel (*130*) found that 2–4 ppm of selenium in clay loam prevented injury to sorghum from red spiders and aphids, but higher concentrations injured the plants. Nutrient solutions containing up to 2.5 ppm of selenium were supplied by Neiswander and Morris (*190*) to plants artifically infested with insects or mites. A concentration in the plant tissues of 100 ppm of selenium practically eliminated red spiders from stocks, roses, and tomatoes. Red spiders were eliminated from carnations by 4 ppm of selenium in the soil. The chrysanthemum aphid did not survive when the foliage of chrysanthemums contained 45 ppm.

The use of sodium selenate (250 mg per square foot) for the control of several greenhouse pests, particularly aphids and mites on chrysanthemums and carnations, has been effective (*19*). Subsequent investigators reported that selenate treatment kept greenhouse plants free from aphids, mites, foliar nematodes, chrysanthemum midges (*6, 37, 112*), and mealy bugs (*53*).

Severe stunting of growth and injury to carnations by the use of selenate in potted plants or in gravel culture has been observed (*5, 283*). By using low-split-dosages of sodium selenate as soil treatment, damage to carnations and chrysanthemums was reduced. Adequate control of red spiders and, subsequently, greater total yield of flowers and early flowers were obtained. There was some stunting of certain varieties of flowers (*7, 53*).

At the present time the dosage recommended for soil treatment for chrysanthemums or carnations is lower than that recommended earlier. At monthly intervals 3.125 gm of Na_2SeO_4 per 100 square feet for 4 months was adequate to control red spiders and mites (*7*). Complete insect control on chrysanthemums obtained by treating the soil with sodium selenate either once with 250 mg per square foot or twice at rates of 125, 62.5, and 31.25 mg per square foot. The soil for carnations was treated twice a year with 250 mg per square foot and 4 times a year with 62.5, 31.25, and 15.6 mg of sodium selenate per square foot (*53*). Sodium selenate has been used successfully for the control of insects on chrysanthemum, carnation, snapdragon, hydrangea, saintpaulia, ageratum, and cyclamen; but it has not proved effective with roses and other woody plants.

Sodium selenate (50–75 ppm) was effective in controlling meadow nematodes, *Pratylenchus* spp., attacking boxwood, when used in powder form (*257*). The leaf-nematode (*Aphelenchoides fragariae*) which attacks several ferns can be controlled by Na_2SeO_4 in pellet form (*139*).

Soil selenization for control of insects was tested under field conditions in Trinidad (*204*). Experiments showed that cotton plants could be rendered toxic to the cotton stainer and the pink bollworm by the application of small amounts of selenate to the soil. Bolls and seed from the first crop were markedly toxic, but those from the second were no longer toxic, owing perhaps to leaching of the selenate from the soil.

In view of the extreme toxicity of selenium to man and the higher animals, the addition of selenium to the soil as a means of insect control may be a dangerous procedure, even with ornamental or other nonfood plants. If the discarded greenhouse soil is used as top dressing for a vegetable garden as is frequently the case, it may present a real hazard. The concentration of selenium in the soil may be sufficiently high to render vegetables distinctly toxic—especially cabbage, kale, cauliflower, broccoli, mustard, radish, and onion. In spite of leaching resulting from rain, dangerous amounts of selenate may remain in the soil for a number of years.

Selenium is a far greater potential public health hazard when used for the control of insects on citrus fruits or apples.

When applied as sprays, certain compounds of selenium are effective insecticides (*81*). The substance most commonly used is a selenide, having the approximate formula $(KNH_4S)_5Se$. The selenide sprays quickly kill mature citrus mites or citrus red spiders, and apparently also destroy the eggs. But selenium compounds are not effective against certain other insects, such as leaf-hoppers and leaf-rollers.

Extensive tests of selenium sprays were reported by Hoskins *et al.* (*102*). They used a spray made by dissolving selenium in a solution of potassium-ammonium sulfide in such proportions that the composition corresponded to the formula $(KNH_4S)_5Se$. This was found to be effective for the control of mites on citrus fruits and grapes, and there was limited injury to fruit and plants. The soil beneath sprayed trees, after 5 years' treatment, contained a maximum of 2 ppm of selenium in the first 6 inches, and penetration to lower depths was slight. The residue upon grapes was somewhat greater on account of the larger surface and probably they absorbed somewhat more selenium from the soil than the citrus fruits.

Selocide (a commercial selenide spray material) was reported by Moore *et al.* (*171*) to control the Pacific mite and the European red mite on apples. The amount of selenium accumulated in the soil after a single application of the spray was regarded negligible. Apples from an orchard sprayed with Selocide were reported to contain no more selenium than those from orchards in which this spray had never been used.

Possible health hazards to farm animals and to human beings, according to White *et al.* (*282*), may attend the use of selenium sprays in citrus groves where garden or forage crops can also be grown. The soil of

California orange groves unsprayed with selenium contained a minute though analytically significant amount of selenium (0.029–0.904 ppm; average 0.067). The soil of sprayed groves contained a tenfold or greater amount (0.566–1.150 ppm; average 0.864) of selenium.

Deposits in soil and residue in treated fruits after Selocide treatment indicate that from 0.08 to 0.33 ppm was present in the flesh of apples, and in the whole fruit the selenium content was from 0.17 to 0.5 ppm. Wheat plants grown in the soil from 1 to 3 years contained from 0 to 0.43 ppm selenium (*103*). The treatment of various varieties of apples with one or more sprays of Selocide to control mites indicates that the addition of one quart of light petroleum oil increased the selenium residue on and in the peel. This increase was highly significant over nonselenium-sprayed fruits (*273*).

The increase of the number of spray applications of Selocide caused a corresponding increase of selenium in skin, flesh, and total apple. The selenium in the soil under the trees gradually increased from 0.56 to 2.83 ppm. The leaf and twig of trees accumulated up to 22.2 ppm of selenium. The late application of Selocide caused significant increase in the selenium content of skin and flesh. Application of the spray in the spring reduced the accumulation of selenium in the fruit. Satisfactory control of red mites was obtained until mid-summer by two spray applications of Selocide in the spring, and an increase of mite population did not occur until late summer (*3, 30*). In orchards, DDT proved most effective for control of codling moths while wettable sulfur, dinitro or selenium compounds were most effective for clover mites (*192*).

Greenhouse red spider mites may become resistant to a parathion, but they are not resistant to other toxicants. Mites from beans were treated with molybdenum and selenium, and the addition of a low level of molybdenum reduced the effectiveness of selenium (*79*). Red mites of avocado and mango did not respond to a proprietary selenium compound (*286*) whereas wheat blight was prevented by the application of Seleson (Se-Hg) preparation when applied 3.76 gm per 3.31 square miles (*106*). Selenious acid (2 ppm) prevents maturation of the larva of flies, mosquitos, and other insects (*231*).

The effectiveness of selenium as an insecticide cannot be denied; however, more studies on the retention of selenium in the soil from selenium sprays and the uptake of selenium from the selenized soil by the usual garden vegetables, hay, and forage plants are needed before the extent of public health hazards can be determined.

OTHER ANIMALS

Selenium poisoning in fishes was described by Ellis *et al.* (*52*). Goldfish, kept in water at room temperature containing sodium selenite, developed anorexia and died in 18–46 days. Catfish, living out-of-doors in running water, died within 48 hours after receiving intraperitoneal injections of 0.15 mg or more of selenium as selenite. Catfish that received a single injection of 0.05 mg of selenium showed no immediate effects; but after about 10 days pronounced exophthalmus and ascites developed and death occurred in 12 to 15 days. There was marked edema of many tissues, particularly the submucosa of the stomach and around the blood vessels in the kidney and livers. Selenium poisoning in the fish produced severe disturbance in the hematopoietic system. The specific gravity of the blood was lower than normal and there was a decrease in red blood cells and hemoglobin.

Experimental studies on rearing fishes and shellfishes indicate that the length of survival time is proportional to the selenium concentration. The addition of 10 ppm of selenium (H_2SeO_3) is lethal to carp in 25 days and corbiculae in 8 days. The carp accumulated 19.3 ppm and mudsnails accumulated 90.3 ppm selenium (*231*).

Duck sickness was produced by the addition of 20 ppm of selenium to the drinking water of the animals. Many of the symptoms were identical with those of *Clostridium* botulism-type C (*265*).

The toxicity of aromatic selenium compounds (hydroxydiphenyl selenides and carboxydiphenyl selenides) to paramecia and amebae is from 20 to 300 times greater than phenols (*110*).

References

1. Anderson, H. D. and A. L. Moxon. 1941. The excretion of selenium by rats on a seleniferous wheat ration. *J. Nutrition* **22**:103–108.
2. Anderson, H. D. and A. L. Moxon. 1942. Changes in the blood picture of the dog following subcutaneous injections of sodium selenite. *J. Pharmacol. Exptl. Therap.* **76**:343–354.
3. Barr, H. E., P. J. Clark and H. Jacks. 1955. Selenium in apples.—The effect of applications of Selocide to the tree and to the soil. *New Zealand J. Sci. Technol.* **B37**:119–125.
4. Bauer, F. K. 1940. Experimentelle Vergiftung mit Selen unter besonderer Berücksichtigung der Wirkung auf das Knochensystem. *Arch. Gewerbepath. Gewerbhyg.* **10**:117–132.
5. Beach, G. 1947. Selenium on carnations, *Florist Rev.* **101**:43.
6. Beach, G. 1949. Some effects of sodium selenate on greenhouse carnations grown in gravel. *Proc. Am. Soc. Hort. Sci.* **53**:507–512.
7. Beach, G. 1950. Some effects of sodium selenate on greenhouse carnations grown in gravel—second report. *Proc. Am. Soc. Hort. Sci.* **56**:423–426.
8. Beath, O. A., J. H. Draize and H. F. Eppson. 1932. Three poisonous vetches. *Wyoming Agr. Expt. Sta. Bull. No.* **189**:1–23.
9. Beath, O. A., J. H. Draize and C. S. Gilbert. 1934. Plants poisonous to livestock. *Wyoming Agr. Expt. Sta. Bull. No.* **200**:1–84.
10. Beath, O. A. 1935. Delayed action of selenium poisoning of livestock. *Science* **81**:617.

11. Beath, O. A., H. F. Eppson and C. S. Gilbert. 1935. Selenium and other toxic minerals in soils and vegetation. *Wyoming Agr. Expt. Sta. Bull. No.* **206**:1–55.
12. Beath, O. A. 1937. The occurrence of selenium and seleniferous vegetation in Wyoming. Part II. Seleniferous vegetation of Wyoming. *Wyoming Agr. Expt. Sta. Bull. No.* **221**:29–64.
13. Beath, O. A., H. F. Eppson, C. S. Gilbert and W. B. Bradley. 1939. Poisonous plants and livestock poisoning. *Wyoming Agr. Expt. Sta. Bull. No.* **231**:1–104.
14. Beath, O. A., C. S. Gilbert, H. F. Eppson and I. Rosenfeld. 1953. Poisonous plants and livestock poisoning. *Wyoming Agr. Expt. Sta. Bull. No.* **324**:1–94.
15. Belogorsky, J. B. and D. Slaughter. 1949. Administration of BAL in selenium poisoning. *Proc. Soc. Exptl. Biol. Med.* **72**:196–198.
16. Bernstein, S. and R. W. McGilvery. 1952. The enzymatic conjugation of *m*-amino phenol. *J. Biol. Chem.* **198**:195–203.
17. Bieri, J. G., C. J. Pollard and R. R. Cardenas, Jr. 1957. Utilization of vitamin A and carotene by selenium poisoned rats. *Proc. Soc. Exptl. Biol. Med.* **94**: 318–320.
18. Blau, M. and R. F. Manske. 1961. The pancreas specificity of Se^{75}-selenomethionine. *J. Nuclear Med.* **2**:102–105.
19. Blauvalt, W. E. 1945. Applying sodium selenate to the soil as an insecticide. *Florists Exchange Hort. Trade World* **105**:16.
20. Blincoe, C. 1960. Whole-body turnover of selenium in the rat. *Nature* **186**:398.
21. Braun, H. A., M. Lusky and H. O. Calvery. 1946. The efficacy of 2, 3-dimercaptopropanol (BAL) in the therapy of poisoning by compounds of antimony, bismuth, chromium, mercury and nickel. *J. Pharmacol. Exptl. Therap.* **87**: 119–125.
22. Brusa, A. and G. P. Oneto. 1954. On the variations of the structure of the ovary and ovules determined by selenium. *Compt. Rend. Assoc. Anat.* **41**: 333–349.
23. Buescher, R. G., M. C. Bell and R. K. Berry. 1961. Effect of excessive calcium on $selenium^{75}$ in swine. *J. Animal Sci.* **20**:368–372.
24. Butcher, E. O. 1957. The effect of several substances on the keratinization of the rat epidermis. *J. Invest. Dermatol.* **29**:377–381.
24a. Butler, G. W. and P. J. Peterson. 1961. Aspects of the faecal excretion of selenium by sheep. *N. Zealand J. Agr. Res.* **4**:484–491.
25. Byers, H. G. 1934. Selenium, vanadium, chromium and arsenic in one soil. *J. Ind. Eng. Chem., News Ed.* **12**:122.
26. Byers, H. G., J. T. Miller, K. T. Williams and H. W. Lakin. 1938. Selenium occurrence in certain soils in the United States, with a discussion of related topics: Third report. *U.S. Dept. Agr. Tech. Bull. No.* **601**:1–74.
27. Carlson, C. W., E. Guenthner, W. Kohlmeyer and O. E. Olson. 1954. Some effects of selenium, arsenicals, and vitamin B_{12} on chick growth. *Poultry Sci.* **33**: 768–774.
27a. Carlson, C. W., P. L. Guss and O. E. Olson. 1962. Selenium content of chick tissues as affected by arsenic. *Poultry Sci.* **41**:1987–1989.
27b. Celander, D. R., M. Jaquo, Jr. and M. D. Naschke. 1962. Biosynthetic labeling of fibrinogen and other proteins with radioselenium. *Federation Proc.* **21**:3E.
28. Challenger, F. 1951. Biological methylation. *Advan. Enzymol.* **12**:429–491.
29. Challenger, F., D. B. Lisle and P. B. Dransfield. 1954. Studies on biological methylation. Part XIV. The formation of trimethylarsine and dimethyl selenide in mould cultures from methyl sources containing C^{14}. *J. Chem. Soc.* pp. 1760–1771.
30. Clark, P. J., H. E. Barr, A. Camden-Cooke and H. Jacks. 1953. Selenium content of apples. *New Zealand J. Sci. Technol.* **B34**:245–247.

31. Claycomb, C. K., D. C. Gatewood, F. M. Sorenson and E. B. Jump. 1960. Presence of Se^{75} in rat saliva after intracardiac injection of radioactive selenite. *J. Dental Res.* **39:**1264.
32. Claycomb, C. K., F. M. Sorenson, D. C. Gatewood, E. B. Jump and M. E. Weaver. 1961. Further studies on the presence of Se^{75} in rat saliva and teeth after intracardiac injection of radioactive sodium selenite. *J. Dental Res.* **40:** 504–510.
33. Clayton, C. C. and C. A. Baumann. 1949. Diet and azo dye tumors: Effect of diet during a period when the dye is not fed. *Cancer Res.* **9:**575–582.
34. Coppa, S. 1949. Blood electrolytes in experimental selenium poisoning. *Folia Med. (Naples)* **32:**449–452.
35. Cowie, D. B. and G. N. Cohen. 1957. Biosynthesis by *E. coli* of active altered proteins containing selenium instead of sulfur. *Biochim. et Biophys. Acta* **26:** 252–261.
36. Czapek, H., and J. Weil. 1893. Über die Wirkung des Selens und Tellurs auf dem Thierischen Organismus. *Arch. Exptl. Pathol. Pharmakol. Naunyn-Schmiedeberg's* **32:**438–455.
37. Davidson, O. W. 1948. The control of greenhouse pests with selenium. Bull. Coop. Ext. Work Agr. Home Econ., New Jersey State Coll. Agric.
38. Davidson, W. B. 1940. Selenium poisoning. *Can. J. Comp. Med.* **4:**19–25.
39. DeMeio, R. H., M. Wizerkaniuk and I. Schreibman. 1955. Enzymatic system synthesizing sulfuric acid esters of phenols. *J. Biol. Chem.* **213:**439–443.
40. Dinkel, C. A., J. A. Minyard, E. I. Whitehead and O. E. Olson. 1957. Progress report of the Reed Ranch substation. *South Dakota State Coll. Circ.* **135:** 1–30.
41. Dolique, R. and J. Giroux. 1943. The fate of selenium after poisoning by sodium selenite and selenate. *Bull. Soc. Chim. France* **10:**60–64.
42. Draize, J. H. and O. A. Beath. 1935. Observations on the pathology of "blind staggers" and "alkali disease." *J. Am. Vet. Med. Assoc.* **86:**753–763.
43. Drill, V. A. 1952. Hepatotoxic agents; mechanism of action and dietary interrelationship. *Pharmacol. Revs.* **4:**1–42.
44. DuBois, K. P., A. L. Moxon and O. E. Olson. 1940. Further studies on the effectiveness of arsenic in preventing selenium poisoning. *J. Nutrition* **19:** 477–482.
45. Dudley, H. C. and H. G. Byers. 1935. Determination of selenium; quantitative determination on animal matter and clinical test in urine. *Ind. Eng. Chem., Anal. Ed.* **7:**3–4.
46. Dudley, H. C. 1936. Toxicology of selenium. I. A study of the distribution of selenium in acute and chronic cases of selenium poisoning. *Am J. Hyg.* **23:** 169–180.
47. Dudley, H. C. 1936. Toxicology of selenium. II. The urinary excretion of selenium. *Am. J. Hyg.* **23:**181–186.
48. Dudley, H. C. and J. W. Miller. 1937. Toxicology of selenium. IV. Effects of exposure to hydrogen selenide. *U. S. Public Health Rept.* **52:**1217–1231.
49. Dudley, H. C. 1938. Toxicology of selenium. V. Toxic and vesicant properties of selenium oxychloride. *U. S. Public Health Rept.* **53:**94–98.
50. Dudley, H. C. and J. W. Miller. 1941. Toxicology of selenium. VI. Effects of subacute exposure to hydrogen selenide. *J. Ind. Hyg. Toxicol.* **23:**470–477.
51. Duhamel, B. G. 1913. Histological lesions in colloidal selenium and selenious acid intoxications. *Compt. Rend. Soc. Biol.* **42:**742–744.
52. Ellis, M. M., H. L. Motley, M. D. Ellis and R. O. Jones. 1937. Selenium poisoning in fishes. *Proc. Soc. Exptl. Biol. Med.* **36:**519–522.

53. English, L. L. 1951. Sodium selenate soil treatments for chrysanthemum and carnation pests. *J. Econ. Entomol.* **44**:208–215.
54. Euler, H. von, H. Hasselquist and B. von Euler. 1956. Biologically active trace elements in organic combination. *Arkiv Kemi* **9**:583–590.
55. Filatova, V. S. 1951. Toxicity of selenic anhydride. *Gigiena i Sanit.* **5**:18–23.
56. Filchagin, N. M. 1960. The effect of methionine on the distribution of Se^{75} in the organs and its renal excretion in healthy rats and in the animals with sarcoma-45. *Patol. Fiziol. i Eksperim. Terapiya* **3**:46–49.
57. Fillippi, E. 1913. Pharmacological studies on selenium and its compounds. *Sperimentale* **67**:565.
58. Fimiani, R. 1949. Prothrombin time in chronic experimental selenium poisoning. *Folia Med.* **32**:458–459.
59. Fimiani, R. 1949. Ascorbic acid in blood and urine in chronic experimental selenium poisoning. *Folia Med.* **32**:452–458.
60. Fimiani, R. 1950. Urinary sulfate in chronic experimental selenium poisoning. *Folia Med.* **33**:466–468.
61. Fimiani, R. 1951. Prothrombin time in experimental chronic selenium poisoning. *Folia Med.* **34**:140–143.
62. Fimiani, R. 1951. Bilirubinemia in experimental selenium intoxication. *Folia Med.* **34**:472–479.
63. Fimiani, R. 1952. Urinary sulfur in chronic selenium intoxication. *Folia Med.* **35**:94–101.
64. Fitzhugh, O. G., A. A. Nelson and C. I. Bliss. 1944. The chronic oral toxicity of selenium. *J. Pharmacol. Exptl. Therap.* **80**:289–299.
65. Fox, W. B. 1943. Some insects infesting the "selenium indicator" vetches in Saskatchewan. *Can. Entomologist* **75**:206–207.
66. Franke, K. W. 1934. A new toxicant occurring naturally in certain samples of plant foodstuffs. I. Results obtained in preliminary feeding trials. *J. Nutrition* **8**:597–608.
67. Franke, K. W. 1934. A new toxicant occurring naturally in certain samples of plant foodstuffs. II. The occurrence of the toxicant in the protein fraction. *J. Nutrition* **8**:609–613.
68. Franke, K. W. and V. R. Potter. 1934. A new toxicant occurring naturally in certain samples of plant foodstuffs. III. Hemoglobin levels observed in white rats which were fed toxic wheat. *J. Nutrition* **8**:615–624.
69. Franke, K. W., T. D. Rice, A. G. Johnson and H. W. Schoening. 1934. Report on a preliminary field survey of the so-called "alkali disease" of livestock. *U.S. Dept. Agr. Circ.* **320**:1–9.
70. Franke, K. W. 1935. A new toxicant occurring naturally in certain samples of plant foodstuffs. X. The effect of feeding toxic foodstuffs in varying amounts and for different time periods. *J. Nutrition* **10**:223–231.
71. Franke, K. W. 1935. A new toxicant occurring naturally in certain samples of plant foodstuffs. XI. The effect of feeding toxic and control foodstuffs alternately. *J. Nutrition* **10**:233–239.
72. Franke, K. W. and V. R. Potter. 1935. A new toxicant occurring naturally in certain samples of plant foodstuffs. IX. Toxic effects of orally ingested selenium. *J. Nutrition* **10**:213–221.
73. Franke, K. W. and W. C. Tully. 1935. A new toxicant occurring naturally in certain samples of plant foodstuffs. V. Low hatchability due to deformities in chicks. *Poultry Sci.* **14**:273–279.
74. Franke, K. W. and A. L. Moxon. 1936. A comparison of the minimum fatal doses of selenium, tellurium, arsenic, and vanadium. *J. Pharmacol. Exptl. Therap.* **58**:454–459.

75. Franke, K. W., A. L. Moxon, W. E. Poley and W. C. Tully. 1936. A new toxicant occurring naturally in certain samples of plant foodstuffs. XII. Monstrosities produced by the injection of selenium salts into hen's eggs. *Anat. Record* **65**:15–22.
76. Franke, K. W. and V. R. Potter. 1936. A new toxicant occurring naturally in certain samples of plant foodstuffs. XIII. The ability of rats to discriminate between diets of varying degrees of toxicity. *Science* **83**:330–332.
77. Franke, K. W. and A. L. Moxon. 1937. The toxicity of orally ingested arsenic, selenium, tellurium, vanadium and molybdenum. *J. Pharmacol. Exptl. Therap.* **61**:89–102.
78. Franke, K. W. and E. P. Painter. 1938. A study of the toxicity and selenium content of seleniferous diets, with statistical consideration. *Cereal Chem.* **15**: 1–24.
78a. Ganther, H. E. and C. A. Baumann. 1962. Selenium metabolism. I. Effects of diet, arsenic, and cadmium. *J. Nutrition* **77**:210–216.
78b. Ganther, H. E. and C. A. Baumann. 1962. Selenium metabolism. II. Modifying effects of sulfate. *J. Nutrition* **77**:408–414.
79. Garman, P. 1950. Parathion-resistant red spiders. *J. Econ. Entomol.* **43**:53–56.
80. Giubileo, M. and R. R. Pollini. 1956. Selenium Physiopathology and clinical data of its intoxication. *Med. Lavoro.* **47**:328–339.
81. Gnadinger, C. B. 1933. Selenium. Insecticide material for controlling red spider. *Ind. Eng. Chem.* **25**:633–637.
82. Gonzalez, C. A. 1943. El problema de las selenizaciones en el estado de Guanajuato. *Fitofilo* **2**:31–69.
83. Gortner, R. A., Jr. and H. B. Lewis. 1939. The retention and excretion of selenium after the administration of sodium selenite to white rats. *J. Pharmacol. Exptl. Therap.* **67**:358–364.
84. Gortner, R. A., Jr. 1940. Chronic selenium poisoning of rats as influenced by dietary protein. *J. Nutrition* **19**:105–112.
85. Gruenwald, P. 1958. Malformations caused by necrosis in the embryo. Illustrated by the effect of selenium compounds on chick embryos. *Am. J. Pathol.* **34**: 77–103.
86. Gusberg, S. B., P. Zamecnik and J. C. Aub. 1941. The distribution of injected organic diselenides in tissues of tumor-bearing animals. *J. Pharmacol. Exptl. Therap.* **71**:239–245.
87. Hadjimarkos, D. M., C. W. Bonhorst and J. J. Mattice. 1959. The selenium concentration in placental tissue and fetal cord blood. *J. Pediat.* **54**:296–298.
88. Hall, R. H., S. Laskin, P. Frank, E. A. Maynard and H. C. Hodge. 1951. Preliminary observations on toxicity of elemental selenium. *Arch. Ind. Hyg. Occupational Med.* **4**:458–464.
89. Halverson, A. W., D. F. Petersen and H. L. Klug. 1951. Fractionation of the "selenium protective factor" in flaxseed. *Proc. South Dakota Acad. Sci.* **30**: 97–102.
90. Halverson, A. W. and C. M. Hendrick. 1955. Negative relation to the selenium protective factor and anti-vitamin B_6 principle of linseed meal. *Proc. South Dakota Acad. Sci.* **33**:95–97.
91. Halverson, A. W., C. M. Hendrick and O. E. Olson. 1955. Observations on the protective effect of linseed oil meal and some extracts against chronic selenium poisoning in rats. *J. Nutrition* **56**:51–60.
92. Halverson, A. W. and K. J. Monty. 1960. An effect of dietary sulfate on selenium poisoning in the rat. *J. Nutrition* **70**:100–102.
92a. Halverson, A. W., P. L. Guss, and O. E. Olson. 1962. Effect of sulfur salts on selenium poisoning in the rat. *J. Nutrition* **77**:459–464.

93. Harshfield, R. D. and H. L. Klug. 1949. The effect of British Anti-Lewisite on selenium toxicity in rats. *Proc. South Dakota Acad. Sci.* **28**:21–27.
94. Heinrich, M. A., Jr. and F. E. Kelsey. 1955. Studies on selenium metabolism: The distribution of selenium in the tissues of the mouse. *J. Pharmacol. Exptl. Therap.* **114**:28–32.
95. Heinrich, M. A. and D. M. MacCanon. 1960. Some effects of sodium selenite on the cardiovascular system. *Toxicol. Appl. Pharmacol.* **2**:33–43.
96. Heinrich, M. A. and D. M. MacCanon. 1961. Respiratory responses to sodium selenite. *Toxicol. Appl. Pharmacol.* **3**:174–181.
96a. Heinrich, M. A., Jr. 1963. Effects of sodium selenite on several blood components. *Toxicol. Appl. Pharmacol.* **5**:267–271.
97. Hendrick, C. M., H. L. Klug and O. E. Olson. 1953. Effect of 3-nitro, 4-hydroxyphenylarsonic acid and arsanilic acid on selenium poisoning in the rat. *J. Nutrition* **51**:131–137.
98. Hendrick, C. M. and O. E. Olson. 1953. The effect of sodium methyl arsonate and calcium methyl arsonate on chronic selenium toxicity in the rat. *Proc. South Dakota Acad. Sci.* **32**:68–71.
99. Hilz, H. and F. Lipmann. 1955. The enzymatic activation of sulfate. *Proc. Natl. Acad. Sci. U.S.* **41**:880–890.
100. Hofmeister, F. 1893–1894. Über Methylirung im Thierkorper. *Arch. Exptl. Pathol. u. Pharmakol. Naunyn-Schmiedeberg's* **33**:198.
101. Horn, M. J., E. M. Nelson and D. B. Jones. 1936. Studies on toxic wheat grown on soils containing selenium. *Cereal Chem.* **13**:126–139.
102. Hoskins, W. M., A. M. Boyce and J. F. Lamiman. 1938. The use of selenium in sprays for the control of mites on citrus and grapes. *Hilgardia* **12**:115–175.
103. Hoskins, W. M. 1949. Deposit and residue of recent insecticides resulting from various control practices in California. *J. Econ. Entomol.* **42**:966–973.
104. Hurd-Karrer, A. M. and M. H. Kennedy. 1936. Inhibiting effect of sulphur in selenized soil on toxicity of wheat to rats. *J. Agr. Res.* **52**:933–942.
105. Hurd-Karrer, A. M. and F. W. Poos. 1936. Toxicity of selenium-containing plants to aphids. *Science* **84**:252.
106. Ishihama, K. and S. Motobashi. 1948. Chemical control of wheat blight. *Noyaku* **2**:27–32.
107. Jaffe, J. J. and H. G. Mautner. 1960. A comparison of the biological properties of 6-selenopurine, 6-selenopurine ribonucleoside and 6-mercaptopurine in mice. *Cancer Res.* **20**:381–386.
108. Jones, C. O. 1909. The physiological effects of selenium compounds with relation to their action on glycogen and sugar derivatives in the tissues. *Biochem. J.* **4**:405–419.
108a. Jones, G. B. and K. O. Godwin. 1962. Distribution of radioactive selenium in mice. *Nature* **196**:1294–1296.
109. Kamstra, L. D. and C. W. Bonhorst. 1953. Effect of arsenic on the expiration of volatile selenium compounds by rats. *Proc. South Dakota Acad. Sci.* **32**:72–74.
110. Kando, S. 1935. Pharmacological studies on aromatic selenium compounds. *Japan. J. Med. Sci. IV.* **9**:29–58.
111. Kesztyus, L. and M. Kiese. 1943. *Klin. Wochschr.* **22**:746. Cited in McConnell and Martin (*194*).
112. Kiplinger, D. C. and G. Fuller. 1946. Selenium studies with some flowering greenhouse plants. *Proc. Am. Soc. Hort. Sci.* **47**:451–462.
113. Klug, H. L. and R. H. Harshfield. 1949. Methionine and selenium toxicity in rats. *Proc. South Dakota Acad. Sci.* **28**:99–102.

114. Klug, H. L., D. F. Petersen and A. L. Moxon. 1949. The toxicity of selenium analogues of cystine and methionine. *Proc. South Dakota Acad. Sci.* **28**:117–120.

115. Klug, H. L., G. P. Lampson and A. L. Moxon. 1950. The distribution of selenium and arsenic in the body tissues of rats fed selenium, arsenic, and selenium plus arsenic. *Proc. South Dakota Acad. Sci.* **29**:57–65.

116. Klug, H. L., A. L. Moxon and G. P. Lampson. 1950. Glutathione and ascorbic acid values in selenium poisoning. *Proc. South Dakota Acad. Sci.* **29**:16–29.

117. Klug, H. L., A. L. Moxon and D. F. Petersen. 1950. The effect of selenium, cystine and low protein diets on rat tissue glutathione and ascorbic acid levels. *Proc. South Dakota Acad. Sci.* **29**:38–44.

118. Klug, H. L., A. L. Moxon, D. F. Petersen and V. R. Potter. 1950. The *in vivo* inhibition of succinic dehydrogenase by selenium and its release by arsenic. *Arch. Biochem.* **28**:253–259.

119. Klug, H. L., R. D. Harshfield, R. M. Pengra and A. L. Moxon. 1952. Methionine and selenium toxicity. *J. Nutrition* **48**:409–420.

120. Klug, H. L., A. L. Moxon, D. F. Petersen and E. P. Painter. 1953. Inhibition of rat liver succinic dehydrogenase by selenuium compounds. *J. Pharmacol. Exptl. Therap.* **108**:437–441.

121. Klug, H. L. and C. M. Hendrick. 1954. Selenium and lung tumors. *Proc. South Dakota Acad. Sci.* **33**:87–89.

122. Knight, S. H. and O. A. Beath. 1937. The occurrence of selenium and seleniferous vegetation in Wyoming. *Wyoming Agr. Expt. Sta. Bull. No.* **221**:3–64.

123. Knott, S. G., C. W. R. McCray and W. T. K. Hall. 1958. Selenium poisoning in horses in North Queensland. *Queensland J. Agr. Sci.* **15**:43–58.

124. Landauer, W. 1940. Studies on the creeper fowl. XIII. The effect of selenium and the asymmetry of selenium induced malformations. *J. Exptl. Zool.* **83**: 431–443.

125. Lardy, H. A. and A. L. Moxon. 1942. The ascorbic acid content of the livers of selenized rats and chicks. *Proc. South Dakota Acad. Sci.* **22**:39.

126. Laszt, L. 1951. Die Wirkung von Natriumselenit bei alloxandiabetischen Ratten. *Schweiz. Med. Wochschr.* **81**:65–68.

127. Leitis, E. and O. E. Olson. 1956. Failure of iron oxide to protect against selenium poisoning. *Proc. South Dakota Acad. Sci.* **35**:193–195.

128. Leitis, E., I. S. Palmer and O. E. Olson. 1956. Various organic arsenicals in the prevention of selenium poisoning. *Proc. South Dakota Acad. Sci.* **35**: 189–192.

129. Leonard, R. O. and R. H. Burns. 1955. A preliminary study of selenized wool. *J. Animal Sci.* **14**:446–457.

130. Leukel, R. W. 1940. Selenized soil as a control for aphids and red spiders on sorghum in the greenhouse. *Phytopathology* **30**:374–376.

131. Levine, V. E. and R. A. Flaherty. 1926. Hypoglycemia induced by sodium selenite. *Proc. Soc. Exptl. Biol. Med.* **23**:251.

132. Lewis, H. B., J. Schultz and R. A. Gortner, Jr. 1940. Dietary protein and the toxicity of sodium selenite in the white rat. *J. Pharmacol. Exptl. Therap.* **68**: 292–299.

133. Lillie, R. D. and M. I. Smith. 1940. Histogenesis of hepatic cirrhosis in chronic food selenosis. *Am. J. Pathol.* **16**:223–228.

134. Lipp, C. C. 1922. Alkali disease. *Vet. Alumni Quart. Ohio State Univ.* **10**: 54–55.

135. Lougee, F. M. and B. S. Hopkins. 1925. Selenium compounds as spray materials. *J. Ind. Eng. Chem.* **17**:456–459.

136. Maag, D. D., J. S. Orsborn and J. R. Clopton. 1960. The effect of sodium selenite on cattle. *Am. J. Vet. Res.* **21**:1049–1053.
137. Madison, T. C. 1860. Sanitary report—Fort Randall. Written Sept. 1857. *In* Coolidge, R. H., Statistical report on the sickness and mortality in the Army of the United States. January, 1855 to January, 1860. *U.S. Congr. 36th, 1st Sess., Senate Exch. Doc.* **52**:37–41.
138. Mahalanobis, S. K. and R. N. Roy. 1954. Effect of selenium on haemoglobin level. *Indian J. Physiol. Allied Sci.* **8**:57–60.
139. Mann, M. D., Jr. 1954. A nematode disease of ferns. *Am. Fern J.* **44**:86–87.
140. Marsh, C. D. and G. C. Roe. 1921. The "alkali disease" of livestock in the Pecos Valley. *U.S. Dept. Agr. Circ.* **180**:1–8.
141. Martin, A. L. 1936. Toxicity of selenium to plants and animals. *Am. J. Botany* **23**:471–483.
142. Mautner, H. G., W. D. Kumler, Y. Okano and R. Pratt. 1956. Anti-fungal activity of some substituted selenosemicarbazones and related compounds. *Antibiotics & Chemotherapy* **6**:51–55.
143. Mautner, H. G. and J. J. Jaffe. 1958. The activity of 6-selenopurine and related compounds against some experimental mouse tumors. *Cancer Res.* **18**: 294–298.
144. McConnell, K. P. 1941. Distribution and excretion studies in the rat after a single subtoxic subcutaneous injection of sodium selenate containing radioselenium. *J. Biol. Chem.* **141**:427–437.
145. McConnell, K. P. 1942. Respiratory excretion of selenium studied with the radioactive isotope. *J. Biol. Chem.* **145**:55–60.
146. McConnell, K. P. 1948. Passage of selenium through the mammary glands of the white rat and the distribution of selenium in the milk proteins after subcutaneous injection of sodium selenate. *J. Biol. Chem.* **173**:653–657.
147. McConnell, K. P. and B. J. Cooper. 1950. Distribution of selenium in serum proteins and red blood cells after subcutaneous injection of sodium selenate containing radioselenium. *J. Biol. Chem.* **183**:459–466.
148. McConnell, K. P. 1952. Selenium toxicity in rats as influenced by choline, betaine and methionine. *Federation Proc.* **11**:255–256.
149. McConnell, K. P. and R. G. Martin. 1952. Biliary excretion of selenium in the dog after administration of sodium selenate containing radioselenium. *J. Biol. Chem.* **194**:183–190.
150. McConnell, K. P. and O. W. Portman. 1952. Toxicity of dimethyl selenide in the rat and mouse. *Proc. Soc. Exptl. Biol. Med.* **79**:230–231.
151. McConnell, K. P. and O. W. Portman. 1952. Excretion of dimethyl selenide by the rat. *J. Biol. Chem.* **195**:277–282.
152. McConnell, K. P. 1953. Elimination of administered selenium in pancreatic juice of dogs. *Ohio Valley section Soc. of Exptl. Biol. Med., Cincinnati, Ohio.*
153. McConnell, K. P. and E. J. Van Loon. 1955. Distribution of Se^{75} in serum proteins as determined by paper electrophoresis. *J. Biol. Chem.* **212**:747–750.
154. McConnell, K. P. and C. H. Wabnitz. 1957. Studies on the fixation of radioselenium in proteins. *J. Biol. Chem.* **226**:765–766.
155. McConnell, K. P. 1959. Selenium-75-binding in dog leucocytes. *Texas Repts. Biol. Med.* **17**:120–122.
156. McConnell, K. P. 1959. Incorporation of Se-75 into cytochrome-c. *Federation Proc.* **18**:285.
157. McConnell, K. P., A. E. Kreamer and D. M. Roth. 1959. Presence of $selenium^{75}$ in the mercapturic acid fraction of dog urine. *J. Biol. Chem.* **234**:2932–2934.
158. McConnell, K. P., D. M. Roth and R. D. Dallam. 1959. Partition of selenium-75 into the intracellular particulate matter of rat liver. *Nature* **183**:183–184.

159. McConnell, K. P. and A. E. Kreamer. 1960. Incorporation of selenium-75 into dog hair. *Proc. Soc. Exptl. Biol. Med.* **105**:170–173.

160. McConnell, K. P., C. H. Wabnitz and D. M. Roth. 1960. Time-distribution studies of selenium-75 in dog serum proteins. *Texas Repts. Biol. Med.* **18**: 438–445.

161. McConnell, K. P. and D. M. Roth. 1961. Selenium in rabbit skeletal muscle myosin. *Federation Proc.* **20**:2990.

161a. McConnell, K. P. and R. S. Levy. 1962. Presence of selenium-75 in lipoproteins. *Nature* **195**:775–776.

161b. McConnell, K. P. and D. M. Roth. 1963. ATP dependent incorporation of selenium into rat liver ribosomes. *Federation Proc.* **22**:234.

162. Meister, A. 1957. "Biochemistry of Amino Acids," pp. 202–213. Academic Press, New York.

163. Miller, J. T. and H. G. Byers. 1935. A selenium spring. *Ind. Eng. Chem., News Ed.* **13**:456.

164. Miller, M. R. 1926. Alkali poisoning of livestock. *Vet. Med.* **21**:268–273.

165. Miller, W. T. and H. W. Schoening. 1938. Toxicity of selenium fed to swine in the form of sodium selenite. *J. Agr. Res.* **56**:831–842.

166. Miller, W. T. and K. T. Williams. 1940. Minimum lethal dose of selenium as sodium selenite for horses, mules, cattle and swine. *J. Agr. Res.* **60**:163–173.

167. Miller, W. T. and K. T. Williams. 1940. Effect of feeding repeated small doses of selenium as sodium selenite to equines. *J. Agr. Res.* **61**:353–368.

168. Minyard, J. A., C. A. Dinkel and O. E. Olson. 1960. The effectiveness of arsanilic acid in counteracting selenium poisoning in beef cattle. *J. Animal Sci.* **19**:260–264.

169. Miura, H. 1958. Selenium poisoning. I. Microdetermination of selenium in biological materials. II. Distribution of inorganic selenium in animal tissues. III. Fate of inorganic selenium in mammals. *Kokumin Eisei* **27**:331–351.

170. Modica, O. 1897. Azione cronica del selenio. *Arch. Farm. et Terap.* (Palermo) **5**:61.

171. Moore, J. B., C. B. Gnadinger, R. W. Coulter and C. C. Fox. 1941. Control of Pacific mite and European red mite on apples. *J. Econ. Entomol.* **34**:111–116.

172. Moxon, A. L. 1937. Alkali disease or selenium poisoning. *South Dakota Agr. Expt. Sta. Bull.* **311**:1–91.

173. Moxon, A. L. 1938. The effect of arsenic on the toxicity of seleniferous grains. *Science* **88**:81.

174. Moxon, A. L., H. D. Anderson and E. P. Painter. 1938. The toxicity of some organic selenium compounds. *J. Pharmacol. Exptl. Therap.* **63**:357–368.

175. Moxon, A. L. and W. E. Poley. 1938. The relation of selenium content of grains in the ration to the selenium content of poultry carcass and eggs. *Poultry Sci.* **17**:77–80.

176. Moxon, A. L. 1939. The selenium content of grasshoppers found feeding on seleniferous vegetation. *Proc. South Dakota Acad. Sci.* **19**:69–70.

177. Moxon, A. L. and K. P. DuBois. 1939. The influence of arsenic and certain other elements on the toxicity of seleniferous grains. *J. Nutrition* **18**:447–457.

178. Moxon, A. L. 1940. Toxicity of selenium-cystine and some other organic selenium compounds. *J. Am. Pharm. Assoc., Sci. Ed.* **29**:249–251.

179. Moxon, A. L. and O. E. Olson. 1940. Can selenium poisoning of livestock be checked? *South Dakota Agr. Expt. Sta. Rept.* **53**:42–44.

180. Moxon, A. L., A. E. Schaefer, H. A. Lardy, K. P. DuBois and O. E. Olson. 1940. Increasing the rate of excretion of selenium from selenized animals by the administration of *p*-bromobenzene. *J. Biol. Chem.* **132**:785–786.

181. Moxon, A. L. 1941. Influence of arsenic on selenium poisoning in hogs. *Proc. South Dakota Acad. Sci.* **21**:34–36.

182. Moxon, A. L., K. P. DuBois and R. L. Potter. 1941. The toxicity of optically inactive *d*- and *l*-selenium-cystine. *J. Pharmacol. Exptl. Therap.* **72**:184–195.

183. Moxon, A. L. and M. A. Rhian. 1943. Selenium poisoning. *Physiol. Rev.* **23**: 305–337.

184. Moxon, A. L., M. A. Rhian, H. D. Anderson and O. E. Olson. 1944. Growth of steers on seleniferous range. *J. Animal Sci.* **3**:299–309.

185. Moxon, A. L. and W. O. Wilson. 1944. Selenium-arsenic antagonism in poultry. *Poultry Sci.* **23**:149–151.

186. Moxon, A. L., C. R. Paynter and A. W. Halverson. 1945. Effect of route of administration on detoxification of selenium by arsenic. *J. Pharmacol. Exptl. Therap.* **84**:115–119.

187. Moxon, A. L., C. W. Jensen and C. R. Paynter. 1947. The influence of germanium, gallium, antimony and some organic arsenicals on the toxicity of selenium. *Proc. South Dakota Acad. Sci.* **26**:21–26.

188. Muehlberger, C. W. and H. H. Schrenk. 1928. The effect of the state of oxidation on the toxicity of certain elements. *J. Pharmacol. Exptl. Therap.* **33**:270.

189. Munsell, H. E., G. M. DeVaney and M. H. Kennedy. 1936. Toxicity of food containing selenium as shown by its effect on the rat. *U.S. Dept. Agr. Tech. Bull. No.* **534**:1–25.

190. Neiswander, C. R. and V. H. Morris. 1940. Introduction of selenium into plant tissues as a toxicant for insects and mites. *J. Econ. Entomol.* **33**:517–525.

191. Nelson, A. A., O. G. Fitzhugh and H. O. Calvery. 1943. Liver tumors following cirrhosis caused by selenium in rats. *Cancer Res.* **3**:230–236.

192. Newton, J. H. and G. M. List. 1949. Codling moth and mite control in 1948. *J. Econ. Entomol.* **42**:346–348.

193. Olson, O. E. and A. W. Halverson. 1954. Effect of linseed oil meal and arsenicals on selenium poisoning in the rat. *Proc. South Dakota Acad. Sci.* **33**:90–94.

194. Olson, O. E., C. W. Carlson and E. Leitis. 1958. Methionine and related compounds and selenium poisoning. *South Dakota Agr. Expt. Sta. Tech. Bull. No.* **20**:1–15.

195. Orstadius, K. 1960. Toxicity of a single subcutaneous dose of sodium selenite in pigs. *Nature* **188**:1117.

196. Painter, E. P. and K. W. Franke. 1935. Selenium in proteins from toxic foodstuffs. III. The removal of selenium from toxic protein hydrolysates. *J. Biol. Chem.* **111**:643–651.

197. Painter, E. P. 1941. The chemistry and toxicity of selenium compounds, with special reference to the selenium problem. *Chem. Rev.* **28**:179–213.

198. Pellegrino, F. and G. Gaizzone. 1928. Action of selenium, tellurium, and cobalt on carbohydrate metabolism. *Arch. Farmacol. Sper.* **45**:75.

199. Peters, A. T. 1904. A fungus disease in corn. *Nebraska Agr. Expt. Sta., Ann. Rept.* **17**:13–22.

200. Petersen, D. F., H. L. Klug, R. D. Harshfield and A. L. Moxon. 1950. The effect of arsenic on selenium metabolism in rats. *Proc. South Dakota Acad. Sci.* **29**:123–127.

201. Petersen, D. F. and R. M. Pengra. 1950. The effect of A. P. F. supplementation of some protein feeds on selenium toxicity in the rat. *Proc. South Dakota Acad. Sci.* **29**:70–74.

202. Petersen, D. F., H. L. Klug and R. D. Harshfield. 1951. Expiration of volatile selenium compounds from selenized rats. *Proc. South Dakota Acad. Sci.* **30**: 73–78.

203. Petersen, D. F. and A. L. Moxon. 1951. Preliminary studies on the effect of ACTH in selenium intoxication. *Proc. South Dakota Acad. Sci.* **30**:126.

203a. Peterson, P. J. and D. J. Spedding. 1963. The excretion by sheep of ^{75}selenium incorporated into red clover (*Trifolium pratense* L.): The chemical nature of the excreted selenium and its uptake by three plant species. *N. Zealand J. Agr. Res.* **6**:13–23.

204. Phillis, E. and T. G. Mason. 1938. Selenization of cotton under field conditions in Trinidad. *Empire Cotton Growing Rev.* **15**:290.

205. Poley, W. E., A. L. Moxon and K. W. Franke. 1937. Further studies of the effects of selenium poisoning on hatchability. *Poultry Sci.* **16**:219–225.

206. Poley, W. E. and A. L. Moxon. 1938. Tolerance levels of seleniferous grains in laying rations. *Poultry Sci.* **17**:72–76.

207. Poley, W. E., W. O. Wilson, A. L. Moxon and J. B. Taylor. 1941. The effect of selenized grains on the rate of growth in chicks. *Poultry Sci.* **20**:171–179.

208. Potter, R. L., K. P. DuBois and A. L. Moxon. 1939. A comparative study of liver glycogen values of control selenium and selenium-arsenic rats. *Proc. South Dakota Acad. Sci.* **19**:99–106.

209. Rhian, M. and A. L. Moxon. 1943. Chronic selenium poisoning in dogs and its prevention by arsenic. *J. Pharmacol. Exptl. Therap.* **78**:249–264.

210. Rigdon, R. H., G. Crass and K. P. McConnell. 1953. Inhibition of maturation of duck erythrocytes by sodium selenite. *A.M.A. Arch. Pathol.* **56**:374–385.

211. Rigdon, R. H., J. R. Couch, D. Brashear and R. Taher Qureshi. 1955. Effect of vitamin B_{12} on selenium poisoning in the rat. *A.M.A. Arch. Pathol.* **59**:66–72.

212. Robinson, W. O. 1933. Determination of selenium in wheat and soils. *J. Assoc. Offic. Agr. Chem.* **16**:423–424.

213. Romanowski, R. D., R. L. Larson, A. W. Halverson and O. E. Olson. 1958. Observations on the protective effect of dietary fat against selenium poisoning in rats. *Proc. South Dakota Acad. Sci.* **37**:76–80.

214. Rosenfeld, I. and O. A. Beath. 1945. The elimination and distribution of selenium in the tissues in experimental selenium poisoning. *J. Nutrition* **30**:443–449.

215. Rosenfeld I. and O. A. Beath. 1946. The influence of protein diets on selenium poisoning. I. *Am. J. Vet. Res.* **7**:52–56.

216. Rosenfeld, I. and O. A. Beath. 1946. The influence of protein diets on selenium poisoning, II. The chemical changes in the tissues following selenium administration. *Am. J. Vet. Res.* **7**:57–61.

217. Rosenfeld, I. and O. A. Beath. 1946. Pathology of selenium poisoning. *Wyoming Agr. Expt. Sta. Bull. No.* **275**:1–27.

218. Rosenfeld, I. and O. A. Beath. 1947. Congenital malformations of eyes of sheep. *J. Agr. Res.* **75**:93–103.

219. Rosenfeld, I. and O. A. Beath. 1947. The influence of various substances on chronic selenium poisoning. *J. Pharmacol. Exptl. Therap.* **91**:218–223.

220. Rosenfeld, I. and O. A. Beath. 1948. Experimentally developed telangiectasis and sawdust liver lesions in rats. *J. Am. Vet. Med. Assoc.* **112**:386–389.

221. Rosenfeld, I. and O. A. Beath. 1953. Distribution of P^{31} and P^{32} in the tissues of normal animals and chronic selenosis. *Nuclear Sci. Abstr.* **7**:61–62.

222. Rosenfeld, I. and O. A. Beath. 1954. Effect of selenium on reproduction in rats. *Proc. Soc. Exptl. Biol. Med.* **87**:295–297.

223. Rosenfeld, I. and H. F. Eppson. 1957. Effect of choline deficiency on chronic selenium poisoning of rats. *Am. J. Vet. Res.* **18**:693–697.

224. Rosenfeld, I. 1960. Effect of selenium on methionine formation *in vivo* and *in vitro*. *Federation Proc.* **19** (Pt. 1):A-4.

225. Rosenfeld, I. 1961. Biosynthesis of seleno-compounds from inorganic selenium by the sheep. *Federation Proc.* **20** (Pt. 1): 10.

226. Rosenfeld, I. 1962. Biosynthesis of seleno-compounds from inorganic selenium by sheep. *Proc. Soc. Exptl. Biol. Med.* **111**:670–673.

227. Rosenfeld, I. 1962. Effect of selenium on methionine formation *in vivo* and *in vitro*. *Proc. Soc. Exptl. Biol. Med.* **109**:624–628.

228. Rosenfeld, I. 1964. Metabolic effects and metabolism of selenium in animals. *Wyoming Agr. Expt. Sta. Bull.* **414**:1–64.

229. Roth, D. M. and K. P. McConnell. 1960. Selenium-75 in the intracellular particulate matter of rat liver. *Federation Proc.* **19**:132.

230. Russell, L. B. and W. L. Russell. 1954. An analysis of the changing radiation response of the developing mouse embryo. *J. Cellular Comp. Physiol.* **43**, Suppl. 1:103–150.

231. Sakurayama, H. 1960. Studies on the selenium poisoning. 7. Experimental studies on rearing fishes, shells and duckweed in selenious acid solution. *Shikoku Igaku Zasshi* **16**:122–127.

232. Sakurayama, H. 1960. Studies on the selenium poisoning. 8. Effects of methionine and bromobenzene upon the excretion of internal selenium. *Shikoku Igaku Zasshi* **16**:128–135.

233. Schneider, H. A. 1936. Selenium in nutrition. *Science* **83**:32–34.

234. Schoening, H. W. 1936. Production of so-called alkali disease in hogs by feeding corn grown in affected areas. *North Am. Veterinarian* **17**:22–28.

235. Schuchardt, P. A., A. W. Halverson and C. O. Claggett. 1955. Occurrence of the selenium protective principle of flax in hull and embryo fractions. *Proc. South Dakota Acad. Sci.* **34**:48–51.

236. Schultz, J. and H. B. Lewis. 1940. The excretion of volatile selenium compounds after the administration of sodium selenite to white rats. *J. Biol. Chem.* **133**:199–207.

237. Seifter, J., W. E. Ehrich, G. Hudyma and G. Mueller. 1946. Thyroid adenomas in rats receiving selenium. *Science* **103**:762.

238. Seifter, J. and W. E. Ehrich. 1948. Goitrogenic compounds: pharmacological and pathological effects. *J. Pharmacol. Exptl. Therap.* **92**:303–314.

239. Sellers, E. A., R. W. You and C. C. Lucas. 1950. Lipotropic agents in liver damage produced by selenium or carbon tetrachloride. *Proc. Soc. Exptl. Biol. Med.* **75**:118–121.

240. Sivjakov, K. I. and H. A. Braun. 1959. The treatment of acute selenium, cadmium and tungsten intoxication in rats with calcium disodium ethylenediaminetetraacetate. *Toxicol. Appl. Pharmacol.* **1**:602–608.

241. Smith, F. F. 1961. Use and limitations of selenium as an insecticide. *U.S. Dept. Agr., Agr. Handbook* **200**:41–45.

242. Smith, M. I., K. W. Franke and B. B. Westfall. 1936. The selenium problem in relation to public health. A preliminary survey to determine the possibility of selenium intoxication in the rural population living on seleniferous soil. *U.S. Public Health Rept.* **51**:1496–1505.

243. Smith, M. I., E. F. Stohlman and R. D. Lillie. 1937. The toxicity and pathology of selenium. *J. Pharmacol. Exptl. Therap.* **60**:449–471.

244. Smith, M. I. and B. B. Westfall. 1937. Further field studies on the selenium problem in relation to public health. *U.S. Public Health Rept.* **52**:1375–1384.

245. Smith, M. I., B. B. Westfall and E. F. Stohlman. 1937. The elimination of selenium and its distribution in the tissues. *U.S. Public Health Rept.* **52:** 1171–1177.
246. Smith, M. I., B. B. Westfall and E. F. Stohlman. 1938. Studies on the fate of selenium in the organism. *U.S. Public Health Rept.* **53:**1199–1216.
247. Smith, M. I. 1939. The influence of diet on the chronic toxicity of selenium. *U.S. Public Health Rept.* **54:**1441–1453.
248. Smith, M. I. and R. D. Lillie. 1940. Part 1. The chronic toxicity of naturally occurring food selenium. *U.S. Public Health Serv., Nat. Inst. Health Bull. No.* **174:**1–13.
249. Smith, M. I. and E. F. Stohlman. 1940. Gastric acidity in chronic selenium poisoning. Part II. *U.S. Public Health Serv., Nat. Inst. Health Bull. No.* **174:** 15–19.
250. Smith, M. I., B. B. Westfall and E. F. Stohlman. 1940. Liver function and bile pigments in experimental chronic selenium poisoning. Part III. *U.S. Public Health Serv., Nat. Inst. Health Bull. No.* **174:**21–44.
251. Smith, M. I. 1941. Chronic endemic selenium poisoning. *J. Am. Med. Assoc.* **116:**562–566.
252. Smith, M. I. and E. F. Stohlman. 1941. Further observations on the influence of dietary protein on the toxicity of selenium. *J. Pharmacol. Exptl. Therap.* **70:**270–278.
253. Svirbely, J. L. 1938. LXI. Vitamin C studies in the rat. The effect of selenium dioxide, sodium selenate and tellurate. *Biochem. J.* **32:**467–473.
254. Tai, T. K. 1956. The influence of certain dietary factors on the growth of rats ingesting synthetic diets containing selenium. *Sheng Li Hsueh Pao* **20:**191–203.
255. Tajiri, T. 1959. Studies on the selenium poisoning. 4. Experimental studies on selenium poisoning in rabbits. *Shikoku Igaku Zasshi* **15:**1680–1692.
256. Tajiri, T. 1959. Studies on the selenium poisoning. 5. Influence of bromobenzene on urinary excretion of selenium. *Shikoku Igaku Zasshi* **15:**1693–1697.
257. Tarjan, A. C. 1950. Investigations of meadow nematodes attacking boxwood, and the therapeutic value of sodium selenate as a control. *Phytopathology* **40:** 1111–1124.
258. Todd, A. T. and H. M. Aldwinckle. 1929. Combination of colloidal lead selenide and radium in treatment of cancer. *Brit. Med. J.* **II:**799–801.
259. Todd, A. T. 1933. Selenide treatment of cancer. *Brit. J. Surgery* **21**(L):619–631.
260. Todd, A. T. 1935. Selenium in the treatment of cancer. *Brit. Med. J.* p. 1293.
261. Todd, A. T., S. Scott and H. Coke. 1935. Discussion on prevention and treatment of metastases in carcinoma mammae. *Proc. Roy. Soc. Med.* **28:**681–694.
262. Trelease, F. F. and H. M. Trelease. 1937. Toxicity to insects and mammals of foods containing selenium. *Am. J. Botany* **24:**448–451.
263. Tucker, J. O. 1960. Preliminary report on selenium toxicity in sheep. *Proc. Am. Coll. Vet. Toxicol.* pp. 41–45.
264. Tully, W. C. and K. W. Franke. 1935. A new toxicant occurring naturally in certain samples of plant foodstuffs. VI. A study of the effect of affected grains on growing chicks. *Poultry Sci.* **14:**280–284.
265. Twomey, A. C. and S. S. Twomey. 1936. Selenium and duck sickness. *Science* **83:**470.
266. Vesce, C. A. 1948. Interpretation of some symptoms in selenium poisoning. *Rass. Med. Ind.* **17:**140–143.
267. Vesce, C. A. 1949. Toxic bone affections and selenium poisoning. *Folia Med. (Naples)* **32:**416–417.

268. Wahlstrom, R. C., L. D. Kamstra and O. E. Olson. 1955. The effect of arsanilic acid and 3-nitro-4-hydroxyphenylarsonic acid on selenium poisoning in the pig. *J. Animal Sci.* **14**:105–110.

269. Wahlstrom, R. C., L. D. Kamstra and O. E. Olson. 1956. Preventing selenium poisoning in growing and fattening pigs. *South Dakota Agr. Expt. Sta. Bull. No.* **456**:1–15.

270. Wahlstrom, R. C., L. D. Kamstra and O. E. Olson. 1956. The effect of organic arsenicals, chlortetracycline and linseed oil meal on selenium poisoning in swine. *J. Animal Sci.* **15**:794–799.

271. Wahlstrom, R. C. and O. E. Olson. 1959. The relation of prenatal and preweaning treatment to the effect of arsanilic acid on selenium poisoning in weanling pigs. *J. Animal Sci.* **18**:578–582.

272. Wahlstrom, R. C. and O. E. Olson. 1959. The effect of selenium on reproduction in swine. *J. Animal Sci.* **18**:141–145.

273. Walker, K. C. 1950. Selenium residue on and in the peel of Washington apples. *Advan. Chem. Ser. No.* **1**:108–111.

274. Von Wasserman, A. V., F. Keysser and M. Wasserman. 1911. Influencing tumors by means of therapeutic agents in the blood stream. Results of chemotherapeutic experiments in tumor animals. *Deut. Med. Wochscr.* **37**:2389–2391.

275. Weisberger, A. S. and L. G. Suhrland. 1956. Studies on analogues or L-cysteine. The effect of selenium cystine on Murphy lymphosarcoma tumor cells in the rat. *Blood* **11**:11–18.

276. Weisberger, A. S. and L. G. Suhrland. 1956. Studies on analogues of L-cysteine and L-cystine. III. The effect of selenium cystine on leukemia. *Blood* **11**:19–30.

277. Westfall, B. B., E. F. Stohlman and M. I. Smith. 1938. The placental transmission of selenium. *J. Pharmacol. Exptl. Therap.* **64**:55–57.

278. Westfall, B. A. 1938. Comparative toxicity of selenium in the presence of various sulfur compounds. Ph.D. dissertation, Univ. of Missouri, Columbia, Missouri.

279. Westfall, B. B. and M. I. Smith. 1940. The distribution of selenium in plasma and liver proteins and its fractionation in tryptic liver digests. *U.S. Public Health Rept.* **55**:1575–1583.

280. Westfall, B. B. and M. I. Smith. 1940. Selenium in the hair as an index of the extent of its deposition in the tissues in chronic poisoning. *U.S. Public Health Serv. Nat. Inst. Health Bull. No.* **174**:45–49.

281. Westfall, B. B. and M. I. Smith. 1941. Further studies on the fate of selenium in the organism. *J. Pharmacol. Exptl. Therap..* **72**:245–251.

282. White, W. B., C. W. Price, A. K. Klein and H. J. Wichmann. 1946. Soil and plant take-up of selenium from spraying orange groves. *J. Assoc. Offic. Agr. Chem.* **29**:349–358.

283. White, H. E. and W. D. Whitcomb. 1946. Sodium selenate for red spider control in Mass. *Proc. Am. Soc. Hort. Sci.* **47**:503–506.

284. Wilson, L. G. 1954. Differentiation and the reaction of rat embryos to radiation. *J. Cellular Comp. Physiol.* **43**:Suppl. 1, 11–38.

285. Wilson, L. G. and R. S. Bandurski. 1956. An enzymatic reaction involving adenosine triphosphate and selenate. *Arch. Biochem. Biophys.* **62**:503–506.

286. Wolfenbarger, D. O. 1950. Red-mite control on avocados and mangos. *J. Econ. Entomol.* **43**:377–380.

287. Wright, C. I. 1941. The effect of sodium selenite on the blood sugar and liver glycogen of rats and rabbits. *U.S. Public Health Rept.* **56**:345–352.

CHAPTER VI

PREVENTION AND CONTROL OF SELENIUM POISONING

It is evident from the preceding chapters that much more research will be needed before the selenium problem is solved. The facts and principles already available point the way to further research and to the development of adequate methods of prevention and control of selenium poisoning. By applying what is now known, much can be accomplished toward reducing losses and depreciation of livestock and possible danger to public health. The following control measures are suggested.

MAPPING OF SELENIFEROUS AREAS

Seleniferous areas that are capable of producing toxic vegetation should be located and mapped. Geological maps showing outcrops of known seleniferous formations serve as guides to such areas. Most states have maps indicating geological formations. Information concerning most of the formations which are seleniferous is given in Chapter II. The distribution of selenium indicator plants and chemical analyses of the various species of plants growing on the soil are important aids.

Because of the great differences in the selenium-absorbing capacity of various plant species, it is essential that the native plants be accurately identified botanically. Soil analyses may prove to be of value if based upon water-soluble selenium, but analyses based upon the total selenium content are unreliable in indicating plant absorption. Both the actual toxicity of the vegetation and the capacity of the soil to produce toxic vegetation need to be considered. If the native forage plants are largely grasses, the vegetation will be relatively nontoxic; but the same soil may be capable of supporting plants with high selenium content such as *Astragalus*, *Stanleya*, section *Oonopsis* of *Haploppapus*, and section *Xylorhiza* of *Machaeranthera*. Suspected areas should be studied further to determine whether or not they produce toxic vegetation.

The maps should indicate the degree of toxicity of the vegetation on the various areas. This is determined not only by the selenium content of the plants, but also by their frequency of occurrence or density of stand. Areas capable of producing toxic wheat and other farm crops, as well as native range plants, should be indicated.

In addition to reconnaissance maps of large areas, detailed maps of individual farms and ranches would be profitable in many cases since it has been found that the fencing off of a few acres on a farm may eliminate the source of considerable livestock injury. The detailed maps of ranches should show safe routes to be followed in trailing livestock from one pasture or range to another.

RECOGNITION OF POISONOUS RANGE PLANTS

As a basis for proper range management, ranchers should become acquainted with the most dangerous species of seleniferous weeds. This would be a great aid in making plans for the grazing and trailing of livestock. The most seleniferous plants include species of *Astragalus, Machaeranthera, Haplopappus,* and *Stanleya.* It would be a relatively easy matter for ranchers to learn to recognize the rather small number of highly seleniferous plants—in most cases not more than about a dozen—that occur in any locality. The photographs, drawings, and descriptions in Chapter III of this book should be helpful, and the state agricultural experiment stations will identify specimens of suspected plants.

On ranges bearing the primary selenium accumulators, the selenium hazard is usually accentuated by the occurrence of several of the more palatable forage plants carrying toxic amounts of selenium. Plants of this type include *Aster* spp., *Atriplex* spp. (saltbush), *Comandra pallida, Castilleja* spp. (paintbrush), *Gutierrezia sarothrae* (snakeweed), *Machaeranthera ramosa,* and *Machaeranthera grindelioides* (Nutt.) Shinners.

LAND MANAGEMENT

Areas known to produce toxic grain should be immediately withdrawn from cultivation of all food plants. A toxic area, a tract of 100,000 acres in South Dakota, has been withdrawn from wheat cultivation by the government. The land purchased by the government had been partly fenced farm and partly open range. A number of the farmers from the purchased land had no funds to carry out soil conservation and, subsequently, wind erosion was rampant (2).

Land management, consisting of plowing and seeding the eroded land with crested wheat grass or other adapted forage, was instituted by the government. A study of proper grazing practices was instituted. The application of sea salts, sulfates, or chlorides did not appear to be of any practical importance as a selenium control measure (5). Plant populations were not indicated, but the selenium accumulation in primary and secondary plants is presumably lower than before the present management was started.

TOLERANCE LIMITS

Tolerance limits of selenium in food for animals should be established and enforced by government inspection. Animals should not be fed toxic hay or grain. Selenium-containing grain may be blended wih sufficient selenium-free feeds to reduce the concentration to the tolerance level. Some seleniferous grains lose a considerable fraction of their selenium if stored for several years. Foodstuffs containing quantities of selenium greater than the established tolerance limits should be diverted to non-food utilization. Means of safe-guarding the public health within the seleniferous areas should be given special consideration.

SELECTION OF ANIMALS

Ranchers should be advised regarding the kinds of livestock best adapted to particular ranges.

GRAZING CONTROL

Over-grazing should be prevented since scarcity of good forage tends to force animals to feed on the highly seleniferous vegetation. Stock raising in some seleniferous areas seems practicable if the ranges are not over-grazed. The native forage grasses contain relatively small amounts of selenium.

Shearing pens and lambing sheds should be located so as to avoid holding sheep for several days on seleniferous ranges of known potential danger. Since sheep are restricted to a limited area during shearing and lambing, the safe forages are soon grazed off, leaving only the less desirable plants.

TRAILING LIVESTOCK

Special care should be given the selection of safe routes for the trailing of livestock from one range to another. Cattle and sheep brought in from a nonseleniferous locality may need special attention during the period of adjustment. The most serious losses of sheep from acute selenium poisoning are likely to occur during trailing and pasturing overnight in regions infested with highly seleniferous weeds and forages.

Choice of routes and places for bedding down should be based on a knowledge of the density and toxicity of the seleniferous vegetation. Since the toxicity of seleniferous plants is known to be correlated with the kind of soil in which they grow, it is important to know the sequence of geological formations along trails. For example, sheep trailed over outcrops of the Niobrara or Steele formations are much more likely to be poisoned than those trailed over the Dakota or Frontier formations. Due consideration should be given annual and seasonal variations. Owing to climatic conditions in some years, many of the usual palatable plants may be low in certain foodstuffs or inferior in quality. Grazing animals may then feed upon perennial seleniferous weeds which supply necessary foodstuffs or minerals not found in other forages.

USE OF HERBICIDES

Eradication of highly seleniferous native range plants and reseeding with forages that are not selenium accumulators may be practicable in some regions. The native seleniferous plants are poisonous themselves and they convert selenium into soluble forms that may be absorbed by desirable range plants. Selective herbicides for the elimination of weeds in Wyoming of several *Astragalus* species, *Artemisia tridentata,* and other weeds were tested. Effective control was obtained by 2,4-D. Other herbicides may be used for the elimination of secondary selenium accumulators or weeds which may absorb soluble selenium from the soil (*1, 4*). *Machaeranthera glabriuscula* (previously called *Xylorhiza parryi,* woody aster), *A. bisulcatus* (two-grooved milk vetch), and *A. pectinatus* (narrow-leafed vetch) were eradicated by treatment with 2,4-D, 2,4,5-T, or 2,4-D ester if the plants were treated at the bud stage or if treatment was repeated for 2 successive years. *M. glabriuscula* (woody aster) is very susceptible to 2,4-D or 2,4,5-T if treated in early spring when the plants are in full bloom (*3*).

Although the above authors do not comment on the probable soil accumulation of selenium from selenium indicator plants, it must be pointed out that decaying and dead plants by leaching would increase the selenium content of the soil. Therefore, it is important that eradication of selenium accumulators by herbicides be followed by manual or mechanical removal of the plants before the soil becomes toxic for all vegetation. The elimination of seleniferous weeds or destruction by means of selective herbicides may require several years because seeds in the soil continue to sprout.

IRRIGATION

Drainage may serve to reduce the available selenium content of irrigated soils. However, only a fraction of the total seleniferous area would be practical to irrigate, since irrigation would depend on the drainage of the soil. Other remedial measures applicable to field conditions should be sought. The application of sulfur or sulfate, which has been suggested, seems neither effective nor practicable. Also, before extensive irrigation is started the soil must be free of seleniferous plants and seeds; if not, irrigation may decrease, rather than increase, the usefulness of the irrigated area (Beath, personal communication from Geological Survey). Unless these control measures are instituted, the soil may become permanently toxic.

SELECTION OF CROPS

Some forage plants, such as grasses and perhaps alfalfa, may safely be grown on low seleniferous soils.

CROPS FOR INDUSTRIAL USE

Nonfood plants, for industrial use, may be cultivated on seleniferous soil. It may be possible to use most of the seleniferous areas for crops that provide sources of fiber, resin, alcohol, oil, plastics, etc.

References

1. Alley, H. P. and D. W. Bohmont. 1958. Big sagebrush control. *Wyoming Agr. Expt. Sta. Bull. No.* **354**:1–7.
2. Anderson, M. S. 1961. Selenium in agriculture. *U.S. Dept. Agr. Handbook* **200**: 53–55.
3. Bohmont, D. W. 1952. Chemical control of poisonous range plants. *Wyoming Agr. Expt. Sta. Bull. No.* **313**:1–29.
4. Bohmont, D. W. 1955. 2,4-D in Wyoming. *Wyoming Agr. Expt. Sta. Circ. No.* **51**, rev. 1–16.
5. Dinkel, C. A., J. A. Minyard, E. I. Whitehead and O. E. Olson. 1957. *South Dakota State College Agr. Expt. Sta. Circ. No.* **135**:8–14.

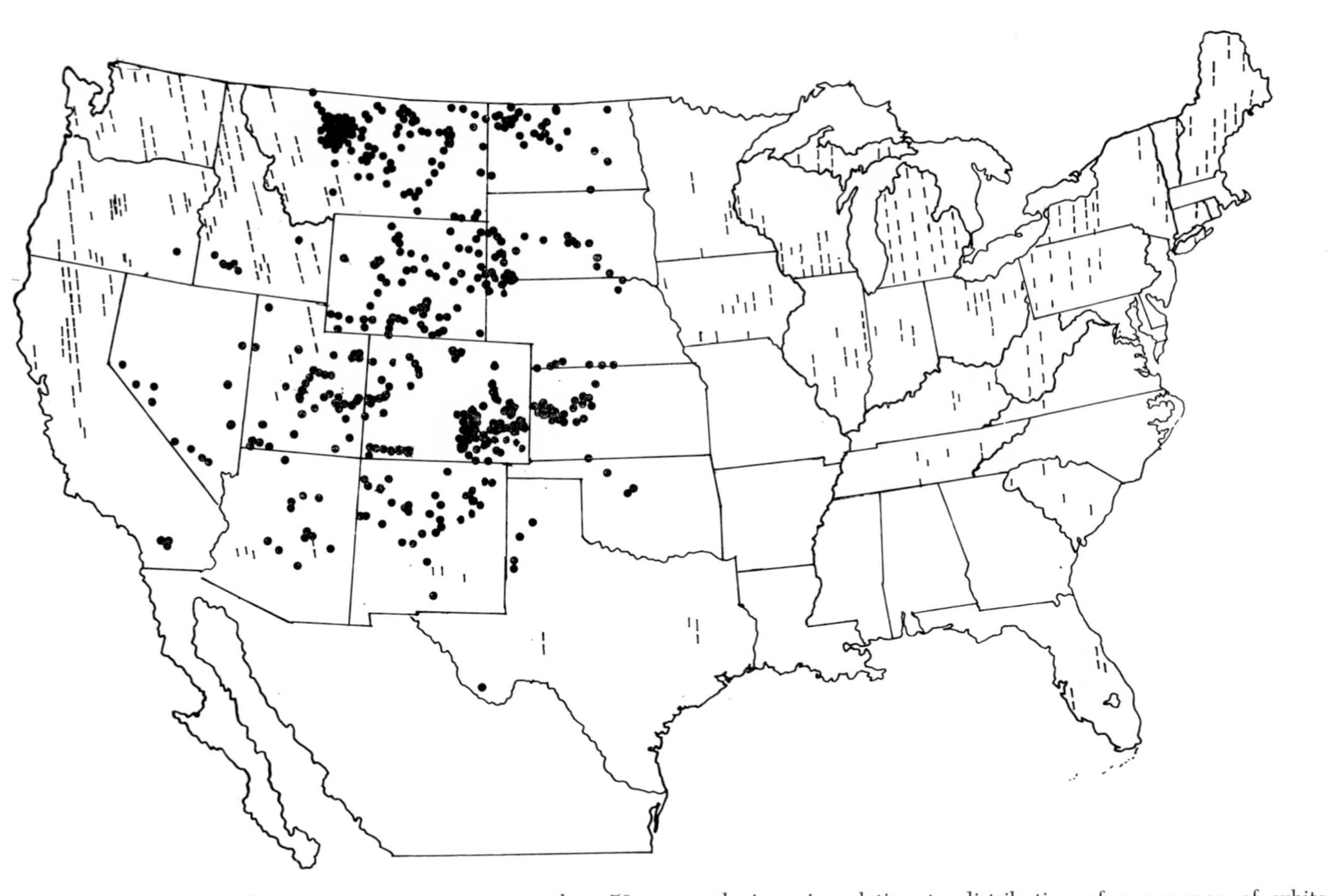

FIG. 39. Distribution of vegetation containing more than 50 ppm selenium, in relation to distribution of occurrence of white muscle disease in livestock. • : seleniferous vegetation; || : white muscle disease occurrence; Modified from Muth and Allaway [illegible]

CHAPTER VII

SELENIUM IN NUTRITION

Selenium previously has been considered as a toxic agent producing various disease conditions in animals by an excess in the diet due to selenium accumulation in the forage from the soil. In this chapter selenium will be discussed in relation to various disease syndromes produced in mammals and birds when selenium deficiency exists in the diet.

Factor 3 as a separate dietary entity preventing necrotic liver degeneration in the rat was reported by Schwarz (*141, 142*). Schwarz and Foltz (*145*) reported that the effective agent in Factor 3 was an organic selenium compound. Concentrates of Factor 3 protected against multiple necrotic degeneration (heart, liver, kidney, and muscle) in the mouse (*43*), and fatal exudative diathesis in chicks (*125, 144*).

Subsequent studies with inorganic selenium compounds proved them to be protective agents as effective as Factor 3 against various disease syndromes in rats, mice, birds, and livestock.

Although priority should be given to the results reported by Schwarz and co-workers on the prophylactic effect of Factor 3-selenium in various disease syndromes in laboratory animals and chicks, in order to maintain the sequence of Chapter V, selenium-responsive diseases in livestock will be discussed first, followed by those in laboratory animals and birds.

SELENIUM IN LIVESTOCK NUTRITION

Congenital white muscle disease (WMD), stiff lamb disease, and nutritional myopathy in calves and lambs have been recognized as a distinct disease syndrome for more than a quarter of a century. It also occurs in deer, and has been produced experimentally in swine. The disease has been recorded in the United States (Fig. 39) (*115b*), New Zealand, Finland, Britain, Japan, Turkey, and Russia. Observations by Muth *et al.* (*113*) indicated that prenatal myopathy in lambs was prevented by the addition of a small amount of selenium to a dystrophogenic diet fed to pregnant ewes. Similar studies were made by a number of investigators and favorable results were obtained with the administration of trace amounts of selenium in the prevention of muscular dystrophy or WMD in livestock.

Causative Agents

Some differences exist in the clinical manifestations and dietetic predisposing conditions that produce degenerative myopathies in young animals in various parts of the world. The feeds that produced the disease in different areas have little in common in botanical classification or in vitamin E content.

The feeding of legumes, cull red kidney beans, Ladino clover cull, second cutting of alfalfa, grass mixed hay, and various grasses may produce the disease syndromes experimentally if the above feeds are grown on areas where the disease is prevalent. The incidence of the disease is higher in areas where gypsum fertilization is practiced in order to increase the yield of forage (*71, 139*), and on irrigated farms (*112*). The incidence of deficiency disease may not always be associated with demonstrable deficiency of selenium in the feed, but may be related to the biological availability of the element (*139, 156*).

Experimental and Field Observations

In New Zealand and some parts of Australia extensive field and experimental observations on selenium deficiency diseases were carried out in connection with selenium-responsive diseases in livestock (*59a, 71, 164a, 167a*). Investigators from New Zealand described a number of disease syndromes which responded to selenium treatment; therefore, these disease syndromes will be discussed separately.

Experimental studies carried out by earlier investigators indicated that some of the deficiency myopathies responded to vitamin E treatment (*18, 85, 178*). However, there is considerable evidence that the muscular dystrophy in calves and lambs is not always associated with low tocopherol content of the ration or milk of the dams and treatment with large doses of tocopherol is not always effective. The mode of action of selenium in producing growth response and preventing WMD suggests that selenium and vitamin E are interrelated in their metabolic functions, but that vitamin E cannot completely replace the need for selenium in livestock.

Synthetic Dystrophogenic Diets

The role of vitamin E and selenium in the nutrition of pigs was studied using diets containing Torula yeast supplemented with sulfur amino acids and all known essential minerals and vitamins except vitamin E (basal ration). The addition of tocopheryl acetate or selenium (sodium selenite) prevented liver necrosis and death of the animals (*54, 170*). Liver necrosis and degenerative changes in cardiac and skeletal muscle of pigs fed vitamin E-deficient Torula yeast diet could be prevented by sodium selenite or by *d*-α-tocopheryl acetate but not by the addition of 0.3 per cent cystine (*126*).

Vitamin E-deficient soybean meal diet fed to pigs produced liver necrosis, massive myocardial transudates, skeletal muscle degeneration, and ceroid deposits in the adipose tissues of the deficient animals. The addition of 0.2 mg of Na_2SeO_3 per kilogram of diet prevented liver necrosis and loss of fluid but had no effect on muscular degeneration or ceroid deposition in the tissues (*64*).

These experiments gave further evidence that degenerative liver necrosis produced by Torula yeast diet or vitamin E-deficient diet in the pigs, as in rats and mice, can be prevented by the addition of a small amount of selenium or α-tocopherol to the diet. The myocardial and skeletal muscle damage and pigmentation in the adipose tissue which is part of vitamin E deficiency syndrome in the pig were not uniformly responsive to selenium administration.

In experimental muscular dystrophy in lambs and calves, highly unsaturated fats have always been used as a stress factor to produce the myopathy. The addition of vitamin E (*17*) and the antioxidant diphenyl-*p*-phenylenediamine (*49*) to the diet have been effective in preventing myopathy in the animals. To separate the dietary factors that contribute to the production of muscular dystrophy in the lamb, the effects of dietary variables were investigated. Torula yeast was used as the source of protein. This protein is deficient in tocopherol, selenium, and sulfur amino acids. The variables added to the basal diet (Torula yeast-coconut oil) were: selenium, Santoquin (1,2-dihydro-6-ethoxy-2,2,4-trimethylquinoline) and the hydroxy analog of methionine (calcium *dl*-2-hydroxy, 4-methyl-thiobutyrate). The addition of antioxidant (0.1%) to the coconut oil-Torula yeast diet prevented muscular dystrophy in the lambs, whereas selenium (1.4 ppm) only delayed the onset of the disease or modified the syndrome, and the hydroxy analog of methionine did not alter the incidence of the disease (*56*). The decreased effectiveness of selenium to prevent the myopathy on an abnormal diet (coconut oil-Torula yeast) for lambs may be due to the lack of utilization of the diet by the animals. The antioxidant in the diet may have altered the diet in some respect to prevent the development of the deficiency diseases.

Natural Dystrophogenic Diets

When forages from enzootic muscular dystrophy areas were fed to ewes, the administration of vitamin E to the ewes was not effective in preventing myopathy in the lambs. The addition of 0.1 ppm selenium (Na_2SeO_3) to the dystrophogenic ewes' diet protected the lambs from

WMD when their mothers were fed prepartum with the selenium-supplemented ration (*113*).

The effectiveness of selenium in the prevention of myopathy in lambs caused by feeding dystrophy-producing forage to the ewes has created interest in the control and the prevention of economically important bovine and ovine disease syndromes. The possibility that selenium deficiency in the diet may be responsible for the irregular and sporadic outbreak of the disease was investigated in various enzootic areas. A known dystrophogenic ration (trefoil-grass hay and raw cull kidney beans) was fed to pregnant ewes. The addition of 1 ppm of selenium (Na_2SeO_3) to the basal ration reduced the incidence of diagnosed muscular dystrophy in the lambs. Linseed oil meal and α-tocopheryl acetate added to the basal ration have also been effective in reducing the incidence of myopathy in the progenies. Selenium assay by activation analysis of the feeds indicated that the basal diet was low in selenium, while linseed oil meal contained 1.18 ppm selenium, which may account for its effectiveness in the prevention of nutritional muscular dystrophy in lambs (*128*).

The evidence obtained by activation analysis—that the basal ration contained only 0.012 and 0.08 ppm of selenium—linked muscular dystrophy in the lamb with selenium deficiency in the ration. However, subsequent studies indicated that the absolute selenium concentration in the forage is not a good index for the demonstrable selenium deficiency. The present evidence suggests that sulfur antagonism can influence the biological availability of the trace amounts of selenium in the diet which are required for the prevention of the disease syndrome (*139*).

Subsequent studies in preventing WMD and improving the rate of growth in lambs by the administration or addition of selenium to the dystrophogenic diet of ewes during gestation or by periodic treatment of lambs in the first few weeks of life were uniformly favorable. The treatment was effective whether sodium selenite or selenate was used either prophylactically or therapeutically (*74, 86, 87, 89, 102, 103, 114, 115, 123, 129, 139, 180, 181*). Literature dealing with selenium-responsive myopathy and selenium treatment in livestock production was summarized by Muth (*115a*) and Wolf *et al.* (*178a*).

The addition of sulfur (0.216%) as Na_2SO_4 to the ewes' diet interfered with the protective effect of selenium. The administration of massive doses of α-tocopherol appeared to prevent the disease in the lambs (*115*). α-Tocopherol given to pregnant ewes was ineffective in preventing muscular myopathy in the lambs (*112, 114*). The inefficient placental transfer of α-tocopherol may be responsible for the variations observed in preventing the disease in the young. Treatment of pregnant ewes in the last 3 months of gestation and lambing with 10 mg of Na_2SeO_3 had no effect on weight gain of the progenies, but treatment of the affected lambs at 3 weeks of age reversed the depression of weights produced by the disease (*181*).

Muscular dystrophy in lambs (produced by dystrophogenic ration fed to ewes) was prevented by the addition of selenium (1.0 ppm per day) and α-tocopherol to the feed of ewes during later gestation and early lactation, although neither gave complete protection at the levels fed. Dystrophy was prevented in the lambs by giving either vitamin E (50 IU) or selenium (0.5 mg) per lamb per day. The addition of the antioxidant diphenyl-*p*-phenylenediamine to the ewes' diet had no effect on the incidence of WMD in lambs (*75*).

Congenital WMD and delayed WMD in hoggets (9- to 12-month-old sheep) are prevalent in New Zealand. The treatment of ewes 1 to 3 weeks before lambing with selenium almost completely prevented the development of WMD in the lambs, while α-tocopherol greatly reduced the incidence of the disease (*45, 69, 71*).

The addition of fats or oils which contain highly unsaturated acids increased the requirements for vitamin E in the diet (*16*). Anti-vitamin E effects of fish liver oil in the induction of WMD in lambs and the prenatal influence of selenium and tocopherol additions to the diet of the ewes were investigated. The addition of fish liver oil to dystrophogenic diet increased the prenatal death, WMD, and sudden death of the progenies. Selenium (0.5 ppm) decreased the severity of the disorders. Vitamin E administration increased the vitamin E concentration in the plasma of ewes and lambs and prevented the development of WMD in the treated animals (*175*). The addition of antioxidants (*N,N′*-diphenyl-*p*-phenylenediamine) to the dystrophogenic diet did not prevent muscular dystrophy in lambs (*74, 75*). Antioxidants which are effective in vitamin E deficiency syndromes in various species of animals do not prevent muscular dystrophy in Herbivora when the dystrophogenic diet is deficient in selenium.

The enzootic muscular dystrophy in north Scotland in suckling calves occurs when the dams are fed rations low in tocopherol; the disease could be prevented by administration of high doses of α-tocopherol either to the dams or to the calves. The oral administration of 0.25 mg selenium per day (Na_2SeO_3) prevented muscular dystrophy in calves and 200 mg α-tocopherol per week was not as effective as selenium, since mild cases of the disease occurred in 3 per cent of the tocopherol-treated group (*165*).

Nutritional muscular dystrophy was produced experimentally in calves by the addition of cod liver oil to the tocopherol-deficient diet. The addition of 1 ppm of selenium to the basal diet did not prevent muscular dystrophy. The addition of 200 IU water-dispersible *d*-α-tocopheryl acetate per calf per day prevented muscular degeneration in all the animals. Environmental factors, dampness, drafts, and bacterial infections were present as a secondary problem in the experiment (*99*). Physiological and environmental stress factors are recognized to be of great importance in increasing the need for vitamin E. An increase of vitamin E in the diet will prevent the disease in the presence of various stresses (*1*). The above studies suggest that selenium is ineffective in preventing muscular dystrophy when physiological and environmental stresses are added to the dietary deficiency.

Experimental studies demonstrated that treatment with selenium was not only effective in preventing muscular dystrophy but also caused a marked increase in weight gain in the young (*48, 79, 102, 103, 123*).

The diseases in livestock responsive to selenium therapy in New Zealand are far greater than those discussed previously; therefore, disease syndromes which are not related to congenital WMD will be discussed briefly.

A disease condition in New Zealand which is designated by some investigators as "ill-thrift" (*103*) or "unthriftiness" (*71*) may be a specific selenium deficiency in livestock (*46–48, 69, 70, 79*). The beneficial effects of selenium in this disease condition were observed under field and experimental conditions by the investigators. Progenies of cattle and sheep responded to treatment by increased growth and decrease in mortality rate (*71*).

Infertility in sheep is frequent in areas in New Zealand where WMD or "unthriftiness" in lambs is prevalent. Increased fertility by selenium administration was most apparent where there was a past history of WMD (*70, 71*).

Periodontal disease in sheep is an important cause of "unthriftiness," and severe losses occur in some areas. Preliminary experiments indicate that after selenium treatment the disease virtually disappeared where the disease previously had been a serious problem (*71*).

Symptoms

Muscular dystrophy affects both skeletal and cardiac muscles of lambs and calves. Usually in lambs there is a predominance of skeletal muscle damage and in calves, cardiac muscle degeneration.

The disease in lambs is characterized by progressive stiffness, resulting in complete disuse of skeletal muscles. The skeletal muscles of the neck or the extremities may be involved, and the involvement of the muscles is bilateral. The bilateral involvement of skeletal muscles impairs both voluntary movement and locomotion and results in muscular weakness (Fig. 40). In animals with impaired locomotion secondary factors such as starvation, exposure, and bacterial infections are the contributing causes of death.

FIG. 40. Muscular dystrophy in lamb showing bilateral involvements of extremities. (By courtesy of O. H. Muth.)

Severely affected cardiac muscle damage, usually in calves, gives rise to dyspnea and general weakness and death within a few hours after symptoms appear or even without appreciable symptoms. Spontaneous recovery may occur without any apparent change in feeding and management. Lambs and calves may recover spontaneously where no severe cardiac involvement is present (*71, 86, 112*).

Diagnosis

Diagnosis may be made by the appearance of clinical symptoms, blood and urine tests or post morten findings. As a result of release of creatine from the degenerating muscle the excretion of creatine is increased, resulting in creatinuria. Blood test consists of the determination of serum glutamic-oxalacetic transaminase (SGO-T) which can establish or confirm the diagnosis. The technique used for the determination is based on the intensity of color produced in the reaction (*166*). The test is not specific, but is a helpful adjunct for confirmation of clinical findings. It provides a guide to the relative muscular damage which may be present, or the detection of the presence of mild, subclinical forms of the disease. A more detailed discussion is presented in the section dealing with Biochemical Changes.

Prophylactic Dose

Muscular Dystrophy

Earlier investigations of Schwarz and co-workers with mice and chicks demonstrated that the preventive dose of selenium against various disease syndromes is very low. Therefore, no selenium intoxication would occur in animals treated with trace amounts of selenium. However, various investigators attempted to inject a single large dose for prolonged effect.

The subcutaneous injection of sodium selenite, 0.075 gm per 100 pounds of weight, to 70 to 80 lambs was lethal to the animals within 24 hours after the injection. However, the injection of 0.01 gm of selenite per 100 pounds of body weight was not toxic and prevented the development of muscular myopathy. Preliminary trials with intramuscular injection of $BaSeO_4$ in oil appeared to be promising in preventing the development of muscular dystrophy in lambs if the $BaSeO_4$ was injected 4 to 8 weeks prior to parturition (*87*). The administration of a single intramuscular dose of selenium (30 mg per 100 lb) to ewes was reported to be fatal to about 90 per cent of the animals within 24 hours (*139*). A considerable difference in the rate of excretion was indicated after the administration of Na_2SeO_3 and $BaSeO_4$ to sheep. Sodium selenite was absorbed rapidly with an accompanying rapid increase in serum selenium and excretion, while $BaSeO_4$ was absorbed and excreted at a slower rate. Tissues, 148 days after injection of $BaSeO_4$, contained below 3–4 ppm and the kidney 57.5 μg per 100 gm tissue (*88*). These selenium levels in the tissues indicate that the authors were using toxic levels of selenium, thereby probably producing functional damage to the organs.

The value of the administration of a single dose of selenium to animals in dystrophogenic areas is fully appreciated. However, it is important that the various factors concerning the toxicity of selenium are evaluated and understood before massive dose injections are instituted. Most investigators used doses of 0.1 to 1.0 ppm selenium mixed with the dystrophogenic diet before parturition. This amount can be added to the diet without any danger of producing toxicity in the animals.

Selenium appeared to be effective whether administered orally, mixed with the feed, or injected subcutaneously prepartum to the animals on dystrophogenic areas or if treatment is started in lambs a few days after birth. Sodium selenate and selenite were used effectively (*47, 48, 71, 87, 89, 113, 128, 181*).

The optimum dose and frequency of administration of selenium to so-called "unthrifty" lambs was 2.5–5.0 mg selenium given at one-month intervals. It improved the growth and decreased the death rate of the animals (*79*).

A limited amount of data is available as to the effective dose in enzootic muscular dystrophy in calves. Sharman *et al.* (*165*) treated a significant number of animals and found that 0.25 mg selenium (Na_2SeO_3) per day per dam was effective in the prevention of muscular dystrophy in calves on 25 farms where the disease was prevalent.

The results of trial experiments on the effect of selenium on ewe fertility indicate that one dose of 5 to 25 mg of selenium prior to mating apparently increased fertility, but the lower dose did not prevent the development of congenital WMD in the progenies (*71*).

Biochemical Changes in Nutritional Myopathy (WMD)

There is a considerable amount of data available on the biochemistry of muscular degeneration. The present discussion on the chemical changes in degenerating muscle will be considered only as related to the experimental findings with selenium.

Chemical composition of dystrophic muscle varies from that of normal animals owing to a decrease in the cell mass and replacement of muscle fibers by hyaline, a clear homogeneous structureless material.

Early studies on the chemical composition of the dystrophic muscles of calves indicated an increase of calcium and sodium and a decrease of potassium and iron. The total nitrogen, creatine, and globulin content of the muscle decreased, but the nucleic acid content increased (*15, 57*). Similar chemical changes in dystrophic muscles were reported in rats, rabbits, and guinea pigs (*61, 72, 111*). The mineral inbalance in the degenerating heart muscle is of great importance since calcification of the organ interferes with functions of the heart. The inorganic salts may comprise nearly one fourth of its nonaqueous components (*34*).

A considerable increase of calcium, phosphorus, and sodium has been reported in bovine and ovine dystrophic muscle that showed either gross or microscopic evidence of calcification (*29, 34, 55, 100, 139*). Selenium or vitamin E therapy in young lambs prevented gross calcification and reduced the calcium, phosphorus, and sodium deposition in the skeletal muscle. The treatment of ewes with vitamin E during gestation did not prevent the increase of calcium, phosphorus, and sodium content of lamb skeletal muscles. Oral prepartum administration of selenium prevented the damage to the muscle and abnormal rise of the inorganic salts in the skeletal muscles of lambs as indicated in Table 49 (*139*).

In normal muscle the creatine level is constant (*20, 97*); however, in dystrophic muscle there is a decrease in creatine (*61, 82, 83, 96*) with subsequent increase in blood and urinary creatine (*104*).

Chemical changes in the composition of blood in dystrophic animals were reported in detail with conflicting results. The possible interest at the present time is the total plasma tocopherol in the dams or in prog-

TABLE 49

Two to Six Week Lamb Skeletal Muscle Analysis[a]

Treatment	mg/100 gm fat-free dry matter				
	Ca	P	Mg	Na	K
1957–1958					
Control[b]	27 ± 4	574 ± 63	123 ± 5	371 ± 15	1,800 ± 48
Basal[c,d]	4,472 ± 25	2,391 ± 558	332 ± 93	1,237 ± 360	1,773 ± 464
Idem + Oral Vit. E/ewes[c]	2,978 ± 12	1,831 ± 281	210 ± 50	1,227 ± 294	1,875 ± 428
Idem + Inj. Vit. E/ewes[c]	4,521 ± 15	2,790 ± 274	342 ± 99	1,168 ± 255	1,897 ± 878
Idem + Oral Se/ewes[b]	28 ± 3	627 ± 57	120 ± 4	413 ± 26	1,638 ± 42
1958–1959					
Basal[c]	5,180 ± 34	3,009 ± 480	337 ± 108	1,122 ± 253	1,750 ± 795
Idem + Oral Vit. E/lambs[b]	47 ± 2	780 ± 12	135 ± 5	331 ± 33	1,663 ± 41
Idem + Inj. Se/lambs[b]	58 ± 3	750 ± 16	165 ± 5	443 ± 32	1,540 ± 52
Idem + Oral Se/ewes[b]	69 ± 4	742 ± 14	121 ± 5	307 ± 50	1,511 ± 75

[a] Schubert *et al.* (*139*).

[b] Group means ± standard errors.

[c] Group ranges.

[d] Basal ration for ewes was Ladino clover chaff and/or clippings from an area where WMD was prevalent.

enies. The plasma tocopherol of the dams may or may not have any correlation with incidence of the disease (*6, 17, 34, 137–139*). Very low tocopherol levels were generally encountered among newborn animals without any manifestations of the disease.

The administration of selenium either to the ewes or to the lambs had no influence on the tocopherol content of plasma. Lambs treated with selenium had low plasma tocopherol levels without any gross manifestation of the disease as indicated in Table 50 (*139*). Analysis for calcium, magnesium, phosphorus, and hemoglobin levels of blood of ewes at prepartum and lambs at 2–6 weeks of age showed no significant differences with the various diets used.

The disease in the lambs is accompanied by severe creatinuria (*177*). In cardiac dystrophy of calves severe creatinuria may be absent, but the nitrogen balance is lower than normal (*14*).

Increased serum glutamic-oxalacetic transaminase (SGO-T) was demonstrated in human progressive muscular dystrophy (*176*), skeletal muscle and liver necrosis (*105*), and acute myocardial infarctions (*80*).

TABLE 50

Ovine Blood Vitamin E as Related to WMD[a]

Year	Ration	Supplement	Blood value	Ewes[b]		Lambs[b] 2–6 weeks	WMD Incidence		
				On trial	Prepartum		Gross	Micro.	No. of Animals
1957–1958	Basal[c]	None	E[d]	208 ± 15	27 ± 5	13 ± 6	11	0	15
	Basal	+ Oral Vit. E/ewes	E	[e]	57 ± 9	20 ± 5	16	0	20
	Basal	+ Oral Se/ewes	E	[e]	24 ± 4	22 ± 3	0	3	16
1958–1959	Basal	None	E	$63 + 3$	13 ± 2	28 ± 9	16	3	20
	Basal	+ Oral Vit. E/lambs	E	[e]	[f]	95 ± 14	0	5	17
	Basal	+ Oral Se/ewes	E		13 ± 5	11 ± 4	0	3	18

[a] Schubert *et al.* (*139*).
[b] Mean ± standard error.
[c] Basal ration grass and Ladino clover for ewes.
[d] Total tocopherols, μg/100 ml plasma.
[e] Control values are representative of all groups when going on trial.
[f] Basal value is representative of all groups of ewes similarly treated.

The SGO-T catalyzes the transfer of an amino group from aspartate to α-ketoglutarate. In tissue breakdown there is a 10- to 100-fold increase of serum transaminase activity due to the release or breakdown of the cell barriers and the enzyme entering the circulatory system.

The value of serum transaminase determination in the Herbivora with muscular dystrophy was recognized by Blincoe and Dye (*19*). Increase in SGO-T activity in cases of muscular dystrophy in lambs and calves was reported by the above investigators. The increase in lambs was more pronounced than in calves. Lambs with skeletal muscle lesions had a range of 687 to 3460 units per milliliter, and calves with heart lesions had a range of 295 to 2360 units per milliliter. Normal values in lambs are 97 to 191 units per milliliter and in calves are 19 to 99 units per milliliter.

Subsequent studies proved that SGO-T is a reliable test in diagnosis of clinical and subclinical WMD in lambs (*85, 90, 171*). Treatment of ewes with selenium during gestation prevented WMD in lambs, but did not inhibit the increase in the SGO-T levels in the lambs. The injection of either 1.0 mg selenium (Na_2SeO_3) at 14-day intervals or weekly injections of α-tocopheryl acetate (525 mg) in lambs reduced their SGO-T levels (*90*).

Pathology

Pathology characteristic of muscular degenerative disease in farm animals was described by various investigators (*13, 86, 112*).

Gross Pathology

Lesions are bilaterally symmetrical and appear as white streaks in the cardiac (Fig. 41) and/or skeletal muscles (Fig. 42). All the striated muscles may be involved in varying degrees. Lesions may vary in size and in appearance from slightly discolored or bleached to distinct striations. Hemorrhages and edema may be present.

In the lamb's heart, lesions appear as white endocardial plaques which may be coalesced and underlie the entire endocardium, giving the appearance of white enamel lining the organ (*112*) (Fig. 43).

In serious cardiac impairment, marked congestion in the lungs occurs and the disease sometimes may be diagnosed as acute pneumonia.

Histopathology

Detailed histological descriptions in the different species of livestock were summarized by Blaxter and Brown (*13*), and MacKenzie (*98*), and described by Muth (*112*). The microscopic lesions appear to indicate a progressive hyaline degeneration with necrosis and a loss of transverse and longitudinal muscle fibers. The fiber becomes amorphous homoge-

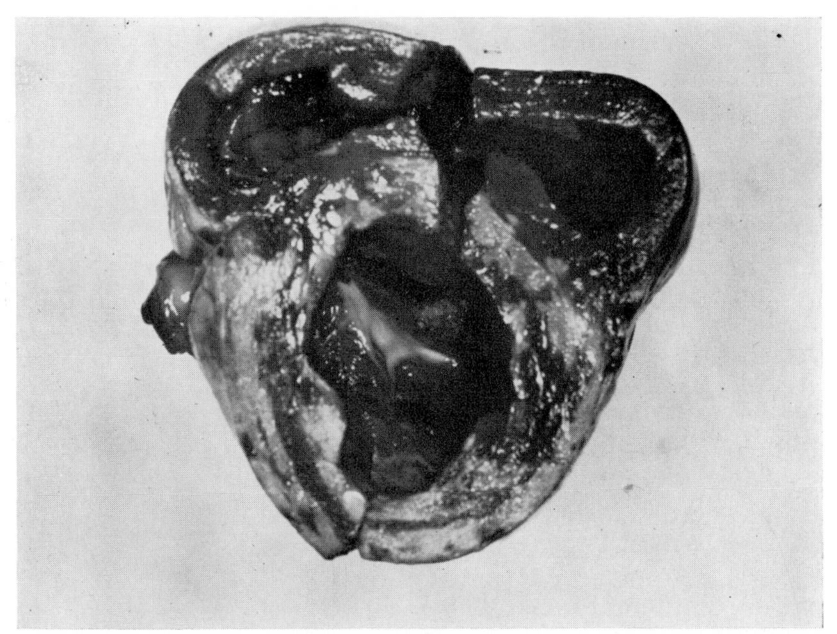

FIG. 41. Cross section through the heart of a 6-week-old calf showing myocardial degeneration with calcification. (By courtesy of O. H. Muth.)

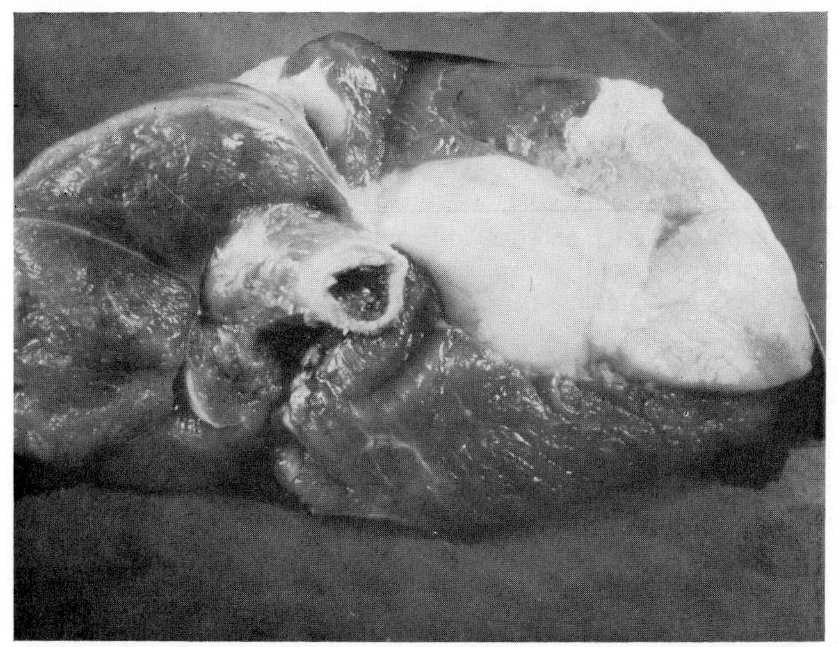

FIG. 42. Skeletal muscle of lamb with distinct white areas and marked striations. (By courtesy of O. H. Muth.)

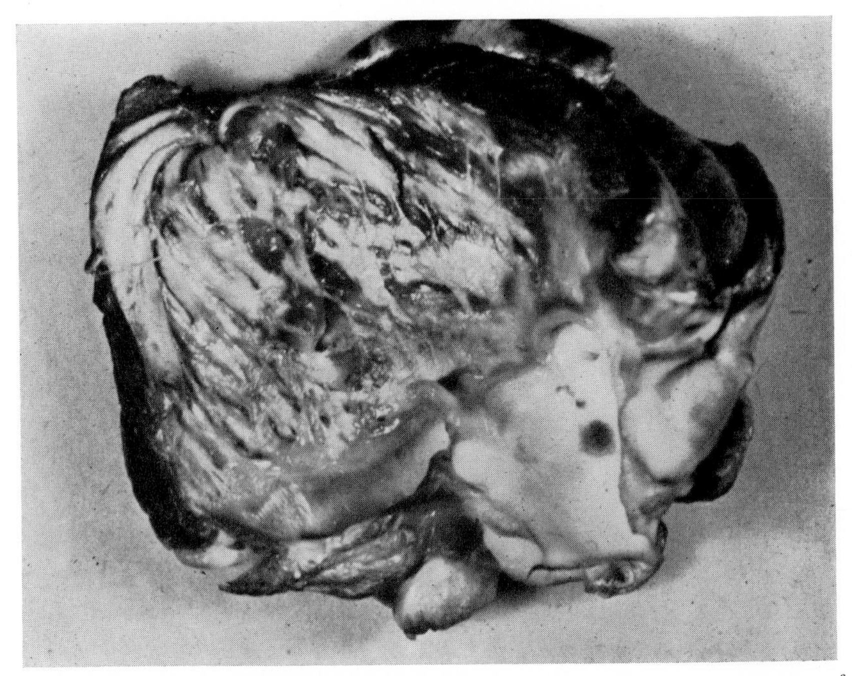

FIG. 43. Characteristic subendothelial lesions in lamb's heart. (By courtesy of O. H. Muth.)

neous, and highly refractile. Vacuoles may appear in the fiber and the hyaline material may be granular. As the disease progresses great masses of cellular elements dominate the picture. Calcification of the necrotic tissue is a variable and secondary phenomenon. This is a typical Zenker's degeneration of the muscles. Regeneration of muscles after hyaline degeneration may occur and the entire muscle may be renewed. The multiplication of the remaining muscle nuclei of the undamaged fibers may take place and produce new muscle cells.

PROPOSED STUDIES

Studies dealing with the minimum prophylactic dose of selenium in livestock during pregnancy and lactation should receive consideration. A single large dose, approximately the chronic toxic dose, of selenium should not be administered to livestock unless studies indicate that selenium has no toxic effect on the animals.

Experimental evidence in rats indicates that the administration of the first subacute toxic dose of selenium interferes with functions of the kidney and intestinal tract. The reduction of kidney functions, as measured by the urinary excretion of Se^{75}, persists as long as 150 days. The urinary excretion of tracer doses of selenium was, on the average, 40 per cent of the injected Se^{75}, while the injection of a toxic dose reduced the excretion to 20 per cent. Tissue retention of selenium is related to the toxic damage to the various organs (*136*). Therefore, detailed study on livestock (sheep, lambs, cattle, calves, and pigs) must be carried out in order to determine the prophylactic and therapeutic doses in contrast to the dose which may produce functional damage to the various organs.

SELENIUM IN LABORATORY ANIMAL NUTRITION

Selenium-responsive deficiency diseases in different species of animals show considerable variations. In Herbivora, discussed previously, the manifestation of the deficiency syndrome is recognized by the development of various degrees of myopathies involving the skeletal and/or cardiac muscles.

In experimental animals the dietary deficiency syndrome responsive to Factor 3 is necrotic liver degeneration in rats (*142*) and cardiac muscle degeneration in mice accompanied by peripheral muscle degeneration, liver and kidney necrosis, and pancreatic dystrophy (*43*). The term "Factor 3" was coined by Schwarz to indicate a third substance of unknown chemical composition which prevented necrotic liver degeneration in rats in addition to cystine and vitamin E (*142*).

Dietary necrotic liver degeneration is recognized as a distinct disease entity. This nutritional deficiency disease may develop in rats if there is a lack of cystine (*174*), vitamin E (*140*), or Factor 3-selenium (*145*). Experimental studies indicate that there exists a remarkable synergistic correlation between Factor 3-selenium and vitamin E against nutritional deficiency syndromes in rats and mice. However, there are several characteristic vitamin E deficiency symptoms which do not respond to the administration of Factor 3 even in large excess. These are resorption of the embryo in pregnant rats (*68*), muscular dystrophy in rabbits (*50*), and encephalomalacia in the chick (*41*). The differential biological response of Factor 3-selenium or selenium compounds from that of vitamin E suggests that they may be two separate and different dietary entities. Cystine, originally believed to play a primary role against liver necrosis, has been shown to contain 1–2 μg of selenium, which may account for some of its biopotency (*155*).

Causative Agents

A variety of diets has been used by various investigators to induce necrotic liver degeneration in rats: cystine-low diet (*174*), cystine-free diet of amino acids in crystalline form (*51*), low casein diet (*35*), and Torula yeast protein diet (*73, 142*). The composition of the various yeast diets which can be used for the production of dietary liver necrosis was discussed by Schwarz (*141, 157*). The composition of the basal diet he developed is similar to the so-called semipurified diets except that 30 per cent Torula yeast is used to supply the protein. This diet has been used by Schwarz since 1949 for the production of dietary necrotic liver degeneration. Table 51 gives the composition of the diet.

The diet is suboptimal in sulfur amino acids, free of vitamin E, and the protein content is from 13 to 15 per cent. Under controlled environmental and dietary conditions the inbred Fisher 344 strain of weanling rats develop and die of nutritional necrotic liver degeneration in about 21 days (*157*).

TABLE 51

Composition of Basal Diet[a]

Torula Yeast[b]	30
Sucrose[c]	59
Lard, vitamin E free[d]	5
Salts[e]	5
Vitamin powder[f]	1

[a] Schwarz (*157*).

[b] Lake State Yeast Corporation, Rinelander, Wisconsin.

[c] Commercial, regular grade.

[d] Vitamin E-free animal fat, stripped by molecular distillation (Distillation Products Division, Rochester, New York).

[e] $CaCO_3$, 543.0 gm; $MgCO_3$, 25.0 gm; $MgSO_4$, 16.0 gm; NaCl, 69.0 gm; KCl, 112.0 gm; KH_2PO_4, 212.0 gm; $FePO_4 \cdot 4H_20$, 20.5 gm; KI, 0.08 gm; $MnSO_4$, 0.35 gm; NaF, 1.0 gm; $Al_2(SO_4)_3 \cdot K_2SO_4$, 0.17 gm; $CuSO_4$, 0.9 gm.

[f] Lactose, 88.68 gm; thiamine•HCl, 40 mg; riboflavin, 25 mg; pyridoxine•HCl, 20 mg; D-calcium pantothenate, 200 mg; choline chloride, 10 gm; niacin, 1 gm; menadione (2-methyl-1, 4-naphthoquinone), 10 mg; folic acid, 20 mg; biotin, 10 mg; and vitamin B_{12}, 1 mg. Vitamin A acetate (1 mg %) and Vitamin D (0.01 mg %) were added to the diets dissolved in a small amount of ethanol (0.5 ml/100 gm of diet).

Experimental Observations

After the recognition of selenium as an integral part of the Factor 3 which prevented dietary necrotic liver degeneration and death in rats, other inorganic compounds (selenium, tellurium, and arsenic) were tested in order to determine their effects on necrotic liver degeneration (*145*). The addition of 6 and 4 μg of selenium (as Na_2SeO_3) per 100 gm of diet gave 100 per cent protection. To give the same protection, 100 μg of selenium (K_2SeO_4) was required per 100 gm of diet, while 100 μg tellurium or arsenic (potassium tellurate or sodium arsenate) per 100 gm of diet was not effective. These results definitely established that in Factor 3 the biologically active substance which prevented nutritional necrotic liver degeneration was combined with selenium, and that inorganic selenium compounds were effective. Molybdenum, cobalt, and osmium, either alone or in combination, were without effect on liver necrosis at a dietary level of 200 to 400 μg per cent (*153*). The discovery that the addition of inorganic selenium compounds to the Torula yeast diet or Torula yeast culture significantly prolonged the survival time of rats and prevented the onset of liver necrotic degeneration was confirmed by many investigators (*4, 23, 58, 62, 81, 151*).

Inorganic selenium compounds, seleno-amino acids, and numerous other organic seleno-compounds, when compared with purified α-Factor 3 preparations (pork kidney powder), gave various degrees of protection against dietary liver necrosis.

Factor 3 was isolated from many natural materials, but on fractionation the kidney yielded at least two chemically closely related substances which were designated α- and β-Factor 3. The α-Factor 3 has a high degree of biological activity and is used as a standard for assay for the biological activity of other compounds against necrotic liver degeneration in rats (*149*).

The ED_{50} (effective dose expressed in μg of selenium per 100 gm of diet) for α-Factor 3 was 0.7 μg of selenium, as determined by activation analysis and standardized in the depleted animals. The biopotencies of selenite, selenocystathionine, selenate, selenocystine, and selenomethionine were of the same order of magnitude, i.e., ED_{50} 2.0–2.5 μg of selenium. The biopotency of these compounds is about one third that of the α-Factor 3 preparation. The ED_{50} of selenic acid and selenium dioxide was somewhat higher due to the instability of these compounds. Elemental selenium was ineffective. The slight protection observed with a high concentration of the element may have been due to the presence of SeO_2 in the sample tested (*149*).

The substitution of a phenyl group for one half of the selenocystine molecule diminished the biological potency about one third. It appears that the groups attached to the selenium in organic seleno-compounds exert a profound influence on its activity against necrotic liver degeneration. The introduction of nitro groups into benzeneseleninic acid enhanced the biological activity. Substitution of a carboxyl group in the *para* position completely abolished the biopotency of the compound. 2-Selenouracil, the analog of 2-thiouracil, was inactive; while 6-selenopurine was quite potent. The potency of 6-selenoctic acid was about one fifth that of the α-Factor 3 preparation and somewhat less than the potency of inorganic selenium compounds or the seleno-amino acids. The introduction of a sulfur atom adjacent to selenium greatly enhanced the protective action of the compound (*148–150*).

It is well known that dietary deficiencies affect and influence the functions of the various hormones. Studies of various hormonal and nutritional stimuli on the course of liver necrosis have suggested that it may be possible to differentiate between true protective and nonspecific effects of various substances by the induction of a hyperthyroid state (*4*). The addition of thyroid hormone to the yeast diet significantly increased the onset of liver necrosis in the rats. The addition of 0.02 mg per cent of sodium selenite prevented liver necrosis, but the survival time of rats fed the highest amount of thyroid powder and selenium was not significantly increased.

The function of vitamin E as an intracellular antioxidant which prevents the accumulation of substances that would lead to peroxidation of tissue lipids and interfere with normal cellular metabolism has been suggested by Tappel and co-workers (*172, 182*). In *in vitro* studies, the antioxidant activity of an organic selenium compound, selenomethionine, was as effective as α-tocopherol in inhibiting the formation of lipid peroxidation products. Other seleno-compounds, in decreasing order of antioxidant activity, were phenyl-selenoglycine, selenocystine, selenohomocysteine, and benzylselenohomocysteine (*183*). On the basis of their studies, Tappell and co-workers advanced the theory that the mechanism of selenium action in the various deficiency syndromes as related to vitamin E deficiency would mainly function by forming lipid antioxidants. These findings are in disagreement with the findings of Green *et al.* (*66, 67*), Edwin *et al.* (*53*), and Diplock *et al.* (*44*), who presented considerable evidence that selenium does not act as an antioxidant and that tocopherol has other functions besides antioxidant activity in the rat. These findings are discussed in more detail under Biochemical Changes.

Effects of antioxidants on dietary liver necrosis *in vivo* were investigated in rats on vitamin E-deficient Torula yeast diet. The antioxidants were grouped according to their ability to reduce or prevent liver damage. Ascorbic acid and methylene blue (0.5%) gave 30–40 per cent protection. Di-tert-amylhydroquinone, Santoquin, and DPPD (*N,N′*-diphenyl-*p*-phenylenediamine) were as effective in preventing liver damage in rats as α-tocopheryl acetate (*146*). The other antioxidants were less effective or inactive against liver damage. It is difficult to postulate the mechanism whereby these chemically unrelated antioxidants have specific properties which function in a manner similar to vitamin E and selenium. The proposed concept that antioxidants have a "sparing" effect on vitamin E merits consideration (*52, 66*).

The role of unsaturated dietary fat in the development of acute liver necrosis in rats and the function of selenium and vitamin E in preventing the damage is not clearly defined at the present time. The addition of even small amounts of unsaturated fatty acids to the diet low in vitamin

E, selenium, and sulfur-containing amino acids greatly accelerated the development of acute liver necrosis in rats (*173*).

The differentiation of Factor 3 as a dietary entity separate from L-cystine and vitamin E was based on their differences in biological actions. Sulfur-containing amino acids (methionine or cystine) do not prevent liver necrosis if they are free from traces of selenium (*155*). If they are supplied in large excesses, they may delay the onset of the disease. This delay is due to the reduction of the vitamin E requirement to only one tenth of the level normally necessary for protection.

A number of pathological conditions which are considered to be a part of vitamin E deficiency syndrome are unaffected by the administration of Factor 3 or selenium (*26, 68, 75, 168*). The ineffectiveness of intramuscular injection of 20 or 100 μg of selenium (Na_2SeO_3) per day in the treatment of muscular dystrophy in the rabbit and the rapid remission of symptoms following the oral administration of 15 mg of DL-α-tocopheryl acetate would suggest that nutritional muscular dystrophy is a more specific deficiency disease in rabbits than in the Herbivora (*50*). The addition of 100 μg of selenium (Na_2SeO_3) and 50 μg of selenium (DL-selenocystine•HCl) to vitamin E-deficient soybean meal diet had no influence on the course of dystrophy in rabbits. The supplementation of the basal diet with α-tocopherol prevented the development of the disease (*76*). The relation of selenium and vitamin E to muscular dystrophy with Torula yeast diet in rabbits was investigated. The rapidly progressing muscular dystrophy in the animals was not prevented by the addition of 1.0 ppm of selenium or by the addition of DL-α-tocopheryl acetate, either alone or in combination (*130*).

Chronic muscular dystrophy developed in young rats receiving vitamin E-low protein diets. The supplementation of the diets with 0.5 ppm of selenium (Na_2SeO_3) failed to protect the young animals against muscular dystrophy (*62*).

The classical vitamin E deficiency symptom, fetal resorption in the pregnant rat, is the basis of the official bioassay procedure for determining the vitamin E activity. Oral or intraperitoneal administration of Factor 3-active selenium compounds, DL-selenocystine•HCl (2.6, 26, and 260 μg), sodium selenite (2.2, 22, and 218 μg), and selenious acid (2.18 mg), did not prevent resorption of the fetus in pregnant rats, while *d*-α-tocopheryl acetate (0.8 mg) was effective (*68*). The addition of SeO_2 to the Torula yeast diet did not prevent impaired reproduction in the rat, but did prevent liver necrosis and hemoglobinuria (*26*).

These findings by various investigators present considerable evidence to support the concept that vitamin E and Factor 3-selenium or selenium compounds are independent dietary entities.

The characteristic degeneration of the enamel organ and whitening of the normally orange-colored incisor teeth of the rat have been described in vitamin E deficiency (*110*). Studies on the effect of selenium in prevention of dental depigmentation are limited and conflicting. The parallelism between the effect of selenium and of vitamin E which prevented liver necrosis and prolonged the survival time of deficient rats does not hold when considering the disturbances causing dental depigmentation (*5, 26*). Irving (*77*), using a different diet and different criteria from that of the above investigators, reported that while 0.9 ppm selenium (Na_2SeO_3) was not as uniformly effective as α-tocopherol for tooth recovery, he suggested that selenium does have a significant role in curing the effects of vitamin E deficiency in the rat incisor tooth.

Symptoms

Factor 3 deficiency in the rat may be described as uneventful in the initial phase, at which time the animals are depleted of protective agent. In the latent phase, one or 2 days before the final breakdown, the animals become weak followed by a transitory state of inactivity, severe tonoclonic convulsions, and death (*106*). Earliest observable symptoms are drop in body temperature, decrease in respiratory rate, and failure to respond to strong stimuli (*152*).

Prophylaxis

As has been noted previously, trace amounts of selenium or vitamin E can prevent the development of multiple necrotic degeneration in rats or mice. Like other micronutrients, Factor 3-selenium is widely distributed in animal tissues and cereals. Brewer's yeast and alcohol-extracted casein are rich sources of Factor 3 (*142, 143*). The Factor 3 activity of inorganic and organic selenium compounds shows considerable variations. Some of these compounds were discussed previously. Other organic seleno-compounds have been evaluated for their biopotencies (*148–150, 157*).

From fractionation studies certain concepts concerning the physical and chemical properties of α-Factor 3 from natural sources were postulated: the active principle is a low molecular weight organic substance, aliphatic in nature, with acidic properties and the selenium most likely is present in the oxidation state of selenite (+4) or selenate (+6). Present observations suggest that α-Factor 3 is an aliphatic seleninic or selenonic acid. A number of aliphatic carboxylic acids containing selenium approached α-Factor 3 in biopotency (*157*).

Biochemical Changes

The metabolic lesion in the final stage of dietary necrotic liver degeneration has been described to be due to acute hypoglycemic shock. The blood glucose level drops below 20 mg per cent and there is a 5-fold increase of lactic acid and almost complete absence of liver glycogen (*107, 152*).

In vitamin E deficiency there is an increased susceptibility of erythrocytes to dialuric acid-induced hemolysis. The addition of 0.5 ppm selenium or *dl*-tocopheryl acetate (200 mg) to the diet of rats prevented autolysis of erythrocytes and erythrocyte fractions when the incubation period was reduced to 15 minutes (*84*). Neither increasing the incubation periods over one hour nor adding selenium, methionine, cystine, methylene blue, and 2,6-di-*tert*-butyl-4-methylphenol had any effect on the sensitivity of the erythrocytes to the hemolyzing action of dialuric acid *in vitro* (*60*).

At the latent period in necrotic liver degeneration a specific metabolic lesion is a decrease of respiration by liver slices from rats maintained on a Torula yeast diet (*25, 135*). The specific breakdown of the respiratory system in the liver, or the respiratory decline, is prevented by tocopherols, tocopherol metabolites, or antioxidants *in vitro* (*65, 108, 109, 134, 154*).

The respiratory decline may be due to a breakdown of enzymes or coenzymes containing sulfhydryl groups. The activity of α-ketoglutarate oxidase in necrotic liver mitochondria from rats fed Torula yeast diet indicates that about one half of the normal oxidase activity was present in the necrotic mitochondria (*26a*). Selenium (15 μg%) or methionine (0.62%) added to the Torula yeast diet after 13 days increased the depleted oxidase over 30 per cent. Vitamin E only slightly altered the rate of the overall system ($<10\%$). These results suggest that selenium, vitamin E, and methionine may act at different but interrelated sites of the oxidase system. Dietary sulfur amino acid supplementation maintains the active sulfhydryl compounds in coenzyme A (*25*) and lipoic acid (*157*) at adequate levels. At which site Factor 3-selenium functions in metabolism is not known at the present time. There are several possibilities, e.g., specific steps in oxidation-reduction reactions, electron transfer systems (*157*), and sulfur-amino acid metabolism (*101, 179*).

Increase of coenzyme A levels in livers with trace amounts of selenium has been reported (*178b, 179*), and evidence of the incorporation of Se^{75} ($Na_2Se^{75}O_3$) in coenzyme A has been presented (*91a*). Vitamin E and cystine deficient diet decreased the coenzyme A content of the liver. The addition of α-tocopherol or selenium to the diet increased the coenzyme level in liver to normal. Selenium and tocopherol had no effect on liver total lipid, cholesterol, phospholipid, or coenzyme Q (*12b*).

The metabolic reaction utilizing Factor 3-selenium in preventing liver necrosis and preventing respiratory decline may utilize different metabolic pathways from those utilized by vitamin E. Alternate metabolic pathways are well known in biochemical reactions. Under such conditions both systems have to be defective before serious metabolic changes occur. Since vitamin E and selenium can take part in oxidation-reduction reactions and participate in hydrogen transfer, this would suggest that the primary lesion may be located in electron transfer (*147*).

The recent discovery of the role of ubiquinone (coenzyme Q) in electron transport (*30*) and the identification of ubichromenol, the cyclized isomer of ubiquinone (*91*), provided a means to determine the relation between cellular oxidation processes and dietary deficiencies of vitamin E and selenium.

The effect of dietary selenium (selenite) in increasing concentrations of both ubiquinone and ubichromenal in tissues is not similar to that of dietary tocopherol in vitamin E-deficient animals. Whereas tocopherol supplementation of the diet increased the ubiquinone concentration in all tissues studied, the administration of selenium to vitamin E-deficient rats significantly increased ubiquinone concentration in the liver but not in the uterus. This may have a bearing on the role of selenium in preventing nutritional liver necrosis in rats, but being ineffective in preventing gestation-resorption (*44, 53, 67*). The above findings provide a biochemical connection for the partial parallelism in the physiological effect of selenium and α-tocopherol.

The effects of tocopherol, vitamin A, selenium, and antioxidants on ubiquinone concentration of tissues of weanling rats maintained on vitamin E-deficient diets indicate that α-tocopherol has two types of functions in preventing deficiency syndromes (*44, 52, 53*). First, it may act in the tissues as an antioxidant, and antioxidants have tocopherol-like action, by sparing vitamin E, thereby preventing vitamin E deficiency in rats. Second, in the rat and the rabbit, α-tocopherol produces an effect upon ubiquinone concentrations which is distinct and different from its antioxidant function. Selenium increases ubiquinone concentration but does not protect against tissue peroxidation in the rat. The finding that selenium is without effect on the ubiquinone concentration in the rat uterus, although it is active in other tissues, may suggest that the nutritional deficiency syndrome which responds to selenium and/or tocopherol may be a specific tissue response. Powerful antioxidants, Santoquin and DPPD, added to the diet had no effect on the ubiquinone level of the tissues (*44, 52, 53*). However, they were able to protect vitamin A and reduce lipid peroxidation in the liver in a manner similar to that of α-tocopherol.

Bieri (*10*) discussed the evidence disputing the idea that antioxidants which are effective in preventing vitamin E deficiency symptoms act by sparing small amounts of tocopherol in the diet or in the body tissues of deficient animals.

Conflicting theories on the antioxidant properties of selenium and tocopherol and their effect on nutritional liver necrosis must be resolved before the mechanism of biochemical effects of these unrelated compounds can be assessed. The significance of the specific tissue ubiquinone response in deficient animals, with selenium and vitamin E treatment at least gives some suggestion why these unrelated compounds have specific effects on such varied disease syndromes which were once considered to be a single vitamin deficiency.

Pathology

Gross pathological changes associated with the dietary necrotic liver degeneration in rats, the cardiac muscle and peripheral muscle degeneration, liver and kidney necrosis, and pancreatic dystrophy in mice have been referred to previously. A list of the pathological manifestations in the various species of animals responsive to Factor 3-selenium are given in Table 52 (*156*).

TABLE 52

Factor 3-Responsive Deficiency Symptoms in Different Species[a]

	Necrosis			Muscular dystrophy	Calcifications	Lung hemorrhage	Pancreas atrophy	Serum protein changes
	Liver	Kidney	Heart					
Rat	+	+	(−)	(+)	+	(+)	(+)	+
Mouse	+	+	+	+		(−)	+	+
Rabbit	+					+		
Mink			+	+				
Hog	+			+				
Sheep			+	+	+			
Calf			+	+	+			
Horse				+				
Trout	+							

KEY: + Pronounced pathological changes; (+) Not always detectable; (—) Occasionally found; Open spaces: not yet investigated. [a] Schwarz and Mertz (*156*).

Gross and microscopic changes associated with the various degenerative diseases are described in every pathological text. The course of dietary necrotic liver degeneration is presented in Table 53 (*147*). Fite (*59*) described the cellular changes in dietary liver necrosis. The nuclear changes observed were karyolysis and karyorrhexis, and he reported the presence of hitherto undescribed granules in the cytoplasm. These granules were distributed evenly and appeared to undergo calcification. These degenerative microgranules were eosinophilic; Fite (*59*) postulated that they developed from degenerating mitochondria.

Studies of liver cells at the various phases of the disease with electron microscopy indicate that degenerative changes occur as early as the seventh day. These changes are elongation and accumulation of microsomes on the surface of mitochondria and early cystic degeneration of microsomes. At the latent phase there are pronounced submicroscopic lesions involving microsomes as well as mitochondria (*127, 147*). These submicroscopic lesions are closely related to the respiratory decline observed in the degenerative liver necrosis in experimental animals (*25, 27, 28*).

TABLE 53
Three Phases of Necrotic Liver Degeneration[a]

	Cellular changes	Duration (days) Fisher strain	Sprague-Dawley strain
Initial phase			
Macros.	:Normal		
Micros.	:Normal	11	25–35
Electron Micros.	:Beginning changes in cytoplasm seen on 7th day.		
Metabol.	:Normal (?)		
Latent phase			
Macros.	:Normal		
Micros.	:Beginning fine changes; degenerative microbodies.	8	10–20
Electron Micros.	:Severe degeneration of cytoplasm and mitochondria.		
Metabol.	:Metabolic insufficiency, respiratory decline		
Terminal phase			
Macros.	:Acute necrosis		
Micros.	:Massive changes	1–2	1–2
Electron Micros.	:———		
Metabol.	:Death		

[a] Schwarz (*147*).

SELENIUM IN CHICK NUTRITION

The disease syndromes associated with vitamin E deficiency in chicks and turkey poults are encephalomalacia, exudative diathesis, muscular dystrophy, gizzard erosion, and hock and adipose tissue disorders. The first three uncomplicated disease syndromes can be produced under proper experimental conditions by the addition of certain dietary stress factors to a vitamin E-deficient diet. The disease syndromes produced by vitamin E-deficient diet responsive to selenium treatment in chicks and poults are exudative diathesis and, to some extent, muscular dystrophy.

Causative Agents

Basal diets used in producing vitamin E deficiency syndromes were prepared by treatment of the diets with ferric chloride or by addition of vitamin E-oxidizing fats to the diet. These procedures served to complicate the disease syndromes and yielded a wide variety of results which made the interpretation difficult. Other dietary stresses such as antibiotics and incompletely balanced proteins or environmental stresses produced irregular and inconsistent disease syndromes in chicks and turkey poults (*1*). The more consistent disease syndrome of exudative diathesis is produced in chicks when Torula yeast is used as the protein source in the diet as indicated in Table 54 (*125, 158*). These diets are nutritionally complete except for vitamin E and biologically available selenium. On these

TABLE 54
Composition of Vitamin E-Deficient Diets

	Grams	Per cent
Torula yeast	40.0[a]	58.5[b]
Cerelose	40.7	28.26
Vitamin E-free lard	5.0	5.0
Calcium gluconate	5.0	—
Cellophane	3.0	3.0
Bone ash	2.0	—
Glycine	0.5	0.5
DL-methionine	0.4	0.3
L-arginine •HCl	0.24	0.24
L-cystine	0.2	—
Salts	2.0[c]	4.2[e]
Vitamins	1.0[d]	1.0[f]

[a] Patterson *et al.* (*125*).

[b] Scott *et al.* (*158*).

[c] Salt supplements in mg/100 gm of diet were: K_2HPO_4, 600; KH_2PO_4, 450; NaCl, 600; $MgSO_4 \cdot 3H_2O$, 250; ferric citrate, 50; $MnSO_4 \cdot H_2O$, 40; $CuSO_4 \cdot 5H_2O$, 2; zinc acetate dihydrate, 1.4; $Al_2(SO_4)_3 \cdot 18H_2O$, 1.6; KBr, 0.8; cobalt acetate tetrahydrate, 0.4; $NiCl_2 \cdot 6H_2O$, 0.2; and $Na_2MoO_4 \cdot 2H_2O$, 0.05.

[d] Vitamin supplements in a cerelose diluent in mg/100 gm of diet were: meso-inositol, 100; calcium pantothenate, 5; niacin, 5; riboflavin, 1; thiamine hydrochloride, 1; pyridoxine•hydrochloride, 1; menadione, 0.027; folic acid, 0.2; biotin, 0.002; and vitamins A and D, 1,000 and 200 units.

[e] Dicalcium phosphate, 2.55; $CaCO_3$, 0.95; NaCl, 0.6; $FeSO_4 \cdot 7H_2O$, 0.054; $MnSO_4 \cdot H_2O$, 0.036; KI, 0.003; $CoCl_2 \cdot 6H_20$, 0.002%.

[f] Thiamine•HCl, 0.2; riboflavin, 0.4; niacin, 2.7; calcium pantothenate, 1.5; pyridoxine•HCl, 0.45; biotin, 0.015; folic acid, 0.08; vitamin K (menadione), 0.08; vitamin B_{12}, 0.0005 mg and vitamin A, 459 IU; vitamin D_3, 30 I.C.U. per 100 gm of diet.

diets chicks develop exudative diathesis within 3 weeks and die by the end of the fourth week. The disease could be prevented by α-tocopherol selenium but not by γ-tocopherol or antioxidants (*122*). Subsequent studies with Torula yeast diets supplemented with higher concentrations of antioxidants prevented exudative diathesis in chicks (*12, 95*). The disease develops in the chicks in the absence of added unsaturated fatty acids and the incidence of the lesions is not affected by supplementary fat in the diet.

Muscular dystrophy can be produced in chicks by the omission of the sulfur amino acids from the Torula yeast diets. The addition of vitamin E to the diet prevents the development of muscular dystrophy and selenium (near subtoxic dose) reduces the incidence of the disease in chicks but does not completely prevent the syndrome (*42, 118*).

Experimental Observations

Exudative Diathesis

Simultaneous reports by Schwarz *et al.* (*144*) and Patterson *et al.* (*125*) proved conclusively that the exudative diathesis in the chick produced by vitamin E-free Torula yeast diets could be prevented by the addition of Factor 3 or inorganic selenium compounds. As a result of these investigations the role of selenium in nutritional diseases in birds became of paramount importance.

The inclusion of Factor 3 (crude or purified fractions), Na_2SeO_3, or selenocystathionine and *d*-α-tocopheryl acetate in the Torula yeast diets prevented exudative diathesis in the chick and stimulated growth (*144*). Similar results were reported by the addition of a nonfat soluble substance of casein, a number of pork tissue fractions, and selenium (selenite) to the Torula yeast diets of chicks. The disease syndrome could also be prevented by the inclusion of 40 units of tocopheryl acetate per kilogram of diet. Dietary tellurium, as tellurite, at 3 ppm and arsenic at 10 ppm were ineffective in preventing the development of exudative diathesis in the chick (*125*).

Subsequent studies confirmed the effectiveness of selenium (inorganic selenium or Factor 3-selenium) in preventing exudative diathesis in chicks and poults, and in some cases it improved the growth rate. Seleniferous milk obtained from lactating cow (given Na_2SeO_3) was more effective in preventing exudative diathesis than selenite, but had no significant effect on growth rate (*101a*). Selenium was effective in preventing exudative diathesis in chicks when added to the Torula yeast diet or a soybean meal diet. When diets other than Torula yeast were used, the growth stimulating effect of selenium was difficult to evaluate. The dietary requirements for selenium are so low that highly purified diets contain enough biologically active selenium to be adequate for growth stimulation (*12a, 32, 41, 56, 131–133, 159–161, 183*).

The disease syndromes responsive to vitamin E and selenium in chicks and poults are given in Table 55.

The nutritional relationship of selenium and vitamin E on Torula yeast diet, isolated soybean protein diet, or purified amino acid diet indicated that selenium was necessary for maximum growth of chicks on Torula yeast diet whether vitamin E was present or absent. The demonstration of specific requirements for selenium without Torula yeast were unsuccessful. Either vitamin E or selenium prevented the exudative diathesis

TABLE 55
Diseases Affected by Vitamin E and Selenium in Chicks and Turkey Poults[a]

Disease	Prophylactic agent	
	Vitamin E	Selenium
Testicular degeneration in male	—	—
Reproduction in female	+	—
Muscular dystrophy	+	Partial
Exudative diathesis	+	+
Encephalomalacia	+	—
Anemia	+	+
Reduced plasma albumin	+	+
Steatitis (yellow fat disease)	+	Not known
Enlarged hock disorders (turkeys)	+	—

[a] References are given in the various sections dealing with the diseases.
+ Complete protection; — Not effective.

that occurred when the above diets were fed, but no growth improvement was obtained from added selenium when the diets were adequate in vitamin E (*119*).

The efficacy of Torula yeast diet to develop vitamin E deficiency syndrome in chicks and poults may be due to the chemical composition of the diet. The yeast is low in selenium, i.e., biologically available selenium, high in ash and unsaturated fatty acid, and may contain a selenium or vitamin E antagonist (*131*). The possibility that the biochemical function of vitamin E in exudative diathesis is as a nonspecific antioxidant in the presence of dietary selenium has been suggested.

The feeding of purified vitamin E-free casein or purified soybean protein diets without added vitamin E or fat to the chicks, showed that the birds developed normally for 6 to 12 months and tocopherols could not be found in serum or eggs. This suggested that α-tocopherol is not essential for growth and development of chicks in the absence of a high concentration of fat (*8, 10, 21*). After feeding a vitamin E-free diet (soybean protein) with lard, sulfur amino acids, and vitamins, the chicks developed exudative diathesis. With higher levels of lard and with selenium in the diet, encephalomalacia occurred, which could be prevented by α-tocopherol or antioxidants (*8, 10*). These investigators suggested that the probable biochemical function of vitamin E in chicks is as a nonspecific antioxidant.

The effectiveness of antioxidants against exudative diathesis depends on the diet used. A large number of antioxidants were found to be ineffective against the disease in chicks fed a diet containing Torula yeast (*158*). Ethoxyquin, at 0.1 per cent, was reported to be effective against exudative diathesis in chicks fed diets containing Torula yeast (*11, 12, 95*). In a Torula yeast-coconut oil ration, 0.1 per cent Santoquin or 1.4 ppm selenium prevented exudative diathesis in the chicks (*56*). The addition of ethoxyquin and *dl*-α-tocopheryl acetate to Torula yeast, soybean protein or purified casein diet, reduced the incidence of exudative diathesis, encephalomalacia, and white striation of breast muscle of chicks. There was complete depression of lipid autoxidation in all tissue except the brain. With the addition of selenium (SeO_2) and cystine to soybean protein, casein, or gelatin diets prevented exudative diathesis and depressed to some degree the lipid peroxidation of fat in some tissues (*11, 12, 169*).

The discrepancy in the above observations concerning the effects of antioxidants on exudative diathesis is difficult to correlate since coconut oil does not contain large amounts of unsaturated fatty acids. Further studies may clarify the functions of antioxidants in exudative diathesis.

The effects of dietary selenium and vitamin E on reproduction were not fully investigated. A few experimental studies on the hatchability of eggs of chickens and turkeys indicate that a lack of vitamin E in the diet lowers hatchability and the addition of vitamin E improves hatchability, but selenium (Na_2SeO_3) is without any effect (*33*).

Feeding semi-purified diets containing Torula or dried Brewer's yeast as the major source of protein to hens indicated that egg production and the hatchability of eggs was markedly lowered. Mortality of the offspring was increased by the use of the Torula yeast diet, but not by the use of a Brewer's yeast diet. The addition of vitamin E to the Torula yeast diet prevented low hatchability and high mortality of chicks. Antioxidants (DPPD, 2,6-di-*tert*-butyl-*p*-cresol) or selenium, when added to the Torula yeast diet (hens), had little or no effect on either hatchability of eggs or chick mortality (*78*).

Muscular Dystrophy

The disease syndrome of muscular dystrophy in chicks has a complex dietary etiology and was described by a number of investigators (*24, 40, 92, 118*). Muscular dystrophy in chicks can be produced by vitamin E-deficient diets low in sulfur amino acids or if these amino acids are omitted from the Torula yeast diet. The addition of vitamin E, methionine, or cystine to the diet will prevent the development of the disease. Under some experimental conditions antioxidants may be effective in the prevention of muscular degeneration in chicks (*56, 93, 94*).

Muscular dystrophy in chicks is less responsive to selenium administration than exudative diathesis (*122*). The effectiveness of a high level (5 ppm) of selenium in reducing (but not preventing completely) the incidence of muscular dystrophy in chicks has been reported by Dam and Søndergaard (*42*). A comparatively high level of selenium (1.0–5.0 mg per kg of diet) was required to reduce the incidence of the disease. The supplementation of the dystrophy-producing diets of chicks severely depleted of vitamin E with either 2.5 mg D-α-tocopheryl acetate or 1.0 mg selenium (Na_2SeO_3) per kilogram of diet had no effect on muscular dystrophy. If the same amounts of selenium and vitamin E were added together to the diets, then the disease was prevented (*164*). These results suggest that selenium as well as vitamin E is involved in the prevention of muscular dystrophy in chicks. The addition of methionine, cystine, or vitamin E singly to the deficient diet completely prevented muscular dystrophy in chicks (*23a, 23b*).

Torula yeast-cerelose diet supplemented with selenium (1 ppm) was as effective as vitamin E in preventing gizzard and skeletal muscular dystrophy in turkey poults (*78a*). Ethoxyquin (0.025%) had only slight effect on the incidence of skeletal dystrophy. Neither DL-methionine (0.4%) nor L-cystine (0.15%) reduced the incidence of dystrophy. It appears that turkey poults resemble more closely certain mammalian species than chicks in the development of nutritional muscular dystrophy.

The functional groups are not the methyl or sulfhydryl groups of methionine since the methyl donors (betaine and choline) and sulfhydryl-containing compounds (sodium thioglycolate and 2,3-mercaptopropanol) did not prevent muscular dystrophy in chicks. Deficiency of arginine and glycine, which are creatine precursors, did not result in a higher incidence of muscular dystrophy. In fact, arginine deficiency prevented the development of muscular dystrophy (*119, 121*).

The interrelation of sulfur amino acids, arginine, selenium, and vitamin E indicates that the synthesis of creatine or the function of methionine as methyl donor are not directly involved in the prevention of muscular dystrophy in chicks. Cystine is essential for the prevention of the disease in chicks. The mechanism whereby a small amount of cystine (0.15%) (*162*) with certain diets prevents muscular dystrophy is not known at the present. Selenium contamination in the sulfur amino acids is negligible since the amount of cystine or methionine used for the prevention of the disease could not contain sufficient amounts of selenium (as contaminant) to be effective. The addition of α-tocopheryl acetate to low-methionine, low-cystine diet completely prevented the development of dystrophy, but there was a decrease in the growth of the chicks (*163*). There is a fundamental biochemical correlation among the metabolisms of sulfur amino acids, arginine, and vitamin E during the development of muscular dystrophy in chicks. The clarification of these interrelations is essential for the understanding of the many metabolic malfunctions of muscles.

Encephalomalacia

This disease does not respond to selenium treatment. It is discussed briefly to indicate that the various syndromes which were once considered as vitamin E deficiency may have different etiology and that these syndromes may be the manifestations of multideficiencies in the diet. The differential response of this disease to selenium and tocopherol suggests that selenium and vitamin E may have different and distinct functions in the biological systems. The lack of biological effects of selenium in this disease could not be related to the failure of selenium to pass through the blood-brain barrier since the injection of selenium into the animals always is followed by an increase of selenium in the brain.

Nutritional encephalomalacia was among the first vitamin E deficiency diseases recognized in the chick, and probably is identical with the so-called "crazy chick" disease (*124*). The predominant clinical signs are ataxia, head retraction, and spasms of leg muscles followed by prostration. The lesions are general disintegration of the cerebellum with brain hemorrhage and edema. Prevention of encephalomalacia by administration of vitamin E was first reported by Dam *et al.* (*37*).

A number of substances, including antioxidants, can substitute for vitamin E and give complete or partial protection against dietary encephalomalacia (*22, 39, 167*).

While selenium is effective in preventing exudative diathesis and some degree of growth repression and can reduce the incidence of muscular dystrophy, it appears to be ineffective in the prevention of encephalomalacia in chicks on vitamin E-deficient diets (*2, 3, 8, 41, 117*).

Symptoms of Selenium-Responsive Diseases in Chicks and Poults

Exudative Diathesis

Exudative diathesis is an edema of subcutaneous fatty tissues with abnormal permeability of the capillary walls (*36*). In severe cases there is an accumulation of fluid throughout the body with the greatest amount of fluid under the ventral skin. Surface distention of the pericardium and edema-associated hemorrhages in the subcutaneous tissues gives a green-

the prevention of hemorrhages in the tissue and not to enhanced hemoglobin formation (*131, 133*).

The postulated mechanisms responsible for the marked outflow of exudate to the subcutaneous tissues may be due to capillary damage (*38*) or to changes in the osmotic pressure of the vascular system (*63*). Bieri and Pollard (*9*) described the following sequence of events in the serum protein changes in exudative diathesis: (1) changes occurred in serum protein concomitant with the appearance of exudate in vitamin E-deficient chicks; (2) decreases in the A/G ratio preceded the onset of the disease by 2 to 3 days; (3) decreases in total protein were evident in some chicks while in others there were no changes; (4) during recovery when chicks appeared normal, A/G ratios were often lower than when the exudates were present. The authors concluded that the damage to the capillaries was the primary lesion in the development of exudative diathesis due to formation of peroxides in the tissues. Vitamin E effect is due to its antioxidant properties. The mechanism of selenium action must be other than that of an antioxidant in the usual sense (*9*). The re-establishment of normal serum protein pattern by vitamin E and selenium is by preventing the effusion in the tissues and not by a direct function in protein synthesis.

An exudative diathesis-inducing diet of chicks (*158*) increased the hemolysis of red blood cells with the addition of dialuric acid solution, while red blood cells of chicks which received the basal diet plus *dl-α*-tocopheryl acetate (25 mg per kg of diet) did not show significant hemolysis *in vitro* (*116*). Studies of the effects of dietary selenium and vitamin E on the hemolysis of red blood cells in vitamin E-deficient chicks indicate that the rate of hemolysis of red blood cells was the same as when the basal diets were fed without selenium. The addition of vitamin E to the diet depressed the rate of hemolysis to a very low level in chicks receiving the basal diets (*60*).

In vivo and *in vitro* measurements of lipid peroxidation in the various tissues of vitamin E-deficient chicks were correlated with the disease syndromes which occur on this diet (*172a*). Some reduction of lipid peroxidation in liver and muscle of vitamin E-deficient chicks was observed when the diet was supplemented with selenium. Vitamin E and cystine were more effective in reducing lipid peroxidation in the tissues of the chicks than selenium (*7*).

Decrease of peroxidative changes in the body fat in chicks which received selenium (5 ppm) has been reported (*41*). The direct addition of cystine and selenium to the tissue homogenate of depleted chicks did not reduce peroxidation (*7, 11*). Ineffectiveness of selenium (Na_2SeO_3) to prevent *in vitro* peroxidation in liver tissues has been reported previously (*94*). Increased *in vivo* lipid peroxidation products in chick liver, heart and leg muscle were reported when chicks were fed Torula yeast diet.

Dietary vitamin E and selenite inhibited lipid peroxidation in the tissues studied. *In vitro* studies, using liver homogenate, showed that selenite was less effective than vitamin E in the prevention of lipid peroxidation. Using a model system for testing the antioxidant activity of organic seleno-compounds, sulfur amino acids, and α-tocopherol, Zalkin *et al.* (*183*) showed that some organic seleno-compounds were as effective antioxidants as α-tocopherol and sulfur amino acids.

The presence of lipid antioxidants were reported in tissue fractions of selenium-fed chickens, rats, and sheep (*67a*). Seleniferous sheep kidney fraction had the highest antioxidant activity. Rat liver fraction contained no lipid antioxidant. Antioxidant activity of the seleno-protein(s) was independent of other antioxidants (α-tocopherol, ascorbic acid, and ascorbic acid plus glutathione).

Several experimental studies indicate that the degree of lipid peroxidation in the various tissues depended on the diet used. In all these experiments *dl*-α-tocopheryl acetate and ethoxyquin prevented lipid peroxidation in all tissues except the brain. Cystine was effective in inhibiting peroxidation only in the muscle tissues. Selenium was partially effective in significantly reducing peroxidation in the liver, but the amount of reduction was not as large as that observed with vitamin E and ethoxyquin. In fact, in lung, lipid peroxidation increased with the addition of selenium or cystine to the diet whenever that tissue was included in the studies. On the basis of these observations the authors concluded that the function of vitamin E in metabolism is as an antioxidant, and it was suggested that selenium and cystine act in a similar manner (*10, 11, 12, 169*).

The fact that vitamin E, antioxidants, and selenium do not prevent lipid peroxidation in the brain but vitamin E or antioxidants prevent encephalomalacia merits comment at the present state of knowledge. This is an interesting biochemical phenomenon where the disease syndrome, encephalomalacia, is prevented by vitamin E and antioxidants, but the biochemical lesion associated with the disease, peroxidation, is not altered in the affected organ.

The increase of lipid peroxidation in the lung with the addition of selenium to the diet poses a question as to whether in chicks, as well as in laboratory animals and livestock, selenium is eliminated by the respiratory system and whether the elimination of selenium by the lung would influence the peroxidation of that tissue.

An alternate biochemical system as to the function of selenium and vitamin E in deficiency disease in rats has been suggested, and it is based upon the effects of vitamin E and selenium upon the ubiquinone (coenzyme Q) content of tissue. Supplementing the deficient diets of turkey poults and pigeons with selenium and α-tocopherol indicated that the ubiquinone level in tissues of the birds showed differences in response to selenium or tocopherol. Increase in ubiquinone level of breast muscle followed vitamin E supplementation, but with selenium the liver showed the most pronounced increase (*44a*). These interrelations have been discussed in some detail in the section dealing with Biochemical Changes in laboratory animals.

The conflicting results of various investigators in some of these studies suggest that a certain amount of caution is needed in the interpretation of the results obtained from *in vitro* and *in vivo* experimentation before ascribing specific biochemical functions of vitamin E or selenium in the various disease syndromes of chicks and poults.

SELENIUM IN HUMAN NUTRITION

The "protein malnutrition" disease, kwashiorkor, may be associated with Factor 3 deficiency (*157*). Preliminary trials were carried out in Jamaica on 2 children having a relatively infrequent disease syndrome which is characterized by a very slow or no weight gain after overcoming the initial acute phase. The daily supplement of 25 μg of selenium as γ, γ'-diselenodivaleric acid gave immediate response in weight gain and increase in food intake. The finding is very preliminary, but it suggests that selenium deficiency in humans may be as important a factor in some disease syndromes as in other animals.

PROPOSED EXPERIMENTATION

The response of various disease syndromes to Factor 3-selenium and selenium compounds suggests studies with selenium indicator plants and seleniferous grains. It would be of considerable theoretical, as well as practical, importance to determine the biological effectiveness of these plants against various disease syndromes in animals. The difference between the toxic and prophylactic dose of selenium provided by these plants should be determined. These studies may furnish information on possible chemical characteristics of seleno-compounds contained in the plants and the effectiveness of the compounds in deficiency diseases.

Studies on the dietary effect of selenium in vitamin E-deficiency syndromes may aid in the dilemma of the metabolic function of vitamin E and resolving the relatively nonspecific diffuse deficiency syndromes now considered as vitamin E deficiency.

References

1. Ames, S. R. 1956. Role of vitamin E (α-tocopherol) in poultry nutrition and disease. *Poultry Sci.* **35:**145–159.
2. Ames, S. R. 1957. Interrelationships of vitamin E with selenium and other nutrients. *Eastern Feed Merchant* 8:40–42.
3. Ames, S. R. and W. J. Swanson. 1958. Growth response to vitamin E in chicks receiving a high-fat diet. *Federation Proc.* **17,** Part 1:181.
4. Aterman, K. 1958. Selenium and liver necrosis in the hyperthyroid rat. *Nature* **182:**1514.

5. Aterman, K. 1959. Selenium, liver necrosis and depigmentation of incisors in the rat. *Brit. J. Nutrition* **13**:38–41.
6. Bacigalupo, F. A., R. Culik, R. W. Luecke, F. Thorp, Jr., and R. L. Johnston. 1952. Further studies on vitamin E deficiency in the lamb. *J. Animal Sci.* **11**: 609–620.
7. Bieri, J. G. 1959. An effect of selenium and cystine on lipid peroxidation in tissues deficient in vitamin E. *Nature* **184**:1148–1149.
8. Bieri, J. G. and G. M. Briggs. 1959. Nonessentiality of vitamin E for normal growth and development of the chick. *Federation Proc.* **18**:517.
9. Bieri, J. G. and C. J. Pollard. 1959. Serum protein changes in vitamin E-deficient chicks. *J. Nutrition* **69**:301–305.
10. Bieri, J. G. 1960. Current aspects of vitamin A, vitamin E, and selenium in poultry nutrition. *World's Poultry Sci. J.* **16**:245–258.
11. Bieri, J. G. 1961. The nature of the action of selenium in replacing vitamin E. *Am. J. Clin. Nutrition* **9**:89–96.
12. Bieri, J. G., H. Dam, I. Prange, and E. Søndergaard. 1961. Effect of dietary selenium dioxide, cystine, ethoxyquin and vitamin E on lipid autoxidation in chick tissues. *Acta Physiol. Scand.* **52**:36–43.
12a. Bieri, J. G. 1963. Selenium as a "dietary protective factor." *Federation Proc.* **22**:318.
12b. Bieri, J. G. and E. L. Andrew. 1963. Metabolic effects of selenium as related to vitamin E. *J. Am. Oil Chem. Soc.* **40**:365–368.
13. Blaxter, K. L. and F. Brown. 1952–53. Vitamin E in the nutrition of farm animals. *Nutrition Abstr. and Rev.* **22**:1–21.
14. Blaxter, K. L., P. S. Watts and W. A. Wood. 1952. The nutrition of the young Ayrshire calf. 8. Muscular dystrophy in the growing calf. *Brit. J. Nutrition* **6**: 125–144.
15. Blaxter, K. L. and W. A. Wood. 1952. The nutrition of the young Ayrshire calf. 9. Composition of the tissues of normal and dystrophic calves. *Brit. J. Nutrition* **6**:144–163.
16. Blaxter, K. L., W. A. Wood and A. M. MacDonald. 1953. The nutrition of the young Ayrshire calf. 11. The toxicity of cod-liver oil. *Brit. J. Nutrition* **7**:34–50.
17. Blaxter, K. L., F. Brown and A. M. MacDonald. 1953. Nutrition of the young Ayrshire calf. 12. Factors affecting the tocopherol reserves, muscle composition and muscle histology of four-day-old calves. *Brit. J. Nutrition* **7**:105–123.
18. Blaxter, K. L. and G. A. M. Sharman. 1953. Prevention and cure of enzootic muscular dystrophy in beef cattle. *Nature* **172**:1006.
19. Blincoe, C. and W. B. Dye. 1958. Serum transaminase in white muscle disease. *J. Animal Sci.* **17**:224–226.
20. Bloch, K., R. Schoenheimer and D. Rittenberg. 1941. Rate of formation and disappearance of body creatine in normal animals. *J. Biol. Chem.* **138**:155–166.
21. Briggs, G. M., M. R. Spivey Fox and J. G. Bieri. 1956. Growth of chicks without dietary vitamin E. *Poultry Sci.* **55**:1134.
22. Bunnell, R. H., L. D. Matterson, E. P. Singsen, L. M. Potter, A. Kozeff and E. L. Jungherr. 1954. Studies on encephalomalacia in the chick. 3. The influence of feeding or injecting various tocopherols or other antioxidants on the incidence of encephalomalacia. *Poultry Sci.* **34**:1068–1075.
23. Bunyan, J., E. E. Edwin and J. Green. 1958. Protective effect of trace elements other than selenium against dietary necrotic liver degeneration. *Nature* **181**: 1801.

23a. Calvert, C. C., M. C. Nesheim, and M. L. Scott. 1962. Effectiveness of selenium in prevention of nutritional muscular dystrophy in the chick. *Proc. Soc. Exptl. Biol. Med.* **109:**16–18.

23b. Calvert, C. C. and M. L. Scott. 1963. Effect of selenium on requirement for vitamin E and cystine for the prevention of nutritional muscular dystrophy in the chick. *Federation Proc.* **22:**318.

24. Cater, D. B. 1951. The effect upon the growth of Rous sarcoma of a diet deficient in vitamin E. *J. Pathol. Bacteriol.* **63:**599–608.

25. Chernick, S. S., J. G. Moe, G. P. Rodnan and K. Schwarz. 1955. A metabolic lesion in dietary necrotic liver degeneration. *J. Biol. Chem.* **217:**829–843.

26. Christensen, F., H. Dam, I. Prange and E. Søndergaard. 1958. The effect of selenium on vitamin E-deficient rats. *Acta Pharmacol. Toxicol.* **15:**181–188.

26a. Connoly, J. D. and K. Schwarz. 1963. Effect of vitamin E, selenium and methionine on α-ketoglutarate oxidase activity of rat liver mitochondria. *Federation Proc.* **22:**652.

27. Corwin, L. M. and K. Schwarz. 1960. Maintenance of α-ketoglutarate and succinate oxidation in vitamin E-deficient liver homogenates by α-tocopherol metabolite, menadione and diphenylphenylenediamine. *Nature* **186:**1048.

28. Corwin, L. M. and K. Schwarz. 1960. Prevention of decline of α-ketoglutarate and succinate oxidation in vitamin E-deficient rat liver homogenates. *J. Biol. Chem.* **235:**3387–3392.

29. Cramer, D. A. 1960. Effects of selenite upon the chemical nature of tissue abnormalities in white muscle disease of lambs. Ph.D. Thesis. Oregon State University, Corvallis, Oregon.

30. Crane, F. L., Y. Hatefi, R. L. Lester and C. Widmer. 1957. Isolation of a quinone from beef heart mitochondria. *Biochim. Biophys. Acta* **25:**220–221.

31. Creech, B. G., G. L. Feldman, T. M. Ferguson, B. L. Reid and J. R. Couch. 1957. Exudative diathesis and vitamin E deficiency in turkey poults. *J. Nutrition* **62:**83–96.

32. Creech, B. G., M. M. Rahman, B. L. Reid and J. R. Couch. 1958. Exudative diathesis in chicks. *J. Nutrition* **64:**55–56.

33. Creger, C. R., R. H. Mitchell, R. L. Atkinson, T. M. Ferguson, B. L. Reid and J. R. Couch. 1960. Vitamin E activity of selenium in turkey hatchability. *Poultry Sci.* **39:**59–63.

34. Culik, R., F. A. Bacigalupo, F. Thorp, Jr., R. W. Luecke and R. H. Nelson. 1951. Vitamin E deficiency in the lamb. *J. Animal Sci.* **10:**1006–1016.

35. Daft, F. S., W. H. Sebrell and R. D. Lillie. 1939. Prevention by cystine or methionine of hemorrhage and necrosis of the liver in rats. *Proc. Soc. Exptl. Biol. Med.* **50:**1–5.

36. Dam, H. and J. Glavind. 1938. Alimentary exudative diathesis. *Nature* **142:**1077–1078.

37. Dam, H., J. Glavind, O. Bernth and E. Hagens. 1938. Antiencephalomalacia activity of *dl,α*-tocopherol. *Nature* **142:**1157–1158.

38. Dam, H. and J. Glavind. 1940. Vitamin E und kapillarpermeabilitat. *Naturwissenschaften* **28:**207.

39. Dam, H., I. Kruse, I. Prange and E. Søndergaard. 1951. Substances affording partial protection against certain vitamin E deficiency symptoms. *Acta Physiol. Scand.* **22:**299–310.

40. Dam, H., I. Prange and E. Søndergaard. 1952. Muscular degeneration (white striation of muscles) in chicks reared on vitamin E-deficient, low-fat diets. *Acta Pathol. Microbiol. Scand.* **31:**172–184.

41. Dam, H., G. K. Nielsen, I. Prange and E. Søndergaard. 1957. The exudative diathesis produced by Torula yeast. *Experientia* **13**:493–494.
42. Dam, H., and E. Søndergaard. 1957. Prophylactic effect of selenium dioxide against degeneration (white striation) of muscles in chicks. *Experientia* **13**:494.
43. DeWitt, W. B. and K. Schwarz. 1958. Multiple dietary necrotic degeneration in the mouse. *Experientia* **14**:28–34.
44. Diplock, A. T., E. E. Edwin, J. Bunyan and J. Green. 1961. The effect of tocopherol, vitamin A, selenium and anti-oxidants on ubiquinone in the rat. *Brit. J. Nutrition* **15**:425–441.
44a. Diplock, A. T., J. Bunyan, E. E. Edwin and J. Green. 1962. Tocopherol, selenium and ubiquinone in the turkey and pigeon. *Brit. J. Nutr.* **16**:109–114.
45. Drake, C., A. B. Grant and W. J. Hartley. 1959. Use of selenium for white muscle disease in lambs. *New Zealand J. Agr.* **98**:252.
46. Drake, C., A. B. Grant and W. J. Hartley. 1959. Selenium and animal health. *Ruakura Farmers' Conf. Week Proc.* Hamilton, N. Zealand, pp. 61–71.
47. Drake, C., A. B. Grant and W. J. Hartley. 1960. Selenium and animal health. Part 1. The effect of α-tocopherol and selenium in the control of field outbreaks of white muscle disease in lambs. *New Zealand Vet. J.* **8**:4–8.
48. Drake, C., A. B. Grant and W. J. Hartley. 1960. Selenium and animal health. Part 2. The effect of selenium on unthrifty weaned lambs. *New Zealand Vet. J.* **8**:9–11.
49. Draper, H. H. 1956. N, N′-Diphenyl-*p*-phenylene-diamine in prevention of vitamin E deficiency in the lamb. *J. Animal Sci.* **15**:115.
50. Draper, H. H. 1957. Ineffectiveness of selenium in the treatment of nutritional muscular dystrophy in the rabbit. *Nature* **180**:1419.
51. du Vigneaud, V., H. M. Dyer and M. W. Kies. 1939. A relationship between the nature of the vitamin B complex supplement and the ability of homocystine to replace methionine in the diet. *J. Biol. Chem.* **130**:325–340.
52. Edwin, E. E., J. Bunyan, A. T. Diplock and J. Green. 1961. Role of tocopherol, selenium and anti-oxidants in the rat. *Nature* **189**:747–748.
53. Edwin, E. E., A. T. Diplock, J. Bunyan and J. Green. 1961. Studies on vitamin E. 6. The distribution of vitamin E in the rat and the effect of α-tocopherol and dietary selenium on ubiquinone and ubichromenol in the tissues. *Biochem. J.* **79**:91–105.
54. Eggert, R. G., E. Patterson, W. T. Akers and E. L. R. Stokstad. 1957. The role of vitamin E and selenium in the nutrition of the pig. *J. Animal Sci.* **16**:1037.
55. Ellis, W. W. 1957. Tissue chemistry and attempted experimental production of white muscle disease. Ph.D. Thesis. Oregon State College. pp. 1–143. Corvallis, Oregon.
56. Erwin, E. S., W. Sterner, R. S. Gordon, L. J. Machlin and L. L. Tureen. 1961. Etiology of muscular dystrophy in the lamb and chick. *J. Nutrition* **75**:45–50.
57. Fenn, W. O. and M. Goettsch. 1939. Electrolytes in nutritional muscular dystrophy in rabbits. *J. Biol. Chem.* **120**:41–50.
58. Fink, H. 1959. New possibilities of preventing the liver-necrosis properties of (roller-dried) skim milk powder. *Milchwissenschaft* **14**:324–327.
59. Fite, G. L. 1954. The pathology of dietary liver necrosis—a preliminary report. *Ann. N.Y. Acad. Sci.* **57**:831.
59a. Gardiner, M. R., J. Armstrong, H. Fels and R. H. Glencross. 1962. A preliminary report on selenium and animal health in western Australia. *Exptl. Agr. Animal Husbandry* **2**:261–269.

60. Gitler, C., M. L. Sunde and C. A. Baumann. 1958. Effect of certain necrosis-preventing factors on hemolysis in vitamin E-deficient rats and chicks. *J. Nutrition* **65**:397–407.
61. Goettsch, M. and E. F. Brown. 1932. Muscle creatine in nutritional muscular dystrophy of the rabbit. *J. Biol. Chem.* **97**:549–561.
62. Goettsch, M. 1961. Failure of certain American yeasts and of selenium to prevent chronic muscular dystrophy in the young rat. *J. Nutrition* **74**:161–166.
63. Goldstein, J. and M. L. Scott. 1956. An electrophoretic study of exudative diathesis in chicks. *J. Nutrition* **60**:349–359.
64. Grant, C. A., and B. Thafvelin. 1958. Selenium and vitamin E. *Nord. Veterinarmed.* **10**:657. Cited by Schultze, M. O. 1960. *Ann. Rev. Biochem.* **29**: 391–412.
65. Green, J., E. E. Edwin, J. Bunyan and A. T. Diplock. 1960. Studies on vitamin E. II. Reversal of respiratory decline in nutritional liver necrosis by intraportal administration of tocopherols and other substances. *Biochem. J.* **75**:456–460.
66. Green, J., A. T. Diplock, J. Bunyan, E. E. Edwin and D. McHale. 1961. Ubiquinone (coenzyme Q) and the function of vitamin E. *Nature* **190**:318–325.
67. Green, J., E. E. Edwin, A. T. Diplock and J. Bunyan. 1961. Role of selenium in relation to ubiquinone in the rat. *Nature* **189**:748–749.
67a. Hamilton, J. W. and A. L. Tappel. 1963. Lipid antioxidant activity in tissues and proteins of selenium-fed animals. *J. Nutrition* **79**:493–502.
68. Harris, P. L., M. I. Ludwig and K. Schwarz, 1958. Ineffectiveness of Factor 3-active selenium compounds in resorption-gestation bioassay for vitamin E. *Proc. Soc. Exptl. Biol. Med.* **97**:686–688.
69. Hartley, W. J., A. B. Grant and C. Drake. 1960. Recent advances in selenium and animal health. *Proc. Lincoln Sheep Farmers' Conf., New Zealand, May, 1960* **10**:29–32.
70. Hartley, W. J., A. B. Grant and C. Drake. 1960. Recent advances in selenium and animal health. *Massey Agr. Coll. Sheepfarming Ann.* pp. 43–48.
71. Hartley, W. J. and A. B. Grant. 1961. A review of selenium responsive diseases of New Zealand livestock. *Federation Proc.* **20,** Part 1:679–688.
72. Heinrich, M. R. and H. A. Mattill. 1943. Lipids of muscle and brain in rats deprived of tocopherol. *Proc. Soc. Exptl. Biol. Med.* **52**:344–346.
73. Hock, A. and H. Fink. 1943. Über eine schwere ernährungsbedingte Stoffwechselstörung und ihre Verhütung durch Cystin. *Hoppe-Seyler's Z. physiol. Chem.* **278**:136–142.
74. Hogue, D. E. 1958. Vitamin E, selenium and other factors related to nutritional muscular dystrophy in lambs. *Proc. Cornell Nutrition Conf. Feed Manf., Ithaca, New York,* pp. 32–39.
75. Hogue, D. E., J. F. Proctor, R. G. Warner and J. K. Loosli, 1962. Relation of selenium, vitamin E and an unidentified factor to muscular dystrophy (stiff-lamb or white muscle disease) in the lamb. *J. Animal Sci.* **21**:25–29.
76. Hove, E. L., G. S. Fry and K. Schwarz. 1958. Ineffectiveness of Factor 3-active selenium compounds in muscular dystrophy of rabbits on vitamin E-free diets. *Proc. Soc. Exptl. Biol. Med.* **98**:27–29.
77. Irving, J. T. 1959. Curative effect of selenium upon the incisor teeth of rats deficient in vitamin E. *Nature* **184**:645–646.
78. Jensen, L. S. and J. McGinnis. 1960. Influence of selenium, antioxidants and type of yeast on vitamin E deficiency in the adult chicken. *J. Nutrition* **72**: 23–28.

78a. Jensen, L. S. and E. D. Walter. 1963. Effect of interrelated factors on expression of a vitamin E deficiency in turkeys. *Federation Proc.* **22,** Part 1:942.

79. Jolly, R. D. 1960. A preliminary experiment to investigate the optimum dose rate and frequency of administration of selenium to unthrifty lambs. *New Zealand Vet. J.* **8:**11–12.

80. Karmen, A., F. Wroblewski and E. S. LaDue. 1955. Transaminase activity in human blood. *J. Clin. Invest.* **34:**126–133.

81. Kelleher, W. J., C. Gitler, M. L. Sunde, M. J. Johnson and C. A. Baumann. 1959. Antinecrogenic property of Torula yeast treated in various ways. *J. Nutrition* **67:**433–444.

82. Knowlton, G. C. and H. M. Hines. 1938. Effect of vitamin E deficiency diet upon skeletal muscle. *Proc. Soc. Exptl. Biol. Med.* **38:**665–667.

83. Knowlton, G. C., H. M. Hines and K. M. Brinkhous. 1939. The effect of wheat germ oil on vitamin E-deficient muscular dystrophy. *Proc. Soc. Exptl. Biol. Med.* **41:**453–456.

84. Krishnamurthy, S. and J. G. Bieri. 1961. An effect of dietary selenium on hemolysis and lipid autoxidation of erythrocytes from vitamin E deficient rats. *Biochem. Biophys. Res. Comm.* **4:**384–387.

85. Kuttler, K. L. and D. W. Marble. 1958. Relationship of serum transaminase to naturally occurring and artificially induced white muscle disease in calves and lambs. *Am. J. Vet. Res.* **19:**632–636.

86. Kuttler, K. L. and D. W. Marble. 1959. White muscle disease in lambs. *Univ. of Nevada Agr. Expt. Sta. Bull.* **207:**2–15.

87. Kuttler, K. L. and D. W. Marble. 1960. Prevention of white muscle disease in lambs by oral and subcutaneous administration of selenium. *Am. J. Vet. Res.* **21:**437–440.

88. Kuttler, K. L., D. W. Marble and C. Blincoe. 1961. Serum and tissue residues following selenium injections in sheep. *Am. J. Vet. Res.* **22:**422–428.

89. Lagace, A. 1961. Effect of selenium on white muscle disease in lambs. *J. Am. Vet. Med. Assoc.* **138:**188–190.

90. Lagace, A., D. S. Bell, A. L. Moxon and W. D. Pounden. 1961. Serum transaminase in the blood of lambs given preventive treatments for white muscle disease. *Am. J. Vet. Res.* **22:**686–688.

91. Laidmon, D. L., R. A. Morton, J. Y. F. Paterson and J. F. Pennock. 1960. Substance SC (ubichromenol): A naturally-occurring cyclic isomeride of ubiquinone-50. *Biochem. J.* **74:**541–549.

91a. Lam, K. W., M. Riegl and R. E. Olson. 1961. Biosynthesis of selenocoenzyme A in the rat. *Federation Proc.* **20:**229A.

92. Machlin, L. J., W. T. Shalkop and P. B. Pearson. 1955. Effect of methionine, sodium sulfate, α-tocopherol and other compounds on muscle degeneration in young chicks. *Poultry Sci.* **34:**1209.

93. Machlin, L. J. and W. T. Shalkop. 1956. Muscular degeneration in chickens fed diets low in vitamin E and sulfur. *J. Nutrition* **60:**87–96.

94. Machlin, L. J., R. S. Gordon and K. H. Meisky. 1959. Effect of antioxidants on vitamin E deficiency symptoms and production of liver "peroxide" in the chicken. *J. Nutrition* **67:**333–343.

95. Machlin, L. J. and R. S. Gordon. 1960. Etiology of muscular dystrophy, exudative diathesis and encephalomalacia in the chicken. *Fifth Intern. Congr. Nutrition, Washington, D.C.* p. 19.

96. MacKenzie, C. G. and E. V. McCollum. 1940. Cure of nutritional muscular dystrophy in the rabbit by α-tocopherol and its effect on creatine metabolism. *J. Nutrition* **19**:345–362.

97. MacKenzie, C. G. and V. du Vigneaud. 1950. Biochemical stability of the methyl group of creatine and creatinine. *J. Biol. Chem.* **185**:185–189.

98. MacKenzie, C. G. 1953. Experimental muscular dystrophy. *In* "Symposium on Nutrition," pp. 136–176. Johns Hopkins Press, Baltimore, Maryland.

99. Maplesden, D. C. and J. K. Loosli. 1960. Nutritional muscular dystrophy in calves. II. Addition of selenium and tocopherol to a basal, dystrophogenic diet containing cod-liver oil. *J. Dairy Sci.* **43**:645–653.

100. Marsh, H. 1932. Diseases of young lambs. *Am. J. Vet. Med. Assoc.* **81**:187–194.

101. Mascitelli-Coriandoli, E., R. Boldrini and C. Citterio. 1958. Selenium effects upon creatinine synthesis in carbon tetrachloride-damaged liver. *Naturwissenschaften* **45**:341–342.

101a. Mathias, M. M., D. E. Hogue, J. K. Loosli and M. L. Scott. 1963. The biological activity of selenium in bovine milk for the chick and rat. *Federation Proc.* **22**: 377.

102. McLean, J. W., G. G. Thompson and J. H. Claxton. 1959. Growth responses to selenium in lambs. *New Zealand Vet. J.* **7**:47–52.

103. McLean, J. W., G. G. Thompson and J. H. Claxton. 1959. Growth responses to selenium in lambs. *Nature* **184**:251–252.

104. Melville, R. S. and J. P. Hummel. 1951. Creatine and glycocyamine metabolism in rabbits in vitamin E deficiency. *J. Biol. Chem.* **191**:383–389.

105. Merrill, J. M., J. Lemley-Stone, J. T. Grace and G. R. Meneely. 1956. Recent clinical experiences with serum-aminopherase (transaminase) determinations. *J. Am. Med. Assoc.* **160**:1454–1456.

106. Mertz, W. and K. Schwarz. 1954. Effect of adrenalin and glucose on the terminal phase of dietary necrotic liver degeneration. *Federation Proc.* **13**:469.

107. Mertz, W. and K. Schwarz. 1955. Glucose imbalance in terminal phase of dietary necrotic liver degeneration. *Federation Proc.* **14**:444.

108. Mertz, W. and K. Schwarz. 1958. Reversal of respiratory decline in necrotic liver degeneration by intraportal antioxidants. *Proc. Soc. Exptl. Biol. Med.* **98**: 808–812.

109. Mertz, W. and K. Schwarz. 1959. Prevention of respiratory decline in necrotic liver degeneration by antioxidants *in vitro*. *Proc. Soc. Exptl. Biol. Med.* **102**: 561–566.

110. Moore, T. and R. L. Mitchell. 1955. Dental depigmentation and lowered content of iron in the incisor teeth of rats deficient in vitamin A or E. *Brit. J. Nutrition* **9**:174–180.

111. Morgulis, S. and W. Osheroff. 1938. Mineral composition of the muscles of rats on a diet producing muscular dystrophy. *J. Biol. Chem.* **124**:767–773.

112. Muth, O. H. 1955. White muscle disease (myopathy) in lambs and calves. I. Occurrence and nature of the disease under Oregon conditions. *J. Am. Vet. Med. Assoc.* **126**:355–361.

113. Muth, O. H., J. E. Oldfield, L. F. Remmert and J. R. Schubert. 1958. Effects of selenium and vitamin E on white muscle disease. *Science* **128**:1090.

114. Muth, O. H., J. E. Oldfield, J. R. Schubert and L. F. Remmert. 1959. White muscle disease (myopathy) in lambs and calves. VI. Effects of selenium and vitamin E on lambs. *Am. J. Vet. Res.* **20**:231–234.

115. Muth, O. H., J. R. Schubert and J. E. Oldfield. 1961. White muscle disease (myopathy) in lambs and calves. VII. Etiology and prophylaxis. *Am. J. Vet. Res.* **22**:466–469.

115a. Muth, O. H. 1963. White muscle disease, a selenium-responsive myopathy. *J. Am. Vet. Med. Assoc.* **142**:272–277.

115b. Muth, O. H. and W. H. Allaway. 1963. The relationship of white muscle disease to the distribution of naturally occurring selenium. *J. Am. Vet. Med. Assoc.* **142**:1379–1384.

116. Muytjens, E. E. 1956. Haemolysis of erythrocytes from vitamin E-deficient chickens. *Biochim. et Biophys. Acta* **20**:553.

117. Nesheim, M. C. and M. L. Scott. 1957. Nutritive activities of selenium for chicks and poults. *Proc. Cornell Nutrition Conf. Feed Mfgrs., 1957.* Ithaca, N.Y.

118. Nesheim, M. C. and M. L. Scott. 1958. Studies on the nutritive effects of selenium in chicks. *J. Nutrition* **65**:601–618.

119. Nesheim, M. C. 1959. Studies on the effect of selenium and other factors on vitamin E deficiency in the chick. *Dissertation Abstr.* **20**:13–14.

120. Nesheim, M. C., S. L. Leonard and M. L. Scott. 1959. Alterations in some biochemical constituents of skeletal muscle of vitamin E-deficient chicks. *J. Nutrition* **68**:359–369.

121. Nesheim, M. C., C. C. Calvert and M. L. Scott. 1960. Effect of arginine deficiency on the chick. *Proc. Soc. Exptl. Biol. Med.* **104**:783–785.

122. Nesheim, M. C. and M. L. Scott. 1961. Nutritional effects of selenium compounds in chicks and turkeys. *Federation Proc.* **20,** Part 1:674–678.

123. Oldfield, J. E., O. H. Muth and J. R. Schubert. 1960. Selenium and vitamin E as related to growth and white muscle disease in lambs. *Proc. Soc. Exptl. Biol. Med.* **103**:799–800.

124. Pappenheimer, A. M. and M. Goettsch. 1931. A cerebellar disorder in chicks, apparently of nutritional origin. *J. Exptl. Med.* **53**:11–26.

125. Patterson, E. L., R. Milstrey and E. L. R. Stokstad. 1957. Effect of selenium in preventing exudative diathesis in chicks. *Proc. Soc. Exptl. Biol. Med.* **95**:617–620.

126. Pellegrini, L. 1958. A study of vitamin E deficiency in pigs fed a Torula yeast diet. Doctoral Thesis, University of Minnesota, St. Paul, Minnesota.

127. Piccardo, M. G. and K. Schwarz. 1958. The electron miscroscopy of dietary necrotic liver degeneration. Symposium on Liver Functions. Publ. 4. Am. Inst. Biol. Sci., Wash., D.C.

128. Proctor, J. F., D. E. Hogue and R. G. Warner. 1958. Selenium, vitamin E and linseed oil meal as preventatives of muscular dystrophy in lambs. *J. Animal Sci.* **17**:1183–1184.

129. Proctor, J. F. 1960. Selenium in its relation to muscular dystrophy and dietary liver necrosis. 1. Muscular dystrophy in the lamb. 2. Studies with laboratory animals. *Dissertation Abstr.* **21**:10.

130. Proctor, J. F., D. C. Maplesden, D. E. Hogue and J. K. Loosli. 1961. Relation of selenium, vitamin E and other factors to muscular dystrophy in the rabbit. *Proc. Soc. Exptl. Biol. Med.* **108**:77–79.

131. Rahman, M. M., C. W. Deyoe, R. E. Davies and J. R. Couch. 1960. Selenium and exudative diathesis in chicks and poults. *J. Nutrition* **72**:71–76.

132. Rahman, M. M., R. E. Davies, C. W. Deyoe and J. R. Couch. 1960. Selenium and Torula yeast in production of exudative diathesis in chicks. *Proc. Soc. Exptl. Biol. Med.* **105**:227–230.

133. Reid, B. L., M. M. Rahman, B. G. Creech and J. R. Couch. 1958. Selenium and development of exudative diathesis in chicks. *Proc. Soc. Exptl. Biol. Med.* **97**:590–593.

134. Rodnan, G. P., S. S. Chernick and K. Schwarz. 1956. Reversal of respiratory decline in necrotic liver degeneration by intraportal tocopherols. *J. Biol. Chem.* **221**:231–238.

135. Rosecran, M., G. P. Rodnan, S. S. Chernick and K. Schwarz. 1955. Acetate-C^{14} utilization in dietary necrotic liver degeneration. *J. Biol. Chem.* **217**:967–976.

136. Rosenfeld, I. 1964. Metabolic effects and metabolism of selenium in animals. *Wyoming Agr. Expt. Sta. Bull. No.* **414**:1–64.

137. Safford, J. W., K. F. Swingle and H. Marsh. 1954. Experimental tocopherol deficiency in young calves. *Am. J. Vet. Res.* **15**:374–384.

138. Safford, J. W., K. F. Swingle and D. E. McRoberts. 1956. Muscular dystrophy in lambs as related to the tocopherol levels in the plasma and milk of ewes and to various feeds. *Am. J. Vet. Res.* **17**:503–509.

139. Schubert, J. R., O. H. Muth, J. E. Oldfield and L. F. Remmert. 1961. Experimental results with selenium in white muscle disease of lambs and calves. *Federation Proc.* **20**, Part 1:689–694.

140. Schwarz, K. 1948. Über die Lebertranschädigung der Ratte und ihre Verhütung durch Tocopherol. *Z. Physiol. Chem.* **283**:106–112.

141. Schwarz, K. 1951. Production of dietary necrotic liver degeneration using American Torula yeast. *Proc. Soc. Exptl. Biol. Med.* **77**:818–823.

142. Schwarz, K. 1951. Production of dietary necrotic liver degeneration using American Torula yeast. *Proc. Soc. Exptl. Biol. Med.* **78**:852–856.

143. Schwarz, K. 1952. Casein and Factor 3 in dietary necrotic liver degeneration; concentration of Factor 3 from casein. *Proc. Soc. Exptl. Biol. Med.* **80**:319–323.

144. Schwarz, K., J. G. Bieri, G. M. Briggs and M. L. Scott. 1957. Prevention of exudative diathesis in chicks by Factor 3 and selenium. *Proc. Soc. Exptl. Biol. Med.* **95**:621–625.

145. Schwarz, K. and C. M. Foltz. 1957. Selenium as an integral part of Factor 3 against dietary necrotic liver degeneration. *J. Am. Chem. Soc.* **79**:3292–3293.

146. Schwarz, K. 1958. Effect of antioxidants on dietary necrotic liver degeneration. *Proc. Soc. Exptl. Biol. Med.* **99**:20–24.

147. Schwarz, K. 1958. Dietary necrotic liver degeneration—an approach to the concept of biochemical lesion. Symposium on Liver Functions. Publ. 4, Am. Inst. Biol. Sci., Wash. D. C.

148. Schwarz, K. and C. M. Foltz. 1958. Factor 3 and 6-selenoctic acid. *Acta Chem. Scand.* **12**:1330–1331.

149. Schwarz, K. and C. M. Foltz. 1958. Factor 3 activity of selenium compounds. *J. Biol. Chem.* **233**:245–251.

150. Schwarz, K. and C. M. Foltz. 1958. Factor 3 potencies of selenium compounds. *Federation Proc.* **17**:492.

151. Schwarz, K. 1959. Der Faktor 3, das selen und die ernahrungbedingte nekrose. *Vitalstoffe-zivilisations krankheiten* Nr. IV, 1–7.

152. Schwarz, K. and W. Mertz. 1959. Terminal phase of dietary liver necrosis in the rat (hepatogenic hypoglycemia). *Metabolism, Clin. Exptl.* **8**:79–87.

153. Schwarz, K., E. E. Roginske and C. M. Foltz. 1959. Ineffectiveness of molybdenum, osmium and cobalt in dietary necrotic liver degeneration. *Nature* **183**: 472–473.

154. Schwarz, K., E. J. Simon and W. Mertz. 1959. *In vitro* effect of tocopherol

metabolites on respiratory decline in dietary necrotic liver degeneration. *Biochim. et Biophysics. Acta* **32**:484–491.

155. Schwarz, K., J. A. Stesney and C. M. Foltz. 1959. Relation between selenium traces in L-cystine and protection against dietary liver necrosis. *Metabolism Clin. Exptl.* **8**:88–90.
156. Schwarz, K. and W. Mertz. 1960. Physiological effects of trace amounts of selenium. *Proc., Conf. Physiological Aspects of Water Quality, Washington, D.C.* pp. 79–104.
157. Schwarz, K. 1961. Development and status of experimental work on Factor 3-selenium. *Federation Proc.* **20**, Part 1:666–673.
158. Scott, M. L., F. W. Hill, L. C. Norris, D. C. Dobson and T. W. Nelson. 1955. Studies on vitamin E in poultry nutrition. *J. Nutrition* **56**:387–402.
159. Scott, M. L. 1957. The identification of an unknown factor as selenium. *Feedstuffs* **29**:20–22.
160. Scott, M. L., J. G. Bieri, G. M. Briggs and K. Schwarz. 1957. Prevention of exudative diathesis by Factor 3 in chicks on vitamin E-deficient Torula yeast diet. *Poultry Sci.* **36**:1155.
161. Scott, M. L. 1958. Selenium as a required trace mineral in animal nutrition. *Proc. Cornell Nutr. Conf. Feed Mfgr., Ithaca, N.Y.* pp. 111–117.
162. Scott, M. L. and C. C. Calvert. 1960. Evidence of a specific need for prevention of nutritional muscular dystrophy in the chick. *5th Intern. Congr. Nutrition, Abstr., Washington, D.C.* **350**, 77–78.
163. Scott, M. L. 1961. Studies on an interrelationship among sulfur amino acids, arginine, selenium and vitamin E in muscular dystrophy in the chick. *Feedstuffs,* **33**: Feb.
164. Scott, M. L. 1962. Anti-oxidants, selenium and sulphur amino acids in the vitamin E nutrition of chicks. *Nutrition Abstr. & Rev.* **32**:1–8.

164a. Setchell, B. P. 1962. Further studies in lambs in N.S.W. on the growth response to selenium and the prevention of muscular dystrophy with selenium and vitamin E. *Australian Vet. J.* **38**:62–65.

165. Sharman, G. A. M., K. L. Blaxter and R. S. Wilson. 1959. Prevention of enzootic muscular dystrophy by selenium administration. *Vet. Record* **71**:536.
166. Sigma Chemical Company. 1960. A simplified method for the colorimetric determination of glutamic-oxalacetic and glutamic-pyruvic transaminases at approximately 500 mμ. *Tech. Bull. No.* **505,** (Rev.) St. Louis, Missouri.
167. Singsen, E. P., R. H. Bunnell, L. D. Matterson, A. Kozeff and E. L. Jungherr. 1955. Studies on encephalomalacia in the chick. 2. The protective action of diphenyl-*p*-phenylenediamine against encephalomalacia. *Poultry Sci.* **34**:262–271.

167a. Skerman, K. D. 1962. Observations on selenium deficiency of lambs in Victoria. *Prod. Proc. Australian Soc. An. Prod.* **4**:22–27.

168. Søndergaard, E., F. Christensen, H. Dam and I. Prange. 1958. *Abstr. Intern. Congr. Biochem. 4th Congr. Vienna,* p. 92. Cited by M. O. Schultze. 1960. Selenium and vitamin E. *Ann Rev. Biochem.* **29**:391–412.
169. Søndergaard, E., J. G. Bieri and H. Dam. 1960. Further observations on the effects of selenium and antioxdants on exudative diathesis in chicks. *Experientia* **16**:554.
170. Stokstad, E. L. R., R. Eggert and E. L. Patterson. 1958. Role of selenium and vitamin E in the nutrition of the pig and the chick. *Abstr. Intern. Congr. Biochem., 4th Congr., Vienna.* p. 92.
171. Swingle, K. F., S. Young and H. C. Dang. 1959. The relationship of serum glumatic oxalacetic transaminase to nutritional muscular dystrophy in lambs. *Am. J. Vet. Res.* **20**:75–77.

172. Tappel, A. L. and H. Zalkin. 1959. Inhibition of lipid peroxidation in mitochondria by vitamin E. *Arch. Biochem. Biophys.* **80**:333–336.

172a. Tappel, A. L. 1962. Vitamin E and selenium in the *in vivo* peroxidation. Symposium on Foods. Avi Publ., Westport, Connecticut.

173. Valberg, L. S., R. A. Young and J. M. R. Beveridge. 1959. The effect of unsaturation of dietary fat and of antioxidants on the development of liver damage. *Can. J. Biochem. Physiol.* **37**:493–499.

174. Weichselbaum, T. E. 1935. Cystine deficiency in the albino rat. *Quart. J. Exptl. Physiol.* **25**:363.

175. Welch, J. G., A. L. Pope, W. G. Hockstra and P. H. Phillips. 1958. The anti-vitamin E effect of fish liver oil in the production of white muscle disease in sheep. *J. Animal Sci.* **17**:1194.

176. White, A. A. and W. C. Hess. 1957. Some alterations in serum enzymes in progressive muscular dystrophy. *Proc. Soc. Exptl. Biol. Med.* **94**:541–544.

177. Whiting, F., J. P. Willman and J. K. Loosli. 1949. Tocopherol (vitamin E) deficiency among sheep on natural feeds. *J. Animal Sci.* **8**:234–242.

178. Willman, J. P., J. K. Loosli, S. A. Asdell, F. B. Morrison and P. Olafson. 1945. Prevention and cure of muscular stiffness (stiff-lamb disease) in lambs. *J. Animal Sci.* **4**:128–132.

178a. Wolf, E., V. Kollonitsch and C. H. Kline. 1963. A survey of selenium treatment in livestock production. *J. Agr. Food Chem.* **11**:355–360.

178b. Yang, C., M. Riegl and R. E. Olson. 1958. Effect of factors protective against dietary hepatic necrosis upon hepatic co-enzyme A levels in the rat. *Federation Proc.* **17**:498.

179. Yang, C. S., G. H. Dialameh and R. E. Olson. 1959. Selenium-sulfur interrelationships in the vitamin E-deficient weanling rat. *Federation Proc.* **18**:553.

180. Young, S., W. W. Hawkins and K. F. Swingle. 1961. Nutritional muscular dystrophy in lambs—administration of selenium to affected and unaffected lambs. *Am. J. Vet. Res.* **22**:416–418.

181. Young, S., W. W. Hawkins and K. F. Swingle. 1961. Nutritional muscular dystrophy in lambs—effect of administering selenium to pregnant ewes. *Am. J. Vet. Res.* **22**:419–421.

182. Zalkin, H. and A. L. Tappel. 1960. Studies of the mechanism of vitamin E action. IV. Lipid peroxidation in the vitamin E-deficient rabbit. *Arch. Biochem. Biophys.* **88**:113–117.

183. Zalkin, H., A. L. Tappel and J. P. Jordan. 1960. Studies of the mechanism of vitamin E action. V. Selenite and tocopherol inhibition of lipid peroxidation in the chick. *Arch. Biochem. Biophys.* **91**:117-122.

CHAPTER VIII

SELENIUM IN RELATION TO PUBLIC HEALTH

The selenium problem is of special importance because of the possibility of human injury from the consumption of grains, vegetables, eggs, dairy products, and meats from affected areas. Extensive investigations of the poisoning of animals have already been made, but the research required on human phases of the problem has barely been touched.

SELENIUM IN LOCAL FOODS

Investigations of the sources of selenium to which man is exposed in seleniferous regions have shown wide occurrence of the element in foods of animal origin, such as milk, eggs, and meat, as well as in vegetables and cereal grains. It is believed that a concentration of 5 ppm in common foods or one tenth this concentration in milk or water is potentially dangerous.

As part of an intensive field survey, Smith and Westfall (*47*) analyzed many samples of foods entering directly into the diets of families in seleniferous regions (Table 56).

TABLE 56
The Selenium Content of Water, Milk, Eggs, Meat, and Bread[a]

Material	Total number of samples	Number of samples showing:			Selenium (ppm)	
		No selenium	Traces	Positive	Minimum	Maximum
Water	44	20	14	10	0.05	0.33
Milk	50	0	6	44	0.16	1.27
Eggs	32	0	0	32	0.25	9.14
Meats	6	0	0	6	1.17	8.00
Bread	11	0	5	6	0.25	1.00

[a] Smith and Westfall (*47*).

The analysis indicates that eggs, meats, and milk contain considerable amounts of selenium. Selenium in wheat and grain is of special interest because of the extensive use of wheat in bread and breakfast foods. The per capita consumption of wheat products is about 160 pounds per year. The selenium content of wheat, wheat products, and some vegetables from seleniferous areas was reported by Williams *et al.* (57), and their data are presented in Chapter IV.

Wheat from Saskatchewan, where highly seleniferous Astragali occur and selenium poisoning of livestock is known, was examined by Thorvaldson and Johnson (*54*). The authors stated that the bulk handling of wheat for export would prevent the selenium content from greatly exceeding 0.44 ppm selenium. Analyses of wheat in Alberta indicate that the selenium content varied from a minimum of 0.1 ppm to a maximum of 1.0 ppm. The results were based on the analysis of 200 samples (55).

Studies on the relation of dental caries in school children and selenium content of eggs, milk, and water in three counties in Oregon—Jackson, Josephine, and Klamath—indicate that in the county (Klamath) in which the selenium content in foods was lowest and the water contained only trace amounts, the children had less decayed, missing, or filled teeth (25).

Surveys on the selenium content of rice, wheat, and broad beans in various parts of Japan indicated that selenium was present in rice (0.16–2.75 ppm), wheat (0.25–1.42 ppm), and broad beans (0.15–1.58 ppm). The source of selenium was the chemical processing of fertilizer which contained 10.5 ppm selenium. Careful disposal of waste liquid from the fertilizer plant was advocated in order to prevent further contamination (*50*, 52). The above authors suggested that raw materials imported from the United States for fertilizer as well as foodstuffs should be checked for their selenium content.

SURVEY OF HEALTH OF RURAL POPULATIONS

An attempt was made by Smith and co-workers (*45*, *47*) to ascertain the effects of selenium on the rural populations of seleniferous areas. It would be expected that the more highly seleniferous foods would be consumed by rural populations subsisting largely on the products of relatively restricted soil areas. A field survey was therefore planned to cover the farming population in selected localities in three of the Great Plains states. The choice of locations was determined by the geological information on distribution of soils derived from Cretaceous shales which usually are high in selenium and where, subsequently, there are high concentrations of selenium in the soil and in the vegetation. Alkali disease on a farm was considered presumptive evidence of the occurrence of selenium in the food products grown there. The survey was limited, with few exceptions, to farms and ranches with reliable histories of alkali disease.

To obtain evidence of selenium ingestion and its possible harmful effects, inquiry was made concerning the health of the members of the families visited; information was secured regarding the extent to which local foods entered into the diets; and wherever possible, general physical examinations were made in an attempt to discover symptoms sufficiently characteristic of selenium poisoning to be of aid in diagnosis. Samples of urine were collected for chemical analysis for selenium, since its presence can furnish evidence of ingestion of the element and may be helpful in appraising the clinical observations.

The survey was conducted from the latter part of April to early June. Little or no home-grown food was consumed at the time, since it was too early for the new supply and not enough food was raised in the area to provide for the entire year. The chief foods that might have contained selenium at that time were meats, milk, and milk products, eggs, and limited amounts of garden vegetables from the preceding year. Home-grown grain is an important food for the animals, but little is used directly by the family.

Members of 111 families were examined. They lived on farms or ranches in the following states and counties: eastern part of Wyoming—Albany and Niobrara counties; southwestern South Dakota—Fall River, Custer, Pennington, Meade, Stanley, Hughes, Jones, Lyman, Tripp, Brule, and Gregory counties; northern Nebraska—Boyd County. Urine samples were collected from 127 subjects representing 90 families.

No symptoms or groups of symptoms were observed that could be considered decisively characteristic of selenium poisoning in man. This was in accord with the experience of local physicians. Vague symptoms of ill health, and symptoms indicative of more or less serious damage to the liver, kidneys, skin, and joints were seen, and the impression was gained that the incidence of such disorders was abnormally high. There are many causes of such disorders, however, and it was impossible to specify the role of selenium, if any, in their causation.

The more pronounced manifestations of disease seen in the 111 families included in the survey (exclusive of vague symptoms of anorexia, indigestion, general pallor, malnutrition, etc.) were the following:

(*a*) Bad teeth, varying from marked discoloration through all stages of decay, were seen in one or more members of 48 families.

(*b*) Yellowish discoloration of the skin, in many cases a very definite icterus, and in some cases seemingly associated with more or less definite liver disease, was seen in about 46 subjects.

(*c*) Skin eruptions of varying degrees of severity, but not conforming to any one type, were seen in 20 subjects.

(*d*) Chronic arthritis with more or less permanent changes in the joints was seen in 15 subjects. All degrees of involvement were noted in this group of patients, varying from the milder types of rheumatoid arthritis to the more severe arthritis deformans. The hypertrophic degenerative type of arthritis was not seen.

(*e*) Diseased nails of the fingers, and in some cases also of the toes, were seen in 8 subjects. They were usually symmetrical, atrophic, brittle, irregular and often presented transverse and at times longitudinal ridges. In some of the cases there was a history of sloughing of the diseased nails at irregular intervals. With the exception of one case there was no history of suppuration, and no evidence of acute or subacute inflammation.

(*f*) Subcutaneous edema (probably cardiorenal origin) was seen in 5 cases and peripheral neuritis of doubtful etiology was seen in two subjects. Fifteen subjects had a history of more or less protracted gastrointestinal disturbances.

Whether or not selenium was implicated in any or all of the above conditions could not be stated with any degree of certainty.

The urinary analysis for selenium showed that 92 per cent of the specimens contained selenium, many of them in appreciable quantities, and some in amounts so high as to suggest probable poisoning, especially if viewed in the light of observations made on animals affected with alkali disease.

An attempt was made to correlate the clinical findings with the urinary selenium concentrations. Analysis of the data, however, did not reveal a constant causal association of health disturbances with concentration of selenium in the urine. It may be assumed that a higher concentration of selenium in the urine probably represents a higher level of intake, and a correspondingly higher concentration in the tissues. Nevertheless, little difference was found in the percentage of symptomatic cases through a wide selenium range in the urine from a trace to 1.33 ppm.

The lack of more definite association of clinical evidence of selenium poisoning with its concentration in the urine does not, however, warrant the assumption of its harmlessness. Indeed, the investigators have a strong impression that some of the signs of ill health, though neither of a specific nor, in most cases, of a serious nature, were the direct results of continual ingestion of small quantities of selenium over a long period of time. The high incidence of symptoms in groups of individuals excreting small quantities of selenium might be a manifestation of irreparable damage due to the intake of selenium in higher concentrations at some time in the past. Indeed, the amount of selenium ingested must, of necessity, vary from time to time with changing availability of locally produced selenium-bearing foods.

To arrive at some conclusions as to the possible diagnostic significance of the most pronounced symptoms observed, all the cases of the entire series were divided into clinical groups according to these symptoms and the number of cases in each clinical group associated with no or with relatively high urinary selenium, respectively, was calculated on a percentage basis, as shown in Table 57. (In the analysis, none or a trace is considered as no selenium, while 0.20 ppm or more is considered as relatively high and assumed to be of probable significance.) Analysis of the data in this manner showed that the incidence of high urinary selenium in the clinical groups of dermatitis and arthritis was no greater than in the symptomless group. Relatively high urinary selenium was most often associated with pathological disturbances of the nails, with bad teeth, with gastrointestinal disorders, and with icteroid skin. The presence of any of these symptoms in an individual living in a seleniferous region may be indicative of chronic selenium poisoning and should suggest the desirability of analyzing the urine for selenium. A careful consideration of the findings in relation to the symptomatology may help to account for some of the obscure ailments in selenium-endemic regions.

TABLE 57

Association of Certain Clinical Groups with Urinary Selenium[a]

Clinical group	Total number of cases with complete data on urinary selenium	Percentage of cases showing	
		No selenium in the urine	0.20 ppm or more selenium
Bad teeth	34	6	47
Icteroid discoloration of the skin	36	11	53
Dermatitis	19	16	31
Arthritis	13	0	30
Gastrointestinal disorders	14	0	57
Pathological nails	7	0	57
Asymptomatic group	22	14	32

[a] Smith *et al.* (*45*).

A more detailed study was made by Smith and Westfall (*47*) in order to correlate the symptomatology with selenium excretion and selenium intake in the diet. With this object in view, a relatively small area of 4 counties was selected from the much larger region covered by the preliminary survey. The area chosen included 3 counties in South Dakota —Lyman, Tripp, and Gregory—and the adjacent Boyd County in Nebraska. In the preliminary survey this area, lying on the west bank of the Missouri River, had been found to be the most highly seleniferous as indicated by the occurrence of selenium in the soil, the incidence of alkali disease in livestock, and the presence of high concentrations of selenium in human urine. Fifty families in the preliminary survey in April, 1936, gave indication of considerable selenium intake in the diet and they were selected for the more intensive study in September of the same year. None of the subjects had lived on seleniferous farms less than 3 years and the majority had lived there from 10 to 40 years.

Specimens of urine for analysis were collected from several members of each family. Samples of foodstuffs entering directly or indirectly into the diets of the families were also taken for analysis; these included water, dairy products, eggs, meats, cereals, and vegetables. Owing to the drought, vegetables were relatively scarce. The cereal grains produced locally are seldom used for human consumption; they are chiefly fed to animals and so constitute only an indirect source of selenium for the rural family.

Table 58 indicates the selenium excretion in the human subjects and the selenium content of foods raised on the farms and consumed by 14

TABLE 58
Relation of Urinary Selenium to Food Selenium[a]

Family No.	Urinary selenium (ppm)	Food selenium (ppm)				
		Milk	Eggs	Meat	Vegetables	Cereal grains
97	0.25, 0.27, 0.32	Trace	0.57	—	Trace	Trace
51	0.20, 0.27	—	1.35	1.60	0.36	1.90
22	0.20, 0.21	0.36	1.40	—	0.41–0.74	Trace
113	0.20, 0.20, 0.24	0.25	1.45	—	0.30–0.82	0
52	0.26	0.25	0.32	—	Trace–0.58	—
83	0.13, 0.38, 0.40	0.34	—	2.19	—	—
27	0.29, 0.56	0.22	—	2.22	—	—
76	0.43, 0.73	0.35	4.08	3.30	0.27–1.05	—
107	0.94	0.39	3.65	—	Trace–0.18	—
47	0.70, 0.80, 0.98	0.57	3.08	—	0.23–2.04	3.30
74	1.03, 1.10	Trace	4.12	—	—	0.45–1.00
78	1.00, 1.14	0.36	5.04	—	1.03–17.80	3.60
16	1.05, 0.36, 1.33	1.14	—	—	2.42	2.50–18.80
19	1.24, 1.98	1.27	—	8.00	1.26	4.20–10.00

[a] Smith and Westfall (*47*).

families (*47*). The selenium concentration of the urine in the whole group varied from 0.20 to 1.98 ppm. The urinary concentration of selenium was fairly uniform for all members of a family group, irrespective of age or other conditions. In only 5 families were there marked individual differences in the urinary concentration of selenuim. Neither age nor any other known factor(s) seemed to account for these differences. In many instances the low values occurred in the urines of the female members of the families. The probable explanation lies in individual dietary habits, and in the lower food intake of females. Some foods on any seleniferous farm carry considerable selenium while others contain little or none.

The urinary selenium concentration of 28 individuals representing 22 families was nearly the same as it had been 5 months previously. This suggests that the absorption of selenium on any given farm at different times of the year remains fairly constant. In only five of the 28 individuals was there a rather marked increase in the urinary selenium above that noted earlier. If there had been more rainfall during the summer and a more abundant supply of garden vegetables, the incidence of increased urinary selenium might have been more frequent.

The frequency of symptoms that were observed in the 100 individuals is indicated in Table 59.

TABLE 59
Frequency of Observed Symptoms and Percentage Distribution[a]

Clinical group	Frequency of occurrence	Percent distribution
No obvious symptoms	24	16.0
Gastrointestinal disturbances	31	20.7
Bad teeth	27	18.0
Icteroid discoloration of the skin	28	18.7
History of recurrent jaundice	5	3.3
Vitiligo	2	1.3
Pigmentation of the skin (chloasma?)	3	2.0
Sallow and pallid color, especially in younger individuals	17	11.3
Dermatitis	5	3.3
Rheumatoid arthritis	3	2.0
Pathological nails	3	2.0
Cardiorenal disease	2	1.3

[a] Smith and Westfall (*47*).

None of the above listed symptoms of the entire group can be regarded as specific effects of selenium and it is not certain that any one is the direct result of continual ingestion of selenium. It seems probable, however, that the high incidence of gastrointestinal disturbances is significant in the light of experimental data on the chronic toxicity and pathology of selenium in lower animals (*46*). The incidence of primary jaundice, recurrent jaundice, and sallow color of younger individuals is higher than the probable occurrence in people not living on seleniferous land. In chronic poisoning in experimental animals with doses of inorganic selenium of similar magnitude to those probably absorbed by the human subjects, microscopic lesions of the liver are frequent (*46*). In experimental animals with mild or moderate chronic selenium poisoning from inorganic as well as from organic selenium, marked bilirubinemia has been observed (*16*). Whether or not any of the human cases have blood changes of a nature similar to experimental animals in chronic selenium poisoning must remain a matter of conjecture until such studies are made.

Recent studies indicate that the high incidence of bad teeth may be correlated with selenium intake. A survey conducted on white, native-born and -reared boys and girls from 10 to 18 years of age living in seleniferous areas in Wyoming indicates a positive correlation between malocclusions and caries of the permanent teeth. A higher percentage of children had gingivitis in the seleniferous than in the nonseleniferous area. The urinary excretion ranged from 0.02 to 1.12 ppm selenium (*53*).

The public health problem is concerned with the continuous ingestion of small doses of organic selenium and the consequent possibility of organic or functional damage in tissues and organs of human beings. Experimental studies of the chronic poisoning of animals have shown that the excretion level of selenium in the urine bears a rather definite relationship to the daily dose ingested. It may be inferred that the human subjects investigated were absorbing from 0.01 to 0.1 or possibly as much as 0.2 mg of selenium per kilogram of body weight per day. The daily intake of 1.0 mg of selenium per kilogram of body weight may produce chronic toxicity in man. The continued ingestion of food selenium as low as 0.2 mg per kilogram of body weight may be harmful (*48*).

The quantitative relationship between the selenium excreted to that ingested and stored in the tissues, the chemical forms of selenium compounds occurring in foods, and the fate of these compounds in the body are some phases of the problem that require further study before the full significance of selenium in public health can be fully evaluated.

SOME CASES OF HUMAN POISONING

Several cases of chronic dermatitis in South Dakota that were apparently caused by the ingestion of seleniferous food were reported by Lemley (*31*). Acute dermatitis was observed on the lips, eyelids, and bearded regions of a rancher who had lived near Reva, South Dakota (Harding County), for more than 30 years and had not suffered previously from a skin disease. Physical examination revealed nothing bearing upon the skin condition. A diagnosis was made as an acute dermatitis venenata of undetermined origin. The patient was referred to the Mayo Clinic, where he remained for 6 weeks. The tentative diagnosis was a moist neurodermatitis with seborrheic characteristics. A biopsy of a skin lesion was reported to be simple chronic inflammation characterized by perivascular accumulations of lymphocytes of unknown etiology. His condition improved while hospitalized and only a few scattered lesions remained, but within 2 weeks after returning to his ranch there was a widespread recurrence of the dermatitis.

Since animals on the patient's ranch and on others nearby suffered from alkali disease, samples of the patient's urine were analyzed for selenium. The finding of about 0.04 ppm of selenium in the urine was considered to be evidence that this was a case of selenium poisoning. Samples of water, meat, vegetables, and dairy products on his ranch contained selenium in appreciable quantities.

Moxon *et al.* (*36*) reported that administration of bromobenzene increased the rate of excretion of selenium from selenized animals. The effectiveness of bromobenzene administration was tested on the above patient and 3 minims was given orally 3 times per day. After 5 days of treatment the patient showed improvement in general health and within 7 days the skin appeared normal, with only a few reddish-brown patches persisting. The above dose was repeated for 3 days each month until the symptoms disappeared. During the time of treatment the amount of selenium excreted by the patient followed a cycle: (1) no selenium excretion on the first day, (2) a maximum excretion of 0.07 ppm on the fourth day, and (3) subsequent decrease to zero within 10 days. This cycle was repeated following each monthly treatment with bromobenzene (*31*).

By avoiding selenium as far as possible in his diet, the patient remained free from symptoms for about a year, but then he had a recurrence of the dermatitis (*32*). Analysis of his foods demonstrated that he had been consuming some canned meat containing 0.40 ppm of selenium. Hospitalization and administration of bromobenzene brought about a rapid disappearance of the lesions.

Several other cases of selenium dermatitis were reported by Lemley (*31*). In a single year, according to Lemley and Merryman (*32*), more than 30 individuals showed some symptoms of selenium poisoning. These individuals came from North Dakota, South Dakota, Montana, Wyoming, and Nebraska. The patients showed various degrees of skin lesions or rashes, follicular rashes over the hairy surfaces of the body, excessive fatigue, and dizziness. In all cases the sources of the selenium were home-grown vegetables, eggs, milk, and meat. Elimination of selenium from their diets resulted in recovery of the patients. Lemley (*31*) and Lemley and Merryman (*32*) used bromobenzene to increase the excretion of selenium. However, subsequent studies with laboratory animals indicate that the oral administration of bromobenzene did not increase the excretion of selenium in the urine. Bromobenzene is extremely toxic and produces severe reactions; thus extreme caution should be exercised in its use in man. No recent studies on the use of bromobenzene in human chronic selenosis are available at the present time; therefore, confirmation of the above reports on the beneficial effects of bromobenzene is needed before it can be recommended for use in routine treatment of chronic selenosis.

The selenium content of drinking water is very rarely high enough to produce toxic manifestations in humans. However, a recent report indicates that well water obtained from the Wasatch geological formation from a depth of about 140 feet contained 9 ppm selenium and produced chronic selenosis in humans. All food consumed by the family was free of selenium. The 5 boys and girls ranging in age from 6 months to 10 years were affected. The parents and the dog also showed some symptoms of poisoning. Physical examination of the children showed no abnormalities other than lassitude, total or partial loss of hair, and discoloration of fingernails, which became brittle and dropped off. Upon discontinuation of the use of the water, regrowth of nails and hair began. The new nails showed abnormal ridges and lumps and the hair was split 3 ways at the ends. The children showed increased mental alertness by doing better work in school (2). This is the first observation where the selenium concentration in water was high enough to produce chronic symptoms in humans similar to alkali disease in livestock.

In rural populations residing in seleniferous areas the continued selenium intake over a period of years may produce unexplained disease syndromes which would warrant suspicion of selenium as a causative agent. The suggested procedures to follow without resorting to expensive diagnostic procedure are: (1) general physical examination; (2) elimination of all foods produced on the farm from the diet, including milk and meat; (3) urinary selenium determination at monthly intervals (decrease in selenium excretion with change of diet would suggest that selenium was either a primary or secondary cause of the disease syndrome); and (4) the proper symptomatic treatment should be instituted to eliminate the discomfort caused by the disease.

HUMAN CHRONIC SELENOSIS IN COLOMBIA, SOUTH AMERICA

The occurrence of chronic selenosis since the 16th century has been recorded in Colombia, South America, by travelers and chroniclers. Benavides and Mojica (3) in a well-written summary have given detailed information on the extent of chronic selenosis in man and animals and on the distribution of selenium in the soil and plants in Colombia. Some of the interesting information given by the above authors is included briefly for historical as well as for scientific value. The food and the disease were described by a priest in 1560: "The corn as well as other vegetables grow well and healthy but in some regions it is so poisonous that whoever eats it, man or animal, loses his hair. Indian women gave birth to monstrous-looking babies who were abandoned by their parents. Some abnormal babies born to Indian mothers were described to be covered with coarse or brittle hair. A number of travelers and priests have repeatedly commented on abandoned malformed Indian babies. Sometimes whole villages were deserted by the Indians."

Travelers, naturalists, and priests from the 17th century on continually described the disease in some regions in Colombia. Naturalists have associated the disease in man and animals with the *soil* and not with fruits, vegetables, or cereals. This conclusion was reached because the same vegetables and cereals were nontoxic in other parts of the country. The soil was high in "caparrosa," the common name for sulfates and other inorganic components of the soil.

The so-called "peladero" soil was described as black, dusty, and rich in graphite in 1856. However, the animals that grazed on the land lost their hair and hoofs and showed malformations of lips and legs; a number of animals aborted; and eggs failed to hatch. Abnormalities in chicks described were similar to those observed in the United States. The "strong peladero" destroyed human hair and nails.

Historians and naturalists attempted to explain the phenomena observed by travelers. Subsequently, the disease was correlated with excessive quantities of magnesium in the soil, phosphorus or iodine deficiency, or microorganisms in the soil. Many other excesses or deficiencies in minerals were related to the disease. More recent studies indicate that there are a number of human cases of chronic selenosis in the "peladeros" or toxic areas. As late as 1936 loss of hair in man and animal was described, at which time it was definitely established that selenium was present in the soil in high concentrations. Reports in 1955 from one district described toxic corn and streams that had no animal life. Men and animals using the streams for drinking water showed loss of hair; small mammals became sterile; and horses suffered hoof damage.

It is interesting to point out that loss of hair and nails reported in the United States (*2*) was observed in Indian children. All cases described in Colombia involved Indians in whom the manifestations of chronic selenosis were evidenced by extensive loss of hair and nails. This may be coincidental, but in human poisoning described in the Caucasian race, loss of hair and nails was not the primary manifestation of the disease.

DENTAL CARIES

Research concerning the influence of trace elements on the susceptibility to dental caries has been mainly confined to the study of fluorine. There is a possibility that other trace elements may have beneficial or harmful effects on dental caries, and the wide variations in the degree of susceptibility to caries may be due to an excess or absence of these elements. In numerous ways there is an obvious parallelism between selenium and fluorides. Fluorides, like selenium, became of interest in human welfare from the toxic standpoint. An excess of fluoride in water caused mottled enamel, while a small amount of fluoride during tooth development is necessary for the formation of highly resistant teeth.

The mechanism of a trace amount of fluoride is partially attributable to the incorporation of fluoride into the crystalline hydroxyapatite lattice in calcifying teeth (*33*).

The early reports on the significant number of "bad teeth" in highly seleniferous areas suggested the possible role of selenium in dental caries. Studies on the deposition of selenium in the teeth indicate that while human teeth in Honolulu were free of selenium (*27*), teeth collected in Washington, D.C., contained a small amount (0.05 ppm) of selenium (*57*). The distribution of selenium in dentine and enamel of teeth indicates that selenium is a normal constituent of these components of the teeth. The deciduous teeth have higher selenium content (2.6 ppm dentine, 4.5 ppm enamel) than the permanent teeth (0.52 ppm dentine, 0.84 enamel) (*23*).

The effects of trace elements, including selenium, were studied by adding the trace elements to the drinking water of rats during pregnancy, lactation, and, subsequently, to the progenies over a period of 120 days. The addition of 5 ppm Na_2SeO_3 to the water increased the caries 38 per cent while 10 ppm Na_2SeO_3 increased carious lesions 54 per cent over the nonseleniferous groups. There was no interference with the deposition of fluoride in the femur (*5*).

Experimental studies on the teeth and jaws of dogs and rats injected with repeated doses of selenium resulted in structural changes in the dentine and variations in size and shape of the mandibular condyles in dogs (*15*), and increase of caries in rats (*56*).

Progressively increasing the level of selenium from 10 to 30 ppm in the cariogenic diet of rats, as the rats increased in age and weight, had no influence on the incidence of dental caries (*37*).

Selenium feeding trials with rats and dogs have not provided any definite answer as to whether there is any causative relationship between selenium intake and susceptibility to dental caries.

The effect of seleniferous diets on the teeth has not been studied except in Oregon by Hadjimarkos and co-workers (*19–21*) in connection with dental caries in school children. Surveys indicate that selenium may be a factor contributing toward the increased susceptibility to dental caries. There appeared to be a direct correlation between urinary selenium excretion and prevalence of dental caries in native-born and -reared school children (*19–22*). The mean urinary selenium concentration in children in these studies in different counties was: 0.074 ppm, Jackson; 0.076 ppm, Josephine; 0.049 ppm, Clatsop; and 0.037 ppm, Klamath. The children with lower level of selenium excretion in the urine had correspondingly less caries. A survey on the selenium content of eggs, milk, and water in relation to dental caries and selenium excretion in urine of school children in 3 counties in Oregon gave good correlation between selenium intake in foods, selenium excretion, and prevalence of dental caries (*25*).

Studies by Hadjimarkos (*25a*) indicate that milk of lactating mothers living in a nonseleniferous area in Oregon contained from 0.013 to 0.053 ppm selenium. At the present time it is difficult to assess the effect of selenium on the pre-development or the post-development of the teeth. Similar surveys in seleniferous and nonseleniferous areas of the United States would assist in evaluating the cause of dental caries as well as the effect of selenium in the diet on the structure of the teeth.

Studies in New Zealand of 5- to 14-year-old boys in 2 districts do not indicate any correlation between urinary excretion of selenium and prevalence of dental caries (*6*). Hadjimarkos (*24*) analyzed their data and reported that the lack of correlation was due to the low selenium level of the 2 groups studied (means values were 0.021 and 0.03 ppm selenium) and the failure of the investigators to differentiate the prevalence of caries in primary and permanent teeth. Since the studies were carried out in that part of New Zealand in which there is widespread selenium deficiency (*28*), it is doubtful that valid comparison can be made with the Oregon studies.

PUBLIC HEALTH HAZARDS IN NONSELENIFEROUS AREAS

No attempt has been made to determine the existence, outside the known seleniferous areas, of public health hazards caused by selenium. This problem is not confined to the United States since grain is exported from the United States to various areas of the world. Although toxic wheat is diluted with nontoxic grain during storing and milling processes, and in well-balanced diets, the consumption of bread and cereals per day is limited, possible harmful effects may occur in individuals who consume more than normal amounts of cereal products or who may have chronic diseases involving the kidney and liver. Selenium, thereby, may play an important role either directly or indirectly in the health of the general population.

Selenium as a public health problem is not confined to the United States. Analyses of grain indicate that selenium is present in Canada, Mexico, Argentina, Colombia, Ireland, Spain, Bulgaria, South Africa, Algeria, Morocco, Israel, Australia, and New Zealand. It is possible that areas not mentioned above may have some degree of public health problems related to the selenium intake.

At the present time one survey has been made on industrial workers in Rochester, New York (*49*). There is no selenium in the soil in that area or within 1000 miles of the region. Industrial workers included in the survey had had no recent exposure to selenium. Random urine samples were collected from 60 men; 70 per cent of the urine contained selenium. Selenium varied from a trace (1–2 μg) to 0.025 ppm of selenium. A second series of studies included repeated daily collection for 4 consecutive days.

The urinary excretion of selenium per day was from 0.02 to 0.1 ppm. The rate of excretion was constant in the individuals included in this study.

Investigating the possible sources of selenium in the above survey indicated that bleached flour and bread contained from 0.26 to 0.33 ppm selenium; rye bread and cracked wheat bread 0.39 and 0.37 ppm, respectively. These studies have given some information concerning the intake of selenium from grain (*49*).

Concentration of selenium in the urine was studied in Washington, D.C. of a few chemists who had direct contact with selenium—and of other persons whose selenium intake, according to their occupations, was from their diets (*57*). The distribution of selenium excreation of the group was somewhat lower than the group studied in Rochester. Soil chemists or chemists leaving seleniferous areas excreted slightly more selenium than people not employed in the chemical field. The concentration of selenium in all urine samples was below 0.1 ppm and varied from 0.002 to 0.04 ppm selenium.

The significance of such low levels of excretion in a small sample of the population from nonseleniferous areas could not be evaluated at the present time. The fragmentary information provided by these studies could give only an indication that small amounts of selenium were present in the diet of every person included in the survey.

SELENIUM AS AN INDUSTRIAL HAZARD

The increasing use of selenium in manufacturing processes presents an important industrial health hazard. Two groups of industries are involved: those that extract, mine, treat, or process selenium-bearing minerals and those that utilize selenium in manufacturing.

Selenium is used in the manufacture of pigments, in the chemical industry, in the manufacture of rubber as a vulcanizing agent, and in rectifiers and photoelectric cells. Selenium and its compounds used in industry are an ever present potential hazard, but the number of workers affected is comparatively low (*13, 26*).

The extent of this hazard depends primarily upon the types of processes being carried on. Selenium-bearing dusts, fumes, vapors, or liquids may present definite hazards, the scope and degree of which are dependent upon the processes involved and the protective devices used to dissipate the noxious materials. The dusts, such as that of elemental selenium, may be of such composition that on inhalation no soluble selenium compound is liberated. But soluble dusts, such as selenium dioxide, selenium trioxide, and certain halogen compounds, may prove toxic due to the ease with which they are absorbed by the tissues of the lung, the alimentary canal, and perhaps the skin. The most toxic vapors, however, may be expected to include hydrogen selenide and certain organic compounds, such as methyl selenide, ethyl selenide, and various aromatic selenides.

Contrary to many reports, there is no danger of selenium intoxication in handling selenium rectifiers. There is no danger to the health of radio and television owners from accidental burning out of selenium rectifiers. In event of a burning rectifier, it is suggested that the power source should be disconnected, the area ventilated, and skin contact with the rectifier residue must be avoided (*9, 44*).

Maximum Permissible Concentration

The maximum permissible concentration of selenium in the air has not been determined and inhalation exposures have been studied only in laboratory animals. In industries where selenium dioxide, selenium trioxide, sodium selenate, and sodium selenite are used, the atmospheric concentration should be below 1.0 mg per cubic meter of air (*40*).

Exposing guinea pigs to hydrogen selenide (0.001–0.004 mg per liter) killed 50 per cent of the animals within 30 days. The accidental exposure of men to hydrogen selenide had immediate and drastic effects. The odor, similar to hydrogen sulfide, produces olfactory fatigue quickly so that toxic concentrations may not be detected after exposure to the gas for several minutes. The gas usually produces a copious flow of tears and nasal mucus which partially alleviates the burning sensation (*14*). Other exposures to hydrogen selenide were described by various investigators (*4, 39, 51*). The threshold limit given by the American Conference of Government Industrial Hygienists for hydrogen selenide is 0.05 ppm selenium or 0.2 mg per cubic meter of air.

Data pertaining to the inhalation hazard with selenium oxychloride are not available at the present time. A minute drop (0.005 ml) of pure selenium oxychloride when applied to the skin of man produced a third degree burn which healed very slowly. Immediate flushing with water rapidly hydrolyzed the $SeOCl_4$ and no burn resulted (*12*). The vapors of selenium oxychloride are toxic but they decompose readily in air; therefore, their irritant and corrosive action on the respiratory tract is not as severe as on the skin. The low vapor pressure limits the concentration to the order of 60 or 70 ppm when in contact with dry recirculated air (*40*).

Symptoms of Exposure to Selenium and Selenium Compounds

Selenium may be absorbed through the lung, alimentary tract, and skin. On rare occasions a skin reaction on the back of the hands of workers, who had handled metallic selenium, has been recorded. In workers exposed to a fine dust of metallic selenium, the dust collected in the upper nasal passages and caused catarrh, nose bleeding, and loss of the sense of smell (*1*). Exposure to elemental selenium in manufacturing processes was described to produce intense and immediate irritation of eyes, nose, and throat, severe burning sensations of the nostrils, immediate sneezing, coughing, nasal congestion, dizziness, and redness of the eye. The most heavily exposed workers had slight difficulty in breathing, edema of the uvula, a few cases of severe dyspnea, and frontal headaches (*8*). It is doubtful that all the observed symptoms are due to elemental selenium since the high temperature used in the processes may have caused elemental selenium to be converted into selenium dioxide.

A majority of workers employed in Japan in the manufacture of selenium rectifiers are minors and children. Long-continued employment in the factory caused hypochromic anemia in the workers and drastic leucopenia. The nails were damaged when they came in direct contact with selenium. Increasing numbers of female workers had irregular menses or menostasis (*38*).

Selenium dioxide and sodium selenite readily form selenious acid which is among the more toxic and irritating compounds of selenium. It penetrates the skin readily and produces local irritation and inflammation. The exposure to SeO_2 dust produces severe dermatitis (*41*), painful inflammation of nail beds due to penetration of dioxide under the nails (*18*), burning of the eye with intense pain, lacrimation, and congestion of the conjunctiva (*34*), and allergic reactions in the eyes (*18*). The toxic effects of SeO_2 dust may be due to its rapid conversion to selenious acid when the dust comes in contact with moist surfaces of the tissues. Cutaneous disorders in workers handling SeO_2 have indicated that the selenite ion was responsible for its toxic action (*29*). Skin lesions produced by SeO_2 resembling hematomas in a state of resorption were described (*17*).

Subacute intoxication with hydrogen selenide may produce nausea, vomiting, metallic taste in the mouth, extreme dizziness, lassitude, and general fatigue including fatigue of the olfactory organ. Garlic odor of the breath was associated with selenium intoxication (*1, 4, 11, 14, 18*). The garlic breath not caused specifically by selenium may be due to the presence of tellurium (*18*).

Acute irritation of the mucous membrane of the respiratory tract, pulmonary edema, severe bronchitis, and bronchial pneumonia have been described in acute hydrogen selenide intoxication (*51*).

Selenium oxychloride can produce rapid tissue destruction on the skin surface with third degree burns which heal very slowly (*12*).

Dimethyl selenide produced acute sore throat and pneumonitis in man (*35*).

It was noted that young, slightly built employees engaged in extraction, purification, and processing of large amounts of selenium were affected more by selenium than the older men of dark, heavy, and stocky build (*10*).

Diagnosis of Exposure

As in animal experiments, selenium intake in man can be detected by the analysis of urine for selenium.

Dudley (*10*) studied men who were employed in industry processing and purification of large quantities of selenium. The daily urinary selenium excretion of these men ranged from 1.0 to 6.9 ppm. Low or trace amounts of selenium were present in urine of men who were not directly employed in the processing of selenium. There was no definite correlation between the severity of the disorders and the selenium excreted in the urine. No significant increase in urinary selenium was reported in subacute hydrogen selenide intoxication in man (*4*).

Preventive Measures

Adequate protective measures should be taken for the prevention of industrial selenium poisoning. Continued sampling of the air for dust and fumes with electrostatic precipitator, and gases and vapors scrubbed through 40–48 per cent HBr with 5–10 per cent free bromine has been suggested as a method of detection (*40*). The determination of selenium will be discussed in the subsequent chapter. Protective measures should include pre-employment examination and industrial cleanliness as well as personal hygiene instructions (*18*).

All dusts should be removed by exhaust ventilation. Workers should wear suitable protective clothing. Adequate washing facilities should be provided and no food should be consumed in the shop. Working with selenium compounds, such as the dioxide, calls for more careful methods of protection. Complete protective clothing, including helmets with a positive air pressure, is necessary for operators engaged in cleaning chambers and flues in those processes which involve sublimation of this chemical.

Treatment

The individual exposed to toxic amounts of selenium should be removed immediately from the toxic area. The affected skin should be washed with water followed by some emollient. Calamine lotion has been recommended for selenium dermatitis and sodium thiosulfate ointment and solution for burns caused by selenium dioxide (*1, 18, 41*). A daily dose of 10 mg (per kilogram of body weight) ascorbic acid intake was suggested as a preventative for workers exposed to selenium compounds (*7, 30*). There is no evidence that increased ascorbic acid intake has any beneficial effects against the disease in man. An increased administration of ascorbic acid had no effect on the development of chronic selenosis in rats (*43*).

Long-Term Effects in Man

The possible long-term effect may be renal and liver damage. Fibrosis in the lung may develop due to continued exposure to dust and gases in the air.

A report described a new aspect of selenium poisoning in a chemist exposed to a high concentration of hydrogen selenide. He developed a severe hyperglycemia which could be controlled only by increasingly large doses of insulin (*42*). Attempts to produce a similar condition in laboratory animals by exposing them to hydrogen selenide produced only transitory hyperglycemia. The authors concluded that individuals exposed to a high dose of selenium may develop diabetes if they have a tendency toward the disease.

Waste Disposal in Industry

Disposal of industrial waste containing selenium is a difficult problem. Burning cannot be carried out in residential areas because the smoke has an obnoxious odor as well as toxic fumes. If the material is dumped and allowed to drain into streams, there is danger of creating a toxic contamination of streams and surrounding soil. Amor and Pringle (*1*) suggested the selenium be reclaimed for further use. This idea in theory may be valid, but it is doubtful that it can be used under industrial conditions.

Industries must recognize the possible contamination of air and water by selenium and institute proper disposal to prevent health hazards in selenium refineries and processing areas.

References

1. Amor, A. J. and P. Pringle. 1945. A review of selenium as an industrial hazard. *Bull. Hyg.* **20**:239–241.
2. Beath, O. A. 1962. Selenium poisons Indians. *Sci. Newsletter* **81**:254.
3. Benavides, S. T. and R. F. S. Mojica. 1959. Seleniosis: Ocurrencia de selenio en rocas, suelos y plantas. Intoxicacion por selenio en animales y en humanos. Publicacion I T-3, Instituto Geografico de Colombia, Bogotá, Colombia.
4. Buchan, R. F. 1947. Industrial selenosis. *Occup. Med.* **3**:439–456.
5. Büttner, W. 1961. Effects of some trace elements on fluoride retention and dental caries. *Arch. Oral Biol.* **6** (suppl.):40.
6. Cadell, P. B. and F. B. Cousins. 1960. Urinary selenium and dental caries. *Nature* **185**:863–864.
7. Cerwenka, E. A., Jr. and W. C. Coopa. 1961. Toxicology of selenium and tellurium and their compounds. *Arch. Environmental Health* **3**:189–200.
8. Clinton, M., Jr. 1947. Selenium fume exposure. *J. Ind. Hyg. Toxicol.* **29**:225–226.
9. Drinker, P. and K. W. Nelson. 1953. Fumes and gases from selenium rectifiers abused by gross overloading. *Arch. Ind. Hyg. and Occup. Med.* **8**:185–189.
10. Dudley, H. C. 1936. Toxicology of selenium. II. The urinary excretion of selenium. *Am. J. Hyg.* **23**:181–186.

11. Dudley, H. C. and J. W. Miller. 1937. Toxicology of selenium. IV. Effects of exposure to hydrogen selenide. *Public Health Repts.* (*U.S.*) **52**:1217–1231.
12. Dudley, H. C. 1938. Toxicology of selenium. V. Toxic and vesicant properties of selenium oxychloride. *Public Health Repts.* (*U.S.*) **53**:94–98.
13. Dudley, H. C. 1938. Selenium as a potential industrial hazard. *Public Health Repts.* (*U.S.*) **53**:281–292.
14. Dudley, H. C. and J. W. Miller. 1941. Toxicology of selenium. VI. Effect of subacute exposure to hydrogen selenide. *J. Ind. Hyg. Toxicol.* **23**:470–477.
15. English, J. A. 1949. Experimental effects of thiouracil and selenium on the teeth and jaws of dogs. *J. Dental Res.* **28**:172–194.
16. Fimiani, R. 1949. Blood bilirubin in chronic experimental selenium poisoning. *Folia Med.* **32**:459–460.
17. Frant, R. 1949. Schadelijke werking van seleendioxyde op de menselijke huid. *Ned. Tijdschr. Geneesk.* **93**:874–876.
18. Glover, J. R. 1954. Some medical problems concerning selenium in industry. *Trans. Assoc. Ind. Med. Officers* **4**:94–96.
19. Hadjimarkos, D. M., C. A. Storvick and L. F. Remmert. 1952. Selenium and dental caries. *J. Pediat.* **40**:451–455.
20. Hadjimarkos, D. M. 1956. Geographic variations of dental caries in Oregon. VII. Caries prevalence among children in the Blue Mountain region. *J. Pediat.* **48**:195–201.
21. Hadjimarkos, D. M. and C. W. Bonhorst. 1958. The trace element selenium and its influence on dental caries susceptibility. *J. Pediat.* **52**:274–278.
22. Hadjimarkos, D. M. and C. W. Bonhorst. 1958. L'influence du selenium sur la susceptibilite a la carie dentaire. *Med. et Hyg.* **16**:620.
23. Hadjimarkos, D. M. and C. W. Bonhorst. 1959. The selenium content of human teeth. *Oral Surg., Oral Med., and Oral Pathol.* **12**:113–116.
24. Hadjimarkos, D. M. 1960. Urinary selenium and dental caries. *Nature* **188**:677.
25. Hadjimarkos, D. M. and C. W. Bonhorst. 1961. The selenium content of eggs, milk and water in relation to dental caries in children *J. Pediat.* **59**:256–259.

25a. Hadjimarkos, D. M. 1963. Selenium content of human milk: Possible effect on dental caries. *J. Pediat.* **63**:273–275.

26. Hamilton, A. and H. L. Hardy. 1949. "Industrial Toxicology," 2nd ed. Paul B. Hoeber, Inc., New York.
27. Hance, F. E. 1938. Selenium. *Hawaiian Planters' Record* **42**:197.
28. Hartley, W. J. and A. B. Grant. 1961. A review of selenium responsive diseases of New Zealand livestock. Symposia and reports. *Federation Proc.* **20**, Part 1: 679–688.
29. Höger, D. and C. Böhm. 1944. *Dermatologica* **90**:217. Cited by Buchan, R. F. 1947. *Occup. Med.* **3**:439–456.
30. Hunter, D. 1950. Toxicology of some metals and their compounds used in industry. *Brit. Med. Bull.* **7**:5–14.
31. Lemley, R. E. 1940. Selenium poisoning in the human. A preliminary case report. *J.-Lancet* **60**:528–531.
32. Lemley, R. E. and M. P. Merryman. 1941. Selenium poisoning in the human subject. *J.-Lancet* **61**:435–438.
33. McClure, F. J. and R. C. Likens. 1951. Fluorine in human teeth in relation to fluorine in the drinking water. *J. Dental Res.* **30**:172–176.
34. Middleton, J. M. 1947. Selenium burn of the eye. *A.M.A. Arch. Ophthalmol.* **38**: 806–811.

35. Motley, H. L., M. M. Ellis and M. D. Ellis. 1937. Acute sore throats following exposure to selenium. *J. Am. Med. Assoc.* **109**:1718–1719.
36. Moxon, A. L, A. E. Schaefer, H. A. Lardy, K. P. DuBois and O. E. Olson. 1940. Increasing the rate of excretion of selenium from selenized animals by the administration of *p*-bromobenzene. *J. Biol. Chem.* **132**:785–786.
37. Muhler, J. C. and W. G. Shafer. 1957. The effect of selenium on the incidence of dental caries in rats. *J. Dent. Res.* **36**:895–896.
38. Nagai, I. 1959. An experimental study of selenium poisoning. *Igaku Kenkyu* (Acta Medica) **29**:1505–1532.
39. Painter, E. P. 1941. The chemistry and toxicity of selenium compounds, with special reference to the selenium problem. *Chem. Rev.* **28**:179–213.
40. Patty, F. H. 1949. "Industrial Hygiene and Toxicology," Vol. II. Wiley (Interscience), New York.
41. Pringle, P. 1942. Occupational dermatitis following exposure to inorganic selenium compounds. *Brit. J. Dermatol. Syphilis* **54**:54–58
42. Rohmer, R., E. Carrot and J. Gouffault. 1950. New aspect of poisoning by selenium compounds. *Bull. Soc. Chim. France* pp. 275–278.
43. Rosenfeld, I. and O. A. Beath. 1947. The influence of various substances on chronic selenium poisoning. *J. Pharmacol. Exptl. Therap.* **91**:218–223.
44. Schwencer, A. 1953. Selenium rectifiers not toxic. *Chem. Eng. News.* **31**:5120.
45. Smith, M. I., K. W. Franke and B. B. Westfall. 1936. The selenium problem in relation to public health. A preliminary survey to determine the possibility of selenium intoxication in the rural population living on seleniferous soil. *Public Health Repts.* (*U.S.*) **51**:1496–1505.
46. Smith, M. I., E. F. Stohlman and R. D. Lillie. 1937. The toxicity and pathology of selenium. *J. Pharmacol. Exptl. Therap.* **60**:449–471.
47. Smith, M. I. and B. B. Westfall. 1937. Further field studies on the selenium problem in relation to public health. *Public Health Repts.* (*U.S.*) **52**:1375–1384.
48. Smith, M. I. and R. D. Lillie. 1940. Part 1. The chronic toxicity of naturally occurring food selenium. *U.S. Public Health Serv., Nat. Inst. Health Bull.* **174**: 1–13.
49. Sterner, J. H. and V. Lidfeldt. 1941. The selenium content of "normal" urine. *J. Pharmacol. Exptl. Therap.* **73**:205–211.
50. Suzuki, Y., K. Nishiyama, Y. Takano, T. Tajiri and I. Sakurayama. 1959. Studies on the selenium content of various foodstuffs, fertilizers and human hairs. *Tokushima J. Exptl. Med.* **6**:243–249.
51. Symanski, H. 1950. Ein fall von selenwasserstoffvergiftung. *Deut. Med. Wochschr.* **75**:1730–1731.
52. Takano, Y. 1959. Studies on the selenium poisoning. Part 6. Selenium content of grains on human hair collected in Japan. *Shikoku Igaku Zasshi* **15**:1861–1865.
53. Tank, G. and C. A. Storvick. 1960. Effect of naturally occurring selenium and vanadium on dental caries. *J. Dental Res.* **39**:473–488.
54. Thorvaldson, T. and L. R. Johnson. 1940. Selenium content of Saskatchewan wheat. *Can. J. Res.* **B18**:138–150.
55. Walker, O. J., W. E. Harris and M. Rossi. 1941. Selenium in soils, grains and plants in Alberta. *Can. J. Res.* **B19**:173–178.
56. Wheatcroft, M. G., J. A. English and C. A. Schlack. 1951. Effect of selenium on the incidence of dental caries in white rat. *J. Dental Res.* **30**:523.
57. Williams, K. T., H. W. Lakin and H. G. Byers. 1941. Selenium occurrence in certain soils in the United States, with a discussion of related topics: fifth report. *U.S. Dept. Agr. Tech. Bull.* **758**:1–69.

CHAPTER IX

CHEMISTRY OF SELENIUM

Selenium was identified as an element in 1817 by the Swedish chemist, Berzelius, in residue from sulfuric acid production. It was named from the Greek word, *selene,* meaning the moon, because of its resemblance to tellurium, an element which had been discovered earlier and was named from the Latin word, *tellus,* meaning the earth.

The chemistry of sulfur, selenium, and tellurium are similar, but their abundance in the earth's crust varies. Sulfur occurs freely in abundant quantities, while selenium and tellurium are rare with an estimated percentage of 10^{-4} and 10^{-9}, respectively, in the composition of the earth.

The distribution of selenium in different geological formations has been discussed in Chapter II. In this chapter, no attempt will be made to review the complex field of the chemistry of selenium. It will be limited to a brief discussion of compounds which may be used or have been used in biological studies. The chemistry of Group VIA elements is reviewed in detail by Sanderson (*62*) and Brasted (*8*).

Sources of selenium. Intensive explorations in the United States have not been fruitful in finding large deposits of selenium. At the present time, selenium is chiefly obtained commercially as a by-product of electrolytic refining of copper.

PHYSICAL AND CHEMICAL PROPERTIES OF SELENIUM

Some of the physical and chemical properties of Group VIA elements are given in Table 60. The data illustrate the variations in properties used for predicting chemical behavior of the elements.

The Group VIA elements—sulfur, selenium, and tellurium—show a great variety of allotropy. The allotropic changes in sulfur have been investigated but the modification of selenium has been studied less extensively. There are three allotropic forms of selenium: (1) "Metallic" hexagonal, crystalline-stable form, lustrous gray to black in color, has high electrical conductivity when exposed to light. (2) Red selenium, monoclinic crystals, obtained by cooling molten selenium, consists of Se_8 molecules as indicated by X-ray studies. The bond distances are 2.34 Å and the bond angles, 105.3° ± 2.3 (*44*). (3) Amorphous selenium may exist as black, amorphous red, or colloidal selenium. This form as well as the red mono-

TABLE 60
Physical and Chemical Properties of Group VIA Elements

	Oxygen O	Sulfur S	Selenium Se	Tellurium Te
Atomic weight	15.9994	32.064	78.96	127.60
Covalent radius, Å	0.73	1.02	1.16	1.35
Atomic radius, Å		1.27	1.40	1.60
Ionic radius, Å	1.40 (−2)	1.84 (−2)	1.98 (−2)	2.21 (−2)
Atomic volume, w/d	0.09 (+6)	0.29 (+6)	0.42 (+6)	0.56 (+6)
Electronegativity	14.0	15.5	16.5	20.5
(Pauling's)[a]	3.50	2.60	2.55	2.30
Oxidation states	−2	6,3,4,−2	6,4,−2	4,6,−2
Electron structure	$s^2 2s^2 2p^4$	[Ne] $3s^2 p^4$	[Ar] $3d^{10} 4s^2 4p^4$	[Kr] $4d^{10} 5s^2 5p^4$

[a] Revision of Pauling's values by Huggins.

clinic crystalline selenium is a poor conductor. The solubilities of allotropic forms are indicated in Table 61.

In the solid state, selenium may exist as the Se_8 molecular form while in the vapor state, decomposition to Se_6 and finally to Se_2 takes place. The crystal structure of oxygen is cubic and of native sulfur is rhombic, while that of tellurium and sublimed selenium is hexagonal.

TABLE 61
Solubility of Allotropic Forms of Selenium

Allotropic form	Water solubility	Other solvents
"Metallic" or gray	Insoluble	Insoluble in alcohol; slightly soluble in CS_2 (2 mg/100 ml); soluble in ether and chloroform
Crystalline monoclinic red	Insoluble	Soluble in CS_2
Amorphous	Reacts with water at 50° forming H_2SeO_3 and hydrogen	Soluble in CS_2, methylene iodide, benzene, or quinoline

The availability of selenium 4*d* orbitals for bonding permits the formation of such compounds as $SeCl_4$ or $SeBr_4$. The most outstanding characteristic of Group VIA elements is their six-electron system of valence orbitals.

Positive oxidation states are +4 and +6, and only a few unstable compounds are in +2 states. The binding in these states is primarily covalent. In the +4 state, the elements show both reducing and oxidizing properties while in the +6 state, they have only oxidizing properties. In selenides, selenium assumes the oxidation state of —2. Polyselenides are known but they are less stable than the polysulfides. Selenium, sulfur, and tellurium often form analogous compounds. The solubilities of some of the selenium compounds which are discussed in this chapter are listed in Table 62.

INORGANIC SELENIUM COMPOUNDS

Selenium Oxides

All selenium oxides are less stable than their sulfur analogs. Selenium differs from sulfur in showing less tendency to become oxidized to the VI state. Its most stable oxide is not SeO_3 but SeO_2. The trioxide, SeO_3, is formed by the action of SO_3 on a selenate [Eq. (1)].

$$K_2SeO_4 + SO_3 \longrightarrow K_2SO_4 + SeO_3 \quad (1)$$

The compound is a white solid occurring in two different forms, resembling the two forms of SO_3. SeO_3 melts at 118°, loses oxygen above 180° giving rise to SeO_2, and decomposes above 240°. Selenium trioxide reacts vigorously with H_2O producing selenic acid, H_2SeO_4.

Selenium Dioxide

Selenium burns in air to SeO_2, a white solid. It can be prepared from a mixture of selenium and concentrated nitric acid and when sublimed gives off a yellowish-greenish vapor which condenses as long crystalline white needles. Selenium dioxide is easily reduced; even specks of oxidizable dust in the air react with it to form red selenium, whereas sulfur dioxide is stable.

Selenium dioxide (SeO_2) dissolves in water readily and absorbs water from moist air. Traces of water can be removed from SeO_2 by drying for several hours in a current of dust-free air at 150° C. If dry selenium dioxide is exposed to a moist atmosphere, it absorbs water and forms crystalline selenious acid (H_2SeO_3).

Selenious Acid

Selenious acid is a weak dibasic acid and unlike sulfurous acid often acts as an oxidizing rather than a reducing agent. It is formed when selenium dioxide is dissolved in water or when selenium is oxidized in the presence of water. It is a white crystalline hygroscopic solid. It quantitatively oxidizes iodide to iodine in acid solution but does not affect bromide or chloride except in high concentrations [Eq. (2)].

$$H_2SeO_3 + 6I^- + 4H^+ \leftrightarrows Se(s) + 2I_3^- + 3H_2O \quad (2)$$

Selenious acid in solution is reduced to elemental selenium when treated with sulfurous acid.

TABLE 62

Solubility of Selenium Compounds[a, b]

Compound	Formula	Water solubility		Other solvents
		Cold	Hot	
Bromides	Se_2Br_2	Decomposes	Decomposes	Decomposes in alcohol; soluble in CS_2, C_2H_5Br, chloroform
	$SeBr_4$	Decomposes	Decomposes	Soluble in CS_2, C_2H_5Br, chloroform, and HCl
	$SeBrCl_3$			Insoluble in CS_2
	Se_2N_2Br	Insoluble	Decomposes	Silghtly soluble in CS^2
Chlorides	Se_2Cl_2	Decomposes	Decomposes	Decomposes in alcohol and ether; soluble in CS_2, CCl_4, chloroform, benzene
	$SeCl_4$	Decomposes	Decomposes	Decomposes in acids and alkalies; slightly soluble in CS_2
Nitride	Se_4N_4	Insoluble	Insoluble	Insoluble in alcohol and ether; slightly soluble in benzene, acetic acid, and CS_2
Oxides	SeO_2	Soluble	Soluble	Soluble in alcohol, acetone, benzene, acetic acid
	SeO_3	Decomposes slightly	Decomposes slightly	Soluble in alcohol and H_2SO_4; insoluble in ether, benzene, chloroform, CCl_4
	$SeSO_3$	Decomposes	Decomposes	Soluble in H_2SO_4; insoluble in SO_3
Oxy-salts	$SeOBr_2$	Decomposes	Decomposes	Soluble in CS_2, CCl_4, chloroform, benzene, H_2SO_4
	$SeOCl_2$	Decomposes	Decomposes	Soluble in CS_2, CCl_4, chloroform, benzene
	$SeOF_2$	Insoluble	Insoluble	Soluble in alcohol, CCl_4
Sulfides	SeS	Insoluble	Insoluble	Insoluble in ether, soluble in CS_2
	SeS_2	Insoluble	Insoluble	Decomposes in HNO_3, aqua regia; soluble in $(NH_4)_2S$

[a] Leddicotte (37).

[b] SeF_4, SeF_6, Se_2I_2 and SeI_4 are unstable and decompose in water.

Selenites are reduced to selenides by an aqueous solution of hydrazine, although some elemental selenium is also formed during reduction. An 85 per cent solution of NH_2NH_2 can be used for the production of metal selenides from selenites. Selenides react with silver nitrate to form Ag_2Se while tellurides are oxidized.

Selenious acid is reduced by thiourea, $CS(NH_2)_2$. This is interpreted as occurring through the decomposition of selenious acid to oxygen which in turn oxidizes the thiourea (*8*) [Eq. (3)].

$$\begin{aligned} H_2SeO_3 &\rightarrow Se + H_2O + O_2 \\ CS(NH_2)_2 + 2O_2 + H_2O &\rightarrow CO(NH_2)_2 + H_2SO_4 \\ 2CS(NH_2)_2 + 3O_2 &\rightarrow 2NH{:}C(NH_2)\cdot SO_3H \end{aligned} \quad (3)$$

The above reaction has been used for selenium determination (*8*).

Selenious acid forms two series of salts, the normal selenites and the acid selenites.

Reaction of Selenites with Sulfhydryl Compounds

The ready reactivity of selenite with cysteine or glutathione is of considerable biological interest. Painter (*50*) suggested the general reactions, Eq. (4), between sulfhydryl compounds and selenious acid:

$$4RSH + H_2SeO_3 \rightarrow RSSR + RS\text{---}\underset{\displaystyle \overset{\downarrow}{RSSR + Se}}{Se}\text{---}SR + 3H_20 \quad (4)$$

Selenite readily oxidizes sulfhydryl compounds forming disulfide and unstable RS–Se–SR compounds. The separation of the seleno-compound from disulfides is difficult due to the instability of RS–Se–SR compounds. Elemental selenium separates more rapidly from basic than from acidic solution.

Aqueous solutions of sodium selenite (0.0025 *M*) and cysteine hydrochloride (0.01 *M*) react to form selenotetracysteine, $Se(C_3H_6NO_2S)_4$, with a yield of 80–85 per cent (*68*).

Further study on the reaction of selenious acid and cysteine indicated that a mixture of at least two components was formed. Selenite oxidized two molecules of cysteine to cystine and probably bound two molecules of cysteine to form selenodicysteine (*34*).

$$HOOC\underset{\displaystyle NH_2}{\underset{|}{C}}HCH_2S\text{---}Se\text{---}SCH_2\underset{\displaystyle NH_2}{\underset{|}{C}}HCOOH$$

The reaction of selenious acid and reduced glutathione (GSH) was reported to be in a mole ratio of 1 : 4 with the formation of a mixture of oxidized glutathione (GSSG), selenodiglutathione, and water (*54*) according to Eq. (5).

$$GSH + H_2SeO_3 \quad GSSG + GS\text{---}Se\text{---}SG + H_2O \quad (5)$$

Catalytic oxidation of glutathione, cysteine, dihydrolipoic acid, and coenzyme A by selenite indicates that selenite is the most active catalyst for the oxidation of glutathione (*72*). Glutathione oxidation was a function of selenite concentration up to 0.01 *M* selenite per mole of GSH. At higher concentrations of selenite there was a loss of catalytic activity due to the reduction of selenite to elemental selenium. Elemental selenium does not act as a catalyst in the reaction. The rate of GSH oxidation increased with increasing pH and the activation energy was 5.9 kcal per mole. Tellurite and arsenite inhibited selenite catalysis. The catalytic oxidation of GSH by selenite proceeds through the formation of selenodiglutathione, an active intermediate in the oxidation.

Selenic Acid (H_2SeO_4)

Selenic acid is formed by the action of powerful oxidizing agents on selenium or selenious acid. The selenate ion is formed quantitatively by oxidation of selenite in $NaHCO_3$ solution by hypobromite (NaBrO). Bromine, chlorine, or H_2O_2 in water can be used for oxidation of selenite [Eq. (6)].

$$\begin{aligned} Se + 3Br_2 + 4H_2O &= H_2SeO_4 + 6HBr \\ H_2SeO_3 + Br_2 + H_2O &= H_2SeO_4 + 2HBr \end{aligned} \qquad (6)$$

Anhydrous H_2SeO_4 remains when the water is removed *in vacuo* at 200°C. It can be distilled without decomposition only under high vacuum. There are two definite hydrates known: $H_2SeO_4{\cdot}H_2O$ and $H_2SeO_4{\cdot}4H_2O$. Selenic acid is a less stable but stronger oxidizing agent than H_2SO_4 and resembles H_2SO_4 in having a high heat of hydration.

The crystal structure is orthorhombic with 4 molecules per unit. Each tetrahedral $SeO_4^{=}$ group is linked to 4 neighboring groups to form puckered layers parallel to the plane (*3*). Selenic acid forms 2 series of salts, selenates and acid selenates.

Halide Compounds

The selenohalide compounds discussed here are those that have been useful in analytical or biological studies.

Bromides. Selenium and sulfur form monobromides while there is no corresponding tellurium bromide. Se_2Br_2 is more stable than the sulfur compound. Sulfur forms no dibromide and selenium dibromide is known only in the vapor state as a decomposition product of $SeBr_4$. Selenium tetrabromide is formed by converting a Se(IV) salt in acid solution with HBr.

Liquid-liquid extraction of $SeBr_4$ from solution with ether or CCl_4 removes $SeBr_4$ from the original solution and on evaporation of the solvents, a solid $SeBr_4$ remains.

Chlorides. Selenium forms Se_2Cl_2 similar to sulfur but there is no Te_2Cl_2. $SeCl_2$ occurs in the vapor as a dissociation product of $SeCl_4$. It is less stable than the very unstable SCl_2. Selenium tetrachloride ($SeCl_4$) is a colorless solid completely dissociated in the vapor state to $SeCl_2$ and chlorine, but it is still more stable than sulfur tetrachloride. Tellurium tetrachloride ($TeCl_4$), as expected from the lower electronegativity of tellurium and greater bond polarity, is more stable than either selenium or sulfur tetrachloride.

Hydrogen Selenide

Hydrogen selenide (H_2Se) is a colorless, very toxic gas closely resembling hydrogen sulfide in odor and general properties, but is less stable. It can be synthesized directly by heating the elements at about 400° or by hydrolysis of metal selenides. The water solubility of H_2Se is greater than H_2S and about 2000 times as strong an acid as hydrogen sulfide. The acidity likely reflects a reduced electron donor ability of HSe^- compared to HS^-.

PREPARATION OF SODIUM OR POTASSIUM SELENITE

Sodium selenite or potassium selenite may be prepared by dissolving SeO_2 [analytical reagent (AR)] in water and neutralizing it with NaOH or KOH.

PREPARATION OF POTASSIUM SELENATE

Since commercial potassium selenate often contains some selenite, for metabolic studies it is advisable to prepare the salt from SeO_2 (AR). The following procedure gives a salt of high purity.

Fifty-two grams of 85 per cent KOH is dissolved in 160 ml water and cooled to 0° C. To the cooled solution, 44 gm of SeO_2 (AR) is added. (About 82 gm of potassium selenite or of a mixture of selenite and selenate may be used instead of SeO_2.)

Twenty-seven to 30 ml of Br_2 (30% excess) is added slowly with cooling to the K_2SeO_3 solution.

One hundred thirty-five grams of KOH is dissolved in 135 ml of distilled water. The cooled KOH solution is added a few drops at a time to the solution of K_2SeO_3 and Br_2 until the Br_2 is decolorized and the solution is strongly alkaline. The flask should be kept at 0° C and stirred continuously while adding the KOH solution to the $K_2SeO_3 + Br_2$ solution. Oxidation of K_2SeO_3 to K_2SeO_4 occurs while the KOH is being added.

The K_2SeO_4 solution is precipitated with about three times its volume of methyl alcohol (AR) and the precipitate is filtered (Whatman No. 3) and redissolved in 100 to 150 ml water. The precipitation with three volumes of methyl alcohol is repeated two to three times and the final precipitate is washed thoroughly with CH_3OH.

The salt may be dried at room temperature, in a vacuum oven at 50° C, or in an oven at 101° C for 6 hours. (Yield: 70 gm or 80% of theoretical K_2SeO_4.)

The test for selenite is made on a 10 per cent acid solution with one drop of dilute $KMnO_4$. If the color persists, no selenite is present. The test for bromide is made with $AgNO_3$ using a dilute acid solution of the selenate. If selenite or bromide is present, the salt is redissolved, reprecipitated, and recrystallized.

A similar procedure may be used for the preparation of sodium selenate, but this salt has water of crystallization.

RADIOCHEMISTRY OF SELENIUM

The radioactive nuclides of selenium are presented in Table 63, which lists their half-life, mode of decay, energy of radiation, and mode of production. The technique of isolation of the radionuclides is made by the

TABLE 63
The Radioactive Nuclides of Selenium

Radio-nuclide	Half-life	Mode of decay	Energy of radiation (MEV)	Methods of production
Se^{72}	9.7 *d*	EC		As-*d*-5*n*, parent As^{72}
Se^{73}	7.1 *h*	β^+, EC	β^+, 1.29, 1.65	Ge^{70}-α-*m*;
		IT	γ, 0.36, 0.066	As-*d*-4*n*
Se^{75}	127 *d*	EC	γ, 0.265, 0.136	Se^{74}-*n*-γ; As-*p*-*n*;
			0.28, 0.405	As-*d*-2*n*
$Se^{77}m$	17.5 *s*	IT	γ, 0.162	Se^{76}-*n*-γ; U fission
$Se^{79}m$	3.90 *m*	IT	γ, 0.096	Se^{78}-*n*-γ; U fission; Br-*n*-*p*
Se^{79}	6×10^4 *y*	β^-	β^-, 0.16	
$Se^{81}m$	56.8 *m*	IT	γ, 0.103	Se^{80}-*n*-γ; Se-*d*-*p*; Br-*n*-*p*; U fission
Se^{81}	18.2 *m*	β^-	β^-, 1.38	Se-*n*-γ; Se-*d*-*p*; Br-*n*-*p*; U fission
Se^{83}	25 *m*	β^-	β^-, 1.5	Se-*n*-γ; Se-*d*-*p*;
			γ, 0.35	U fission, Th fission
Se^{84}	3.3 *m*	β^-		U fission; parent Br^{83}

conventional analytical chemistry. These methods are precipitation, solvent extractions, volatilization, chromatography, and/or electrolysis. Identification of isotopes is made by the characteristic radiation and half-life (the time required for one half of the isotopes in a sample to decay). The half-life of many selenium isotopes ranges from a few seconds to 6×10^4 years.

Among the radioactive isotopes listed in Table 63, only Se^{75} is useful for biological studies. It has a relatively long half-life (127 days) which allows long-term studies. The decay of Se^{75} was discussed by Schardt and Welker (*65*) and its radiations by Jensen *et al.* (*30*).

$Selenium^{75}$ can be used as an analytical adjunct to determine and check the accuracy of methods of procedure (*25, 31, 60*), to trace its distribution, and to study the metabolism of selenium in biological systems.

ORGANOSELENIUM COMPOUNDS

A comprehensive and systematic review of the various aspects of organic chemistry of selenium was made by Campbell *et al.* (*9*). The nomenclature for organoselenium compounds is similar to that of sulfur compounds. The organic selenium compounds discussed here are those compounds that have been used or may have some value in biological studies.

Some organic reactions of selenium compounds which may function in biological systems were summarized by Painter (*50*). Organic diselenides, selenium ethers, and seleninic acids (acetic, β-propionic, *n*-propyl, and benzyl) were synthesized and their decomposition studied in alkaline solution by Painter *et al.* (*49*). Decomposition of the seleno-compounds was similar to the corresponding sulfur compounds.

DIMETHYL SELENIDE

Considerable evidence has been presented to indicate that dimethyl selenide is a metabolic product of inorganic selenium in many biological systems (*11*). Dimethyl selenide is a volatile liquid of pungent odor. It can be prepared from metal selenides and methyl sulfates [Eq. (7)].

$$Na_2Se + 2CH_3OSO_3Na \rightarrow Se(CH_3)_2 + 2Na_2SO_4 \quad (7)$$

SELENO-AMINO ACIDS

Selenocystine and its derivatives and selenomethionine were synthesized by the methods used for their sulfur analogs.

Selenocystine has been prepared by treating methyl α-amino-β-chloropropionate with sodium benzyl selenide. The amino acid β-(benzylseleno)-alanine was formed and this compound was reduced with sodium in liquid ammonia; the benzyl group cleaved and the fraction containing the amino group gave selenocystine after air oxidation (*51*).

```
                NH2
                |
Se—CH2—CH—COOH
|
Se—CH2—CH—COOH
                |
                NH2
```

Selenocystine

Two other methods for the preparation of selenocystine have been described. In the first method the α-amino-β-chloropropionic acid was treated with barium hydrogen selenide or calcium hydrogen selenide and the product was oxidized to produce selenocystine. The second method was the treatment of benzyl chloromethyl selenide with phthalimidomalonic ester followed by hydrolysis and reduction. Both methods gave low yields of selenocystine (*75, 76*).

Derivatives of benzyl selenol have been used for the synthesis of selenohomocystine and selenomethionine (*33, 52*). The compounds were prepared by treating 5-(β-bromoethyl)-hydantoin with sodium benzyl selenide in ethanol to give 5-(β-benzylselenoethyl)-hydantoin. Hydrolysis with NaOH gave α-amino-γ-(benzylseleno)-butyric acid. Reduction of this amino acid with sodium in liquid ammonia gave selenohomocystine, and by methylation of the reduced form selenomethionine was obtained.

$$H_3C{-}Se{-}CH_2{-}CH_2{-}\underset{\displaystyle NH_2}{\underset{|}{CH}}{-}COOH$$

Selenomethionine

$$HOOC\underset{\displaystyle NH_2}{\underset{|}{C}}HCH_2CH_2SeSeCH_2CH_2\underset{\displaystyle NH_2}{\underset{|}{C}}HCOOH$$

Selenohomocystine

Synthesis of selenomethionine from sodium methylselenide and γ-amino-butyrolactone was described by Plieninger (*58*).

All the seleno-amino acids synthesized by above methods were the DL-isomers. In general, the seleno-amino acids have the same degree of instability as their sulfur analogs. Selenocystine is less stable than selenomethionine. Hydrolysis of Se^{75}-wool protein with 3 *N* and 6 *N* HCl indicated that the stronger acid solution decomposed selenocystine and cystine in wool and reduced their recovery (*59*). It should be pointed out that a mixture of seleno-amino acids and their sulfur analogs cannot be separated either by resins or paper chromatography. R_f values of seleno-amino acids are the same as those of the corresponding sulfur compounds when the same solvents are used (*55, 59, 71, 73*). Selenocystine in water solution on electrodialysis decomposed to give elemental selenium (*45*).

Selenocystamine, selenohypotaurine, and selenotaurine were synthesized by Pichot *et al.* (*56a*). The method of synthesis was as follows:

Selenocystamine hydrochloride is prepared by the addition of potassium selenothiocyanate to *N*-bromoethylphthalimide with a yield of about 40 per cent. The oxidation of selenocystamine hydrochloride with brominated water converted it to selenohypotaurine with a yield of 97 per cent. Selenotaurine may be prepared from selenocystamine or selenohypotaurine by oxidation with chlorine. The compounds were purified and separated on ion exchange resin. Selenotaurine is unstable when crystallized.

$(NH_2CH_2CH_2Se)_2 \cdot 2HCl$	$NH_2CH_2CH_2SeO_2H$	$NH_2CH_2CH_2SeO_3H$
Selenocystamine	Selenohypotaurine	Selenotaurine

Homocyclic and Heterocyclic Seleno-Compounds

Selenium analogs of antifungal, bacteriostatic, and carcinostatic thio-compounds were synthesized and the biological effectiveness studied by a few investigators. Dingwall (*17*) reviewed the literature dealing with the biological effectiveness of these organoselenium compounds. A few of those compounds will be discussed briefly.

2-Phenylselenosemicarbazide, its sulfur and oxygen analogs and a series of their *para*-substituted benzaldehyde derivatives were synthesized (*40*). The dipole moments, infrared and ultraviolet spectra of some analogous carbamyl (thiocarbamyl and selenocarbamyl) compounds were investigated. The compounds of selenium were more acidic than their sulfur analogs. The carbon-selenium double bond was more polar than the carbon-sulfur double bond. The biological effectiveness (bacteriostatic) of the selenium compounds on a molar basis was 10 to 1000 times more effective than their sulfur analogs while the oxygen compounds generally showed slight activity.

Selenopurine and selenopyrimidine derivatives have been prepared by similar methods used for the preparation of the thio-analogs by Mautner (*39*). 6-Selenopurine was prepared by the addition of hydroselenide or selenourea in absolute alcohol to 6-chloropurine and the mixture was refluxed for 18 hours with hydroselenide and one hour with selenourea. The methylation of selenopurine in alkaline solution with methyl iodide yielded 6-methylselenopurine.

2-Selenouracil was prepared by the addition of ethylformyl acetate to selenourea and allowing it to stand at room temperature for 3 hours. 2,4-Diselenouracil was prepared by the addition of hydroselenide to 2,4-dichloropyrimidine and refluxed for 3 hours. 2-Selenothymine was prepared by a solution of sodium ethylformyl propionate, selenourea, and sodium in absolute alcohol heated to reflux for 3 hours. 6-Selenopurine, 6-methylselenopurine, 2-selenouracil, 2,4-diselenouracil, and 2-selenothymine were isolated following acidification of the refluxed mixtures and cooling.

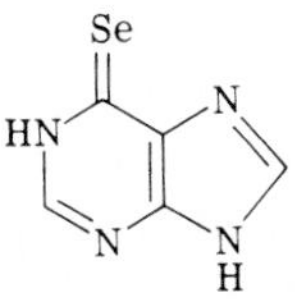

6-Selenopurine 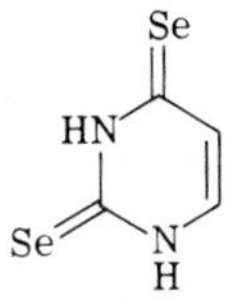   2,4-Diselenouracil 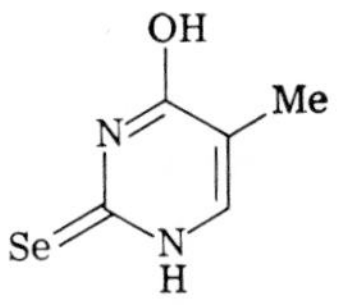   2-Selenothymine

The most useful carcinostatic and bacteriostatic compounds were those in which the size of the new atom or group was similar to the group or atom that was replaced. 6-Selenopurine was unstable and its effectiveness implies selective rapid action. The ultraviolet spectra of the above compounds and their sulfur and oxygen analogs were studied. Acidic dissociation was found to increase from the oxygen to the sulfur analogs (*39*).

6-Amino-8-selenopurine, 6-hydroxy-8-selenopurine, and 6-morpholyl-8-selenopurine were synthesized by reaction of six substituted 4,5-diaminopyrimidines with selenious acid (*10*). In these compounds the selenium was placed within the purine nucleus.

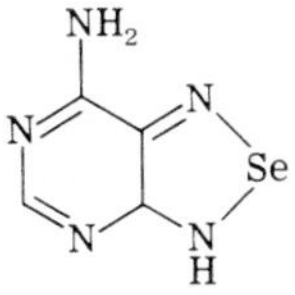

6-Amino-
8-selenopurine

These compounds may be useful as possible purine antimetabolites for cancer therapy (*64*).

Selenoguanine, selenocytosine, and related compounds were synthesized by Mautner *et al.* (*43*). 2-Amino-6-selenopurine (selenoguanine) was prepared in excellent yield by the reaction of hydroselenide with 2-amino-6-chloropurine in a manner analogous to the synthesis of 6-selenopurine. 4-Amino-2-selenopyrimidine (selenocytosine) was prepared by the reaction of diselenouracil with ammonia analogous to the synthesis of thiocytosine from dithiouracil (*27*). 2,4-Diseleno-5-methylpyrimidine (diselenothymine) was synthesized by the addition of sodium hydroselenide to 2,4-dichloro-5-methylpyrimidine. By the addition of ammonia the diselenothymine was converted to 5-methylselenocytosine (4-amino-5-methyl-2-selenopyrimidine).

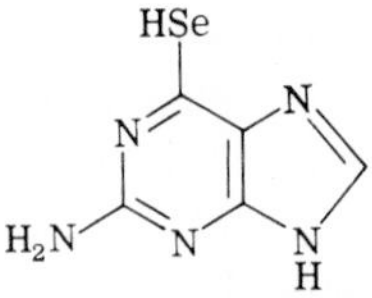

Selenoguanine 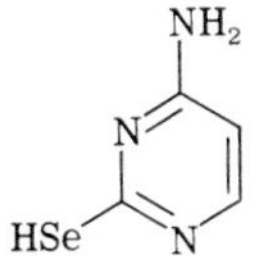   Selenocytosine 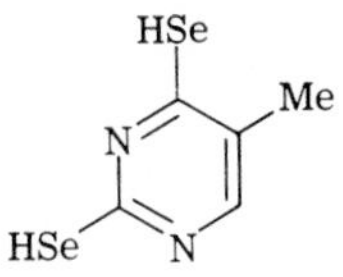   Diselenothymine

Selenoguanine possesses an appreciably higher therapeutic index against murine neoplasms than thioguanine.

Other seleno-substituted heterocyclic compounds—2-selenopyridine, *N*-methyl-2-selenopyridine, 2-methylselenopyridine, and 2,2′-dipyridyl diselenide—were synthesized by Mautner *et al.* (*42*).

The acidic and basic dissociation constants of the selenium compounds were compared with those of the isologous oxo- and thio-compounds. These studies indicated that 2-selenopyridine is a stronger acid than 2-thiopyridine, which in turn is a stronger acid than 2-oxypyridine. The compounds were suggested to be tautomeric form in which the dissociating hydrogen is released from the ring of nitrogen and the ability to withdraw electrons from this nitrogen increases as oxygen is replaced with sulfur and selenium. The ultraviolet spectra of 2-selenopyridine and thiopyridine were investigated in neutral (water) and in cationic (70% sulfuric acid, pH 5.65) forms. The stability of the seleno-compound may increase its biological usefulness. Changes in acid dissociation and lipid solubility of barbiturates were noted when the oxygen in the 2-position was replaced by sulfur or selenium (*41*).

The considerable effectiveness of cysteamine and 2-aminoethylisothiouronium salts (AET) against ionizing radiation has been indicated (*19*, *56b*). Chu and Mautner (*13*) prepared selenium analogs as potential antiradiation agents. The selenium analog of AET was prepared by the reaction of selenourea in isopropyl alcohol with 2-bromoethylamine hydrobromide. The selenouronium salt was treated with sodium hydroxide and yielded 2-selenoethylguanidine which was isolated as the flavianate salt. The reaction of 2-aminoethylisoselenouronium hydrobromide with boiling water resulted in the formation of 2-aminoselenazoline.

The following reaction sequence indicates the preparation of the above selenium compounds [Eq. (7a)].

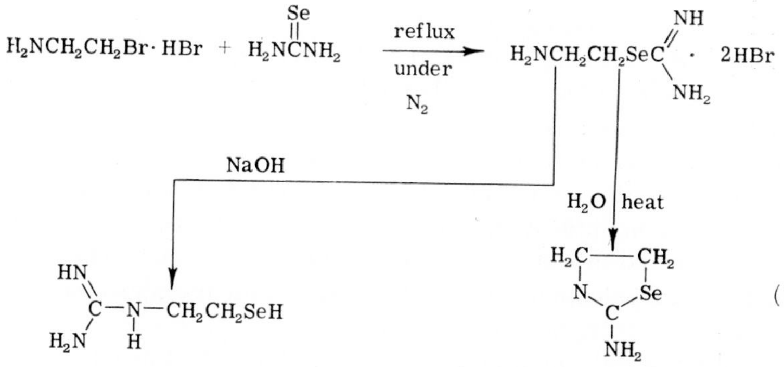

$$H_2NCH_2CH_2Br \cdot HBr + H_2N\overset{\overset{\displaystyle Se}{\|}}{C}NH_2 \xrightarrow[\text{under } N_2]{\text{reflux}} H_2NCH_2CH_2SeC(=NH)NH_2 \cdot 2HBr$$

$$\xrightarrow{NaOH} \; HN{=}C(H_2N){-}NH{-}CH_2CH_2SeH \quad \text{2-Selenoethylguanidine}$$

$$\xrightarrow{H_2O,\ \text{heat}} \; \text{2-Aminoselenazoline (ring: } H_2C{-}CH_2,\ N{=}C(NH_2){-}Se) \tag{7a}$$

2-Selenoethylguanidine

2-Aminoselenazoline

SELENOPANTETHINE

A selenium analog of pantethine was prepared by the condensation of pantothenic acid with selenocystamine (*26*). The light brown oil residue was obtained as the condensation product. Selenopantethine was separated by elution with acetone from a column of activated alumina. The compound is highly hygroscopic yellow glass.

$$[HOCH_2CMe_2CH(OH)CONHCH_2CH_2CONHCH_2CH_2Se]_2$$
Selenopantethine

METHODS OF DETERMINATION

The separation of selenium by distillation, ion exchange procedures, and electrolytic separation is described by Kolthoff and Elving (*35*). The method for the determination of selenium by distillation as $SeBr_4$, precipitation of selenium and titration with thiosulfate will be described. This method has been in use in the authors' laboratories for about 30 years. Other methods will be discussed according to their value for the determination of selenium in biological material.

The procedure recommended below includes many of the modifications described by Klein (*32*). This method is adapted to the determination of quantities of selenium of more than 0.01 mg. If smaller amounts are to be estimated, semi-micro or micro methods, or neutron activation analyses may be used.

The reagents listed for the General Method are given in detail for the determination of selenium in plants, plant extracts, water, animal tissues, urine, soil, and rocks.

REAGENTS

I. Sulfuric nitric acid: Mixture of 2 parts concentrated HNO_3, and 1 part of concentrated H_2SO_4.
II. Mercuric oxide fixative: 5% HgO in concentrated HNO_3.
III. Nitric acid: concentrated (AR)
IV. Hydrobromic acid-bromine: 1.5% Br_2 in HBr, 48%. (Diluted 1:4 with water when used for distillation.)
V. Sulfur dioxide: Free of Se.
VI. Hydroxylamine hydrochloride: 10% solution in water.
VII. Selenium stock solution (1 mg Se per milliliter for standard: Prepared from purified selenium, or SeO_2 or Na_2SeO_3.) The compound is dissolved in water containing about 5 to 8% of 48% HBr.
VIII. Standard selenium solution: Prepared from the above stock containing 0.1 mg Se per milliliter.
IX. Sulfur dioxide in water: SO_2 gas is slowly bubbled for about 3 minutes into water.

X. Phenol: 5% solution.

XI. Sodium thiosulfate solution: 0.005 *N*. The solution is stored in a brown bottle in the dark. One milliliter of the freshly prepared solution is equivalent to 0.1 mg of Se. (It is necessary to check it with the standard Se solution on the day of titration.)

XII. Starch indicator: 0.5% aqueous solution.

XIII. Iodine solution: 0.005 *N* (in 2.5% KI). The solution is stored in a brown bottle in a cool, dark place. (One milliliter is equivalent to 1 ml of the standard thiosulfate solution, but the exact ratio is established on the day of titration.)

XIV. Gum arabic solution: 5% solution of gum arabic is prepared in water. The solution should be prepared as needed or preserved by saturating it with benzoic acid.

APPARATUS

An all-glass distillation apparatus is used for selenium analysis as indicated in Fig. 44.

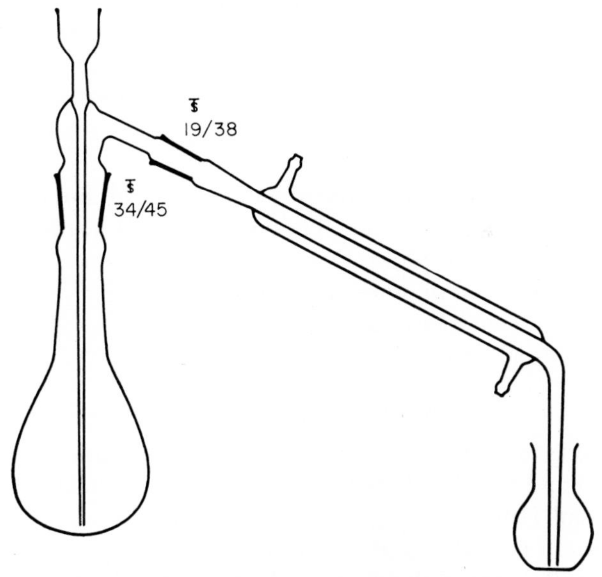

FIG. 44. Distillation apparatus used in selenium analysis.

GENERAL METHOD

Samples of dried or fresh material may be used for analysis. Samples (plants or feces) may be dried quickly by placing them in a forced draft oven at about 60° C or plants may be placed on wire screens in a well-ventilated room. Prolonged drying at a higher temperature or air-drying results in loss of Se, therefore, is to be avoided.

If fresh plant is used, it should be ground and thoroughly mixed. If a water extract of plant material is analyzed, sodium peroxide is added until the extract has a slightly alkaline pH. Water must be removed by evaporation to reduce the volume of the extract to approximately that of the H_2SO_4 used.

For Se analysis of dry plant material, a 3-gm sample (estimated to contain 300 to 3000 ppm Se) or a 6- to 10-gm sample (less than 300 ppm Se) may be used. If fresh material with low Se content is used, a 40- to 50-gm sample can be used.

The sample is digested with low flame in the flask (see Apparatus) with 150 ml of H_2SO_4-HNO_3 (reagent I), 10 ml of HgO (reagent II), and a few boiling chips (allowing 30 minutes with intermittent stirring before digestion is started). If foaming occurs, heating is discontinued until it subsides or an antifoaming agent may be added. Digestion is continued with a higher flame until the material slightly darkens. (With some types of material, additional HNO_3 must be used for complete oxidation. In this case the digest is cooled, 10 ml of concentrated HNO_3 is added and heated; this operation may be repeated until all the organic material is destroyed. Trials may be made to determine whether or not additional portions of HNO_3 are required for complete recovery of the Se from the material used.) Finally, the digest is heated until the liquid turns pale yellow (but not black) or until SO_3 fumes appear. It is necessary to oxidize the organic material sufficiently and to expel the excess HNO_3, otherwise the Br_2 subsequently added will be reduced. But any prolonged fuming of SO_3 should be avoided, because continued heating at this temperature causes loss of Se.

Se is separated from all other elements except arsenic, tin, germanium, small amounts of antimony, and tellurium (partly) by distillation with HBr and Br_2 from acid solution [Eq. (8)].

$$H_2SeO_3 + 4HBr = SeBr_4 + 3H_2O \tag{8}$$

The digest is cooled and about 75 ml of water is added. The digest is again cooled and 60 ml of HBr-Br_2 (reagent IV) is added. In the receiving flask, 5 ml HBr-Br_2 (reagent IV) is added to cover the end of the delivery tube. (HBr-Br_2 in the receiver insures retention of the Se as $SeBr_4$.) Free Br_2 should distill at the beginning, indicating an excess of the reagent. If this does not occur, the distillation is stopped and cooled and 10 ml of HBr-Br_2 (reagent IV) is added. The volume of the distillate should be 75–100 ml. The distillate contains the Se as H_2SeO_3 [Eq. (9)].

$$SeBr_4 + 3H_2O = H_2SeO_3 + 4HBr \tag{9}$$

The condenser is rinsed with a small amount of water; the rinse water is collected in the receiving flask. In the analysis of some substances, it may be necessary to reoxidize the residue with perchloric acid and redistill.

If wax or other insoluble material is visible in the distillate, this is removed by filtration on an asbestos mat. The mat is rinsed with 3 small portions of water. (The total volume of distillate and rinse water should not exceed about 150 ml.) The filtered distillate is transferred to a beaker and decolorized with SO_2 (using a slight excess); 2 ml of hydroxylamine hydrochloride (reagent VI) is added; and the beaker is covered and allowed to stand on a steam bath for 30 minutes [Eq. (10)].

$$H_2SeO_3 + 2H_2SO_3 = Se + 2H_2SO_4 + H_2O$$
$$H_2SeO_3 + 2NH_2OH \cdot HCl = Se + N_2O + 4H_2O + 2HCl \qquad (10)$$

The precipitate is allowed to settle overnight. If the selenium precipitate stands too long, it may partially redissolve.

The Se appears as a pink, red, or black precipitate. The precipitated selenium is filtered on an asbestos mat in a crucible with gentle suction. The beaker is rinsed with several small portions of distilled water, pouring these into the crucible.

The precipitate is then dissolved in about 4 ml of dilute $HBr\text{-}Br_2$ (reagent IV) (diluted 1:2 or 1:4 depending upon the amount of the precipitate) and allowed to stand for a few minutes to dissolve the selenium [Eq. (11)].

$$Se + 2Br_2 + 3H_2O = H_2SeO_3 + 4HBr \qquad (11)$$

The precipitate on the wall of the crucible is washed down with a few drops of dilute $HBr\text{-}Br_2$, using a fine capillary pipette. Gentle suction is applied and the Se solution is drawn through the asbestos mat; the procedure is repeated twice with 2 ml of dilute $HBr\text{-}Br_2$. The mat is rinsed with a minimum amount of water so as to keep the volume of the filtrate, including washings, below 25 ml.

If the amount of Se is estimated to be small (i.e., less than 2.5 mg), the filtrate is titrated directly. Larger amounts of precipitate are diluted to 50, 100, or 200 ml in a volumetric flask. Aliquots of 10 to 30 ml can be used for titration.

Duplicate Se standards are made from reagent VIII (0.1 mg Se per ml). The range may vary from 1.0 to 2.5 mg. Reagent blanks in duplicate are made with water and approximately the average volume of dilute $HBr\text{-}Br_2$ that is present in the distillate.

To the distillate, standards, and reagent blanks, a solution of SO_2 (reagent IX) is added, drop by drop, until the bromine color nearly disappears [Eq. (12)].

$$H_2SO_3 + Br_2 + H_2O = H_2SO_4 + 2HBr \qquad (12)$$

If too much SO_2 is added and the solution is completely decolorized, dilute $HBr\text{-}Br_2$ (reagent IV diluted 1:20 with water) is added dropwise until a light-yellow color reappears. Then 3 drops of the phenol solution (reagent X) are added for the final decolorization. It is desirable to reduce the color to light yellow before adding the phenol since tribromophenol is precipitated with excess Br_2; but the presence of precipitate does not affect the titration.

To a blank, a known volume (about 3 ml) of the iodine solution (reagent XIII) is added, followed by 3 drops of starch solution (reagent XII), and is titrated with the thiosulfate solution (reagent XI) to a colorless end point. The amount of thiosulfate is recorded [Eq. (13)].

$$2Na_2S_2O_3 + I_2 = Na_2S_4O_6 + 2NaI \tag{13}$$

The other blank is titrated in a similar manner and the results of the thiosulfate equivalent of the I_2 are averaged.

Titration of standards and distillate is carried out by the addition of an excess of thiosulfate (reagent XI) (2–4 ml) and 5 drops of starch. After 30 seconds the excess of thiosulfate is back titrated with iodine (reagent XIII). If the end points in titration are passed, thiosulfate or iodine may be added and the sample retitrated; for each sample it is necessary to know the total thiosulfate and the total iodine used. 1 ml 0.005 N $Na_2S_2O_3 \approx 0.005$ N iodine ≈ 0.0987 mg Se.

Equation (14) describes the essential features of the reaction between the selenious acid and the sodium thiosulfate (*47*):

$$H_2SeO_3 + 4Na_2S_2O_3 + 4HBr = Na_2S_4SeO_6 + Na_2S_4O_6 + 4NaBr + 3H_2O \tag{14}$$

DETERMINATION OF SELENIUM IN VARIOUS MATERIALS

For titration of the small amounts of Se likely to be present in water, urine, animal tissues, blood, rocks, and soils, it is advisable to dilute the standard Se solution, the sodium thiosulfate solution, and the iodine solution 1 to 5; for plants with high Se content the reagents are used without dilution.

WATER

In recognition of the possible health hazard by selenium in water, the U. S. Public Health Service recommends for drinking water 0.05 mg Se per liter shall constitute grounds for rejection of water supply.

Determination of selenium in water requires 2 or more liters of water. The pH is adjusted to alkaline with sodium peroxide and the water is evaporated almost to dryness on a steam bath. If a high concentration of organic matter is present, it may be necessary to digest with a small amount of the sulfuric-nitric acid (reagent I) on low flame. Digestion is repeated until the organic matter is oxidized. Distillation of Se is carried out in the same manner as described under General Method.

The distillate is treated by bubbling SO_2 into the liquid until the yellow color of bromine disappears (5–10 seconds longer).

The solution is transferred to either a 50 or 100 ml volumetric flask. One ml gum arabic (reagent XIV) and 2 ml hydroxylamine (reagent VI) are added. The flask is stoppered and allowed to stand one hour. Simultaneously, the standard from the selenium stock solution containing from 0.01 to 0.1 mg Se is treated in the same manner as the water sample. Visual comparison can be used to determine the amount of selenium by comparing the sample with the standards (*2*).

The sample may be transferred to a cuvette with 4 cm light path and read against a similarly prepared reagent blank at 415 mμ. To obtain the concentration of selenium, standards are prepared in the same manner as the sample and read at the same time. By using $SnCl_2$ instead of hydroxylamine hydrochloride and omitting gum arabic, the sensitivity of the determination can be increased (*35*). The modification of Lambert *et al.* (*36*) for the determination of trace amounts of Se in water is based on the quantitative oxidation of iodide by selenious acid. The iodine is determined colorimetrically at 320 mμ.

A number of modifications for Se analysis of effluents and water have been suggested; the following modifications have considerable value. After destruction of the organic matter by wet oxidation, the selenium is distilled as the bromide. Selenious acid is reduced to elemental selenium with ascorbic acid and measured colorimetrically as a colloidal sol against standards. Visual color measurement has been recommended for the colloidal solution (*1*).

A modification of the American Public Health Association method for determination of selenium in water has been suggested (*23*). In addition to the nitric-sulfuric acid, a small volume of perchloric is used for oxidation of the organic matter. The selenium is precipitated with ascorbic acid. The turbidity under standard conditions of acidity of sample and standard gave reproducible colors and accurate results.

Plants

Three to five grams of finely ground, dried samples or 20–50 gm of fresh sample (depending on the Se content) is oxidized and distilled as indicated in General Method.

For assay of plants containing high levels of selenium, the residue remaining after distillation is heated to incipient fumes of SO_3, cooled, and 5 ml $HClO_4$ is added. The residue is mixed with the acid and heated to fuming. The $HClO_4$ oxidation is repeated once more. The digest is cooled, two 25 ml portions of water are added, followed by 25 ml $HBr\text{-}Br_2$ solution and distilled until the temperature reaches 130° C. The distillates are then combined. The selenium content is determined by titration as indicated in General Method. In low selenium samples the selenium may be determined by methods described for water analysis.

URINE

The selenium in urine may be determined as follows: urine, 1 volume; HBr-Br_2 (reagent IV), 1 volume; concentrated H_2SO_4, 1 volume. The reagents are added slowly in the order given (*67*). A distillate of about 1.5 volumes is needed to insure complete recovery of the Se. Fifty to 100 ml of urine is sufficient if the Se content is 0.01 mg per 100 ml. The selenium after distillation may be determined by titration or according to the methods described in water analysis.

The analysis of urine may also be carried out according to the General Method by adding 30–50 ml of H_2SO_4 and 80–100 ml H_2SO_4-HNO_3 (reagent I) to 100 ml of urine. When nearly all the HNO_3 has been driven off, the digest is cooled, 50 ml of water is added, and it is heated again to completely remove the HNO_3. This method gives better recovery of selenium. The distillate may be treated according to the methods described for water analysis or titrated as indicated in General Method.

Polarographic determination of selenium in urine over a concentration range of 0.063 to 0.175 m*M* (0.5 to 14 μg/ml in 10 ml sample) with an average error of 2 per cent has been described (*20*). Loss of selenium in urine during storage can be reduced by the addition of HNO_3 or by placing the urine in a deep freeze.

FECES

The method of drying is discussed in General Method and 10–25 gm of feces is generally used for Se determination. Procedures are the same as given in General Methods.

A few experiments with Se^{75} indicate that a second oxidation of the residue according to the method given for plants will increase the recovery of Se.

ANIMAL TISSUES

Fresh tissue (25–50 gm) is macerated and placed in a distillation flask; 50 ml of concentrated H_2SO_4, 150 ml of H_2SO_4-HNO_3 (reagent I), and 10 ml HgO (reagent II) are added to the tissue. There may be considerable foaming; therefore, the flask should be cooled or an antifoaming agent added. After the foaming recedes, the flask is heated and the procedure is the same as in General Method except that it is necessary to increase the amount of HBr-Br_2 (reagent IV) from 60 ml to about 75 ml for the distillation.

BLOOD

For the digestion of blood (50 ml) the concentrations of the reagents are reduced as follows: concentrated H_2SO_4, 30 ml; H_2SO_4-HNO_3 (reagent I), 95 ml; HgO (reagent II), 10 ml. The digestion, distillation, and titration are the same as given in General Method.

A number of modifications have been suggested by various investigators for the oxidation of organic matter. Oxidation mixtures of nitric-perchloric, nitric-perchloric-sulfuric, and nitric-sulfuric acids were tried (25).

Tissues containing excess lipid should be treated in the following manner: The tissue is dried at 100° C in an oven overnight and then ground and extracted with chloroform several times. The chloroform is removed by filtration and the tissue air-dried. For oxidation of the organic matter, a mixture of 60 per cent $HClO_4$ and concentrated HNO_3 (1:3) with copper nitrate catalyst may be used (57). The perchloric acid addition may produce violent foaming; therefore, the sample must be cooled in ice during the addition.

Another modification involves the precipitation of selenium from the usual nitric-sulfuric acid digest of the sample, the addition of HC1, and the colorimetric determination of selenium with diaminobenzidine (7). The colorimetric method is given under micro-determination.

Water Extracts of Plants or Soils

The same digestion mixture and method may be used as for blood. The volume of the extract may be reduced by evaporation after adjusting the pH to slightly alkaline with sodium peroxide; the volume used for digestion should not greatly exceed that of the H_2SO_4 in the digestion mixture.

The distillate may be treated with ascorbic acid and the colloidal selenium may be determined according to the method given for water or by titration as described in General Method.

Soils and Rocks

A sample of air-dried soil (5–10 gm preferably ground to pass a 75- or 100-mesh sieve) is placed in the distillation flask and 100 ml HBr-Br_2 (reagent IV) is slowly added. The presence of considerable carbonate in the soil causes foaming and necessitates the addition of enough acid to provide an excess of 50 to 75 ml of HBr after the carbonate has been neutralized. With soils containing considerable organic matter, it may be necessary to use more HBr-Br_2 (reagent IV) in order to make certain that, when the mixture is distilled, 1 or 2 ml of free Br_2 will be distilled over. Additional water may be needed. The mixture is distilled as described in General Method and the distillation is continued until the residue is thickened.

Although one distillation may be sufficient, it is advisable to redistill the residue. A few types of rocks (e.g., siltstone from the Phosphoria Formation) require several distillations with HBr-Br_2 to remove the Se completely. With some rocks, it is advisable to oxidize the sample with H_2SO_4-HNO_3 (reagent I) before distillation. Some difficulty may be encountered in expelling the excess HNO_3 during the initial oxidation. To overcome this, the addition of 1 or 2 gm of starch to the mixture will accelerate the decomposition of the HNO_3.

Atmosphere

Atmospheric dust may be sampled for selenium with an electrostatic precipitator, and fumes, gases, or vapors may be scrubbed through hydrobromic acid containing 5–10 per cent Br_2. After the samples have been collected, the selenium may be separated by distillation and selenium concentration may be estimated by gravimetric, volumetric, or colorimetric methods. A rapid and simple determination for selenium in dust vapors was described by Berton (*6*). A known volume of air is passed through a filter paper moistened with strong solution of cyanide which will dissolve Se and SeO_2. The adsorbed selenium on the filter paper is reduced with SO_2 to form red elemental selenium. Comparison of color with a known amount of standard can be used to estimate the selenium concentration in the atmosphere.

Comments

The inadequacies and inaccuracies of the most frequently used methods for the determination of selenium have been recognized for some time. Therefore, innumerable modifications have been suggested. The usefulness of some of the modifications is doubtful. However, all workers recognized that the values reported in the literature are relative and comparable since the same method is used in each experimental series. Gorsuch (*25*) studied the effect of variations in oxidation conditions and oxidation mixture on the recovery of selenium by the use of Se^{75}. He reported that the oxidation mixture used for the destruction of the organic matter and the rate of oxidation had considerable influence on the recovery of selenium. Recovery with an oxidation mixture of nitric and sulfuric was from 78 to 80 per cent of the added Se^{75}. Some data were obtained on recoveries of Se^{75} from sheep excreta (collected during repeated injections of Se^{75}) and tissues (*60*).

Table 64 gives some indication of the accuracy of the methods and the amount of selenium retained in the various fractions in the determinations of biological materials. The data presented on blood and feces indicate that the selenium determination for blood or feces by the use of the present method has an over-all error of approximately 40 per cent when compared with the homogenized undigested sample.

The recovery by the method, described under General Method and used for the determination of selenium as indicated by Se^{75} recovery in the various tissues, was as follows: in liver, kidney, and various segments of the intestinal tract, the recoveries were 98 to 102 per cent. In the heart, spleen, lung, and muscle, recovery on the average was 89.5, 80, 75, and 75 per cent, respectively. The recovery for skin and brain was between 60 and 70 per cent.

The discrepancies in the recoveries of selenium in many cases may have been due to retention of selenium in the residue and passage of colloidal selenium through the asbestos mat with the HBr filtrate. High lipid content of skin and brain was probably connected with the increased error in the determination in these tissues. Some of the lipids were retained in the residue while others were distilled over. Some losses occurred which could not be accounted for in any of the fractions.

TABLE 64
Recovery of Se^{75} in the Various Fractions in the Determination of Selenium[a]

	Oxidation with $H_2SO_4 + HNO_3$			Direct distillation (HBr-Br_2)		
	% Se^{75} recovered[b]			% Se^{75} recovered[b]		
	Residue	HBr filtrate	Se fraction[c]	Residue	HBr filtrate	Se fraction[c]
Urine	5.3 ± 1.5		93.4 ± 2.0	5.9 ± 2	4.2 ± 2	78.1 ± 8.3
Feces	8.35 ± 2.1	7.4 ±2	66.8 ± 8.1			
Blood	4.0 ± 1.9	5.93 ± 2.7	61.4 ± 2.9			

[a] Rosenfeld and Eppson (*60*).
[b] On filter mats less than one per cent.
[c] Per cent of selenium recovered in the precipitate.

The decreased recovery of selenium in the blood, heart, spleen, and feces may be directly connected to the *form* of selenium present in these organs. There is evidence that considerable amounts of selenium are present in the blood as the volatile selenium compound, dimethyl selenide, which has a boiling point of 55° C.

ESTIMATION OF WATER-SOLUBLE SELENATE, SELENITE, AND ORGANIC SELENIUM

Soil or Rock

Two hundred grams of finely ground, air-dry soil in 500 ml of distilled water is placed in a mechanical shaker and rotated overnight. (Alternative procedures are to reflux the mixture for 30 minutes or to heat it for several hours on a steam bath and then let stand overnight.) About one half of the clear liquid is filtered with suction through a thick, shredded filter paper mat in a Büchner funnel or a Pasteur-Chamberland filter.

A. A 25 ml aliquot of filtrate is analyzed for total water-soluble Se by the General Method. Se in this aliquot represents the sums of organic Se, selenate, and selenite.

B. To 25 ml filtrate, 25 ml of 48% HBr is added; the solution is saturated with SO_2 and 2 ml of hydroxylamine (reagent VI) and heated on a steam bath for 30 minutes. The precipitated Se represents chiefly selenate and selenite.

C. To 25 ml filtrate, 25 ml of 12 *N* H_2SO_4 is added; the solution is saturated with SO_2 and heated on a steam bath for 30 minutes. The precipitate represents all Se originally present as selenite. Selenite also can be precipitated quantitatively from the slightly acid aqueous solutions by ascorbic acid (5). Selenate does not interfere with the reaction. All determinations should be carried out in duplicate.

The selenium may be determined titrimetrically or colorimetrically.

$A - B =$ water-soluble organic Se
$B - C =$ selenate
$C =$ selenite

Plant Extracts

The total Se (5–10 gm dry sample) is determined by the General Method; for determination of water-soluble Se, 50 gm of the sample is treated with 500 ml of boiling water, cooled, and filtered. The volume of water may be doubled if the plant material forms a gelatinous mass. Using aliquots of the filtrate, water-soluble, organic Se, selenite, and selenate can be estimated as described for the soil extract (5). The bound selenium in the plant can be estimated by subtracting the total water-soluble Se from the total Se in the plant.

MICRO METHODS FOR DETERMINATION OF SELENIUM

The importance of detecting trace amounts of Se was prompted by the recognition of the function of minute amounts of selenium in various disease syndromes. The methods reviewed for the determination of trace quantities of selenium are colorimetric, fluorometric, spectrophotometric, isotopic dilution and neutron activation methods. Only the methods which were used for the determination of selenium in biological materials will be considered in this review.

Colorimetric Method

Hoste (28) and Hoste and Gillis (29) reported a sensitive method for determining selenium by 3,3′-diaminobenzidine (DAB). This compound reacts with selenium forming an intense yellow compound, piazselenol. Oxidizing agents interfere, and iron, copper, and vanadium react with the reagent. The interference from iron was eliminated by addition of a fluoride or phosphoric acid and interference from copper by oxalic acid. Cheng (*12*) studied the specificity and sensitivity of DAB and recommended a procedure of increased specificity, sensitivity (50 ppb Se), and rapidity.

The method used for biological material will be given in detail. This method is a compilation of modifications of Cheng's method.

Reagents and Instruments

I. Digest mixture: 60% $HClO_4$ and concentrated HNO_3 (1:3).
II. Copper nitrate.
III. $HNO_3 + HCl$ (1:1).
IV. NH_4OH conc., reagent grade.
V. 0.5% DAB in water (stored in refrigerator).
VI. Standard selenium solution (selenious acid) prepared by dissolving 1.6335 gm in 1 liter of water. It is standardized gravimetrically or by titration and the working standard is prepared by diluting the above solution to contain 5–10 μg Se per milliliter.
VII. Formic acid: 2.5 *M*.
VIII. EDTA: 0.1 *M* in water (disodium salt of ethylenediaminetetraacetic acid).
IX. Toluene. Reagent grade.
X. Micro-Kjeldahl flasks.
XI. Instrument for measuring absorption at 420 mμ.

Wet Ashing

The detailed method for ashing was supplied by Yang and Olson (personal communication).

A defatted tissue sample of 0.2 to 2.0 gm (depending on the Se concentration) is placed in a micro-Kjeldahl flask. The digestion mixture is added slowly (5–20 ml, depending upon the size of sample), and a few milligrams of copper nitrate is added. The flask should be surrounded by ice. After the reaction stops and the solution is almost clear (with small sample), the micro-Kjeldahl flask is placed on a gentle flame, hot plate, or steam bath and digested for about 4 hours. A reflux condenser is essential to prevent the loss of Se due to volatilization. After the digestion is completed, the clear solution is transferred to a beaker and evaporated to near dryness on a steam bath or hot plate. (This step must be watched carefully since long-continued drying can cause considerable loss of Se.) If there is any insoluble residue, more acid mixture should be added for complete digestion.

When the fumes of $HClO_4$ are nearly gone, 30–50 ml of HNO_3-HCl (reagent III) is added and the solution is heated gently until the excess acid is removed and the residue is nearly dry. The residue is dissolved in water and a small amount of concentrated NH_4OH is added and the pH is adjusted between 1 and 2.

An alternate ashing procedure for samples with small amounts of organic material is as follows: a few-milligram sample containing 2–10 μg of Se is added to a micro digestion tube. A few drops of 70 to 72% $HClO_4$ is added and the contents are heated gradually to 205° C in a glycerol bath until the solution is clear and the residue is almost dry. The cooled, digested sample may be treated with one drop of saturated hydrazine sulfate solution and heated in boiling water. A red precipitate or pink color is produced according to the amount of selenium (*21*). The precipitate may be redissolved in acid, pH adjusted with NH_4OH between 1 and 2, and Se determined colorimetrically.

An aliquot of the ashed sample or *in toto,* containing not more than 30 μg Se, is placed in a glass-stoppered test tube (50–60 ml) and about 10 ml water, 1 ml of formic acid (reagent VII; pH adjusted between 2–3), 1 ml of DAB (reagent V) and 1 ml of EDTA (reagent VII) are added. The volume is made up to 20 ml with water. Standards (10, 20, and 30 μg Se) and reagent blanks are prepared in a similar manner.

The reaction is allowed to proceed at room temperature for 30 minutes (maximum, 50 minutes). The pH is adjusted to between 6 and 7 with 7 *M* NH_4OH and 10 ml of toluene is added. The sample is mixed by vigorous shaking for 30 seconds. The toluene layer is decanted and centrifuged for a few minutes. The absorbence of the toluene layer is determined at 420 mμ using a reagent blank. The calibration curve follows Beer's law over the range of 5 to 25 μg of Se in 10 ml of toluene at wavelengths of 340 to 420 mμ. Selenium content, 1–10 μg per 6 ml of toluene and 10–100 μg of Se per 10 ml toluene, at 420 mμ follows Beer's law (*12*).

Sawicki (*63*) reported 2 sensitive colorimetric reagents for selenium determination: (1) 4-dimethylamino-1,2-phenylenediamine and (2) 4-methylthio-1,2-phenylenediamine. The first reacts with selenious acid to give a bright red color in 1 *N* HCl and the second forms a blue-purple color in 50% H_2SO_4. Both colors are stable with appropriate media and produce piazselenols. The limit of identification is 0.05 μg of Se and the concentration limit is 1 to 4,000,000.

Selenium in some organic seleno-compounds has been determined colorimetrically by oxidizing the seleno-compounds to selenious acid and the selenium sol is stabilized with chlorpromazine•hydrochloric acid (*16*).

Fluorometric Method

The sensitivity of fluorometric measurement of the colored selenium-diaminobenzidine (DAB) complex compared to that of the photometric has been the basis for the use of this instrument in determining trace amounts of Se in biological materials.

The sensitivity of this procedure as reported by various investigators varied from 0.02 μg in the range of 0.1 to 210 μg Se(*15*). A method with increased sensitivity, specificity, and preciseness for the measurement of Se by fluorometric method in mixed herbage, different species of plants, and soil samples for as little as 0.02 μg of Se was described (*74a*). In this procedure an arbitrarily defined oxidation end point must not be exceeded, because it will increase the interfering fluorescence and a loss of Se may result.

A study on the reaction of trace amounts of selenious acid with an excess of DAB was investigated by Parker and Harvey (*53*). They concluded that the colored reaction product is a monopiazselenol and not the diapiazselenol as was previously suggested (*12, 29*). The absorption and fluorescence spectra of the monopiazselenol were determined and Cheng's colorimetric procedure was adapted to the fluorometric determination. This procedure was applicable to as little as 0.02 ppm Se when a 2 gm sample was used.

Spectrophotometric Method

A method for the removal of selenium from organic compounds (steroids) by the use of Raney nickel was reported. The method consists of separation of Se from the steroids with Raney nickel and oxidation of the selenium to selenious acid with concentrated HNO_3. The selenium in the sample was measured by a spectrophotometer at 330 mμ, and range of the determination was 10 to 150 μg of Se (*69*).

The accuracy of a method for separating trace amounts of Se from organic samples was studied by the use of carrier Se^{75} (as selenious acid). The factors responsible for the discrepancies present in the method were studied. The method adapted consists of a micro modification of the spectrophotometric method using DAB (reagent IV) and incorporation of Se^{75} in the technique to determine and check the losses which may occur during the course of the analysis (*31*).

Neutron Activation Method

Analysis by neutron activation has been a useful and highly sensitive method for determining trace elements. The technique used involves exposure of a small (of the order of 1 cm^2 wet tissue), wet ashed and dried or otherwise prepared tissue to thermal neutrons or a mixture of thermal and slow neutrons (*70*). Several of the elements present in the sample may become radioactive and the newly formed radioactive isotope may be measured by standard radiochemical techniques.

The sensitivity attainable by neutron activation analysis has been reported (*70*), and the decay of Se^{75} was described by Edwards and Gallagher (*18*). Nondestructive analysis of selenium by neutron activation was described by Okada (*48*).

For determining small amounts of the commoner elements by this method, contamination probably is a more serious problem than for the determination of selenium. However, in any determination of elements below 1.0 ppm, contamination must be carefully controlled.

USE OF SELENIUM COMPOUNDS

INDUSTRIAL USES

The most interesting industrial uses of selenium are those depending upon its remarkable photoelectric properties. The electrons of selenium are susceptible to excitation by light and the element may be used as a photo-switch that is "on" when illuminated and "off" when dark. Selenium generates an electric current when light shines on it and this property is utilized in simple instruments for measuring light intensity. The photographic exposure meter consists of a selenium cell connected with deflecting galvanometer that measures the current generated.

The selenium cell has nearly the same spectral sensitivity as the human eye; however, there is a lag in response that prevents its use in television and sound-reproducing apparatus. The selenium cell is simple in construction and unlike the vacuum-tube photoelectric cell requires no external source of current. It is suitable for use in colorimeters and pyrometers and in photometers for astronomical work, and it has been adapted for measurements of ultraviolet light and X-rays.

The selenium cells make it possible to transmit photographs and sketches along a wire (for newspaper illustrations), to make synchronous records of sound, moving pictures, and to construct street lights, buoys, and electric signs which light up automatically at dusk and extinguish themselves at dawn. It is used for burglar alarms and for opening and closing doors automatically.

Selenium is used in the glass industry to decolorize the greenish tint due to iron impurities. When added in slight excess to glass, colors ranging from light yellow to ruby red can develop. This ruby-red glass is used for household tablewares, warning signals, and automobile tail lights.

Selenium is used as pigment in plastics, glazes, inks and paints. It is also used in the manufacture of rubber to increase resilience and reduce friction wear. It is used in the manufacture of covering of electric cables as well as in the vulcanization of rubber.

In metallurgy, selenium is used in the production of stainless steel, copper-base alloys, magnesium alloys, and manganese alloys.

In the chemical industry selenium is used in printing inks, lubricants, linseed, and tung oils to prevent oxidation and decrease the deterioration of these materials. Metal selenides are used as catalysts in the conversion of heavy oils into fuel oils. Selenium is used in the preparation of many organic compounds such as terpenes, steroids, bile acids, unsaturated hydrocarbons, aldehydes, and ketones. As a dehydrogenating as well as a hydrogenating agent, selenium is used for determining the chemical structure of steroids, vitamins, and hormones.

Selenium has been used as a chemical catalyst, as a flame-proofing agent for textiles, and as a sensitizer in photographic emulsions. Active selenium sulfide is sensitive to mercury vapors and this characteristic is used for copying documents as well as detecting mercury vapors in the air, in industry, or in laboratories where mercury is used extensively.

Therapeutic Agent

The use of selenium as a therapeutic agent for dermatologic and other conditions has been considered on the basis of its similarity to sulfur in its chemical and physical properties. The therapeutic agent was prepared by heating a 50:50 mixture of selenium sulfide and bentonite at a temperature above the fusion point of SeS. The mass obtained was cooled, ground to a fine powder and was readily suspendible in an aqueous vehicle (*46*). Various forms of this composition were tested and found to be effective in certain skin conditions. The combination of selenium sulfide-bentonite mixture with a high concentration of suitable detergent (of low sensitization properties) is now marketed under the trade name "Selsun" as a shampoo (*4*).

The suggested mode of action of Selsun is twofold. One is due to the detergent action; the other is due to an activation of previously nonreactive sulfhydryl groups (*22*).

Matson (*38*) reviewed the literature dealing with therapeutic effects of selenium sulfide -detergent suspension in seborrhic dermatosis. He discussed the mechanism of action of the mixture, as well as the chemical nature of selenium sulfide.

Using tissue culture techniques, 2.5 per cent selenium sulfide suspensions were tested for their toxicity. The suspension was not more toxic to the skin than the vehicle used for suspension (*66*). The selenium sulfide suspension was effective in the treatment of granulated eyelids (blepharitis marginalis) (*14, 24*).

In view of the great affinity of selenium for keratinized structures, the advisability of using selenium compounds in the treatment of disease of the scalp has been questioned. Even when a relatively nonreactive mixture (selenium sulfide) is used, the liberation of selenium-containing ions cannot be excluded with certainty (*61*). Some unfavorable reactions were reported in the use of Selsun as a therapeutic agent indicated by the shedding of hair and local irritation of skin (*18a, 25a*).

A similar suspension for treatment of dermatitis and mange for cats and dogs has been prepared under the trade name "Seleen" and is found to be effective.

Diagnostic Use of Se^{75}-Selenomethionine

The use of radioactive isotopes in clinical diagnosis has advanced rapidly during the last decade. Scanning devices and procedures for detection of localized radioactivity in organs has encouraged the use of isotopes as diagnostic aids. Radioactive pharmaceuticals have been used for visualization of lesions in kidney, spleen, thyroid, brain, and bone by scanning techniques.

Current diagnostic methods for evaluation of pancreatic malfunctions furnish useful information but present problems in their clinical application. Previous attempts by isotopic scanograph for delineation of the pancreas were unsuccessful. Radioactive zinc, manganese, and externally labeled I^{131}-iodotyrosine (*43b*) were used for these studies, but they proved to be unsatisfactory for scanning studies of the pancreas.

Distribution studies of Se^{75}-selenomethionine in dogs indicated that the compound had sufficient pancreas specificity (*6b*) to be useful for study of pancreatic function by isotope scanning methods (*6a*). Earlier studies indicated that the amino acid uptake by the pancreas was a reflection of the rapid rate of synthesis of its digestive enzymes (*74a*). Sulfur- or carbon-labeled amino acids are not suitable for scanning owing to the radiation characteristics of the elements in their structures (*74b*).

The high degree of localization of Se^{75}-selenomethionine in the pancreas and the radiation characteristics of Se^{75} may provide a direct method for visualization of pancreas in man. Blau and Bender (*6a*) using Se^{75}-selenomethionine scanned the pancreas of more than 50 patients. They reported that in about two thirds of the patients, they were able to visualize the pancreas. The estimated dose, 3–3.5 μc of Se^{75}-selenomethionine per kilogram of body weight, is administered to the patient and the total body radiation is approximately 0.6 rad over several months (*6a*).

There are no known precautions and no known contraindications to the use of Se^{75}-selenomethionine for scanning of human pancreas. The total selenium in the compound is approximately 50 μg of selenium (*43a*) which is below the level ingested in food and water daily by every person in the United States.

The procedure devised for human studies favors the synthesis of pancreatic enzymes and avoids any stimulus which would produce pancreatic secretion (*6a*). Prolonged food deprivation increases the uptake of the seleno-amino acid by the liver (*6b*). The following procedure was adapted by Blau and Bender (*6a*) for human studies: Three to four hours after a high protein breakfast, the pancreas is stimulated to empty by a dose of mixed secretin and pancreozymin (Cecekin Vitrum); one hour later, the calculated dose of Se^{75}-selenomethionine is administered intravenously; scanning is started one-half hour after injection of the compound.

Modification of the above procedure and clinical experience of other investigators with Se^{75}-selenomethionine in patients with no pancreatic diseases and in pancreatic carcinoma was given in a report by Squibb's Radiopharmaceuticals Services (*43a*). Se^{75}-selenomethionine is furnished by the company for diagnostic use under the trade name of "Sethotope."

The use of Se^{75}-selenomethionine should be regarded at the present time as an important step toward nonsurgical means of pancreatic visualization. Subsequent studies may indicate the usefulness of the procedure and may offer a unique opportunity to evaluate pancreatic morphology and function by isotope methods.

References

1. A.B.C.M.-S.A.C. Committee. 1956. Recommended methods for the analysis of trade effluents. Prepared by the joint A.B.C.M.-S.A.C. Committee on methods for analysis of trade effluents. Methods for the determination of chromium, lead and selenium. *Analyst* **81**:607–614.
2. American Public Health Association. 1955. "Standard Methods for the Examination of Water, Sewage and Industrial Wastes," 3rd ed. New York.
3. Bailey, M. and A. F. Wells. 1951. The structures of inorganic oxy-acids: The crystal structure of selenic acid. *J. Chem. Soc.* pp. 968–973.
4. Baldwin, R. M. and A. P. Young, Jr. 1951. U. S. Patent No. 2,694,669.
5. Beath, O. A. and H. F. Eppson. 1947. The form of selenium in some vegetation. *Wyoming Agr. Expt. Sta. Bull. No.* **278**:1–15.
6. Berton, A. 1953. Simple and rapid determination of dust and vapors of selenium and selenium dioxide in air. *Chim. Anal.* **35**:91.

6a. Blau, M. and M. A. Bender. 1962. Se^{75}-Selenomethionine for visualization of the pancreas by isotope scanning. *Radiology* **78**:974.

6b. Blau, M. and R. F. Manske. 1961. The pancreas specificity of Se^{75}-selenomethione. *J. Nuclear Med.* **2**:102–105.

7. Bonhorst, C. W. and J. J. Mattice. 1959. Colorimetric determination of selenium in biological materials. *Anal. Chem.* **31**:2106.
8. Brasted, R. C. 1961. "Comprehensive Inorganic Chemistry," Vol. 8, 306 pp. Van Nostrand, New York.
9. Campbell, T. W., H. G. Walker and G. M. Coppinger. 1952. Some aspects of the organic chemistry of selenium. *Chem. Rev.* **50**:279–349.
10. Carr, A., E. Sawicki and F. E. Ray. 1958. 8-Selenopurines. *J. Org. Chem.* **23**: 1940–1942.
11. Challenger, F. 1951. Biological methylation. *Advan. Enzymol.* **12**:429–491.
12. Cheng, K. L. 1956. Determination of traces of selenium. 3,3′-diaminobenzidine as selenium (IV) organic reagent. *Anal. Chem.* **28**:1738–1742.
13. Chu, S. H. and H. G. Mautner. 1962. Potential antiradiation agents. II. Selenium analogs of 2-aminoethylisothiouronium hydrobromide and related compounds. *J. Org. Chem.* **27**:2899–2901.

14. Cohen, L. B. 1954. Use of selsun in blepharitis marginalis. *Am. J. Ophthamol.* **38**:560–562.
15. Cousins, F. B. 1960. A fluorometric microdetermination of selenium in biological material. *Australian J. Exptl. Biol. Med. Sci.* **38**:11–16.
16. Dingwall, D. and W. D. Williams. 1960. Studies in organoselenium compounds. Part I. Determination of Se. *J. Pharm. and Pharmacol.* **13**:12–19.
17. Dingwall, D. 1962. Review article. Selenium analogues of biologically active sulphur compounds. *J. Pharm. and Pharmacol.* **14**:765–776.
18. Edwards, W. F. and C. J. Gallagher, Jr. 1961. The decay of Se^{75}. *Nuclear Phys.* **26**:649–657.
18a. Eisenberg, B. C. 1955. Contact dermatitis from selenium sulfide shampoo. *A.M.A. Arch. Dermatol.* **72**:71–72.
19. Eldjarn, L. and A. Pihl. 1956. On the mode of action of X-ray protective agents. I. The fixation *in vivo* of cystamine and cysteamine to proteins. *J. Biol. Chem.* **223**:341–352.
20. Faulkner, A. G., E. C. Knoblock and W. C. Purdy. 1961. The polarographic determination of selenium in urine. *Clin. Chem.* **7**:22–29.
21. Feigl, F. 1961. Detection of selenium in organic spot-test analysis. *Anal Chim. Acta* **24**:501–504.
22. Flesch, P. 1953. On the mode of action of selenium sulfide. *J. Invest. Dermatol.* **21**:223–225.
23. Fogg, D. N. and N. T. Wilkinson. 1956. The determination of selenium in effluents. *Analyst* **81**:525–531.
24. Fritz, M. H. 1955. The treatment of dandruff and granulated eyelids with selenium sulfide (Selsun). *Clin. Med.* **2**:695–696.
25. Gorsuch, T. T. 1959. Radiochemical investigations on the recovery for analysis of trace elements in organic and biological materials. *Analyst* **84**:135–173.
25a. Grover, R. W. 1956. Diffuse hair loss associated with selenium (Selsun) sulfide shampoo. *J. Am. Med. Assoc.* **160**:1397–1398.
26. Gunther, W. H. H. and H. G. Mautner. 1960. Pantethine analogs. The condensation of panthothenic acid with selenocystamine, with bis-(beta-aminoethyl) sulfide and with 1,2-dithia-5-azepane (a new ring system). *J. Am. Chem. Soc.* **82**:2762–2765.
27. Hitchings, G. H. and G. B. Elion. 1954. The chemistry and biochemistry of purine analogs. *Ann. New York Acad. Sci.* **60**:195–199.
28. Hoste, J. 1948. Diaminobenzidine as a reagent for vanadium and selenium. *Anal. Chim. Acta* **2**:402–408.
29. Hoste, J. and J. Gillis. 1955. Spectrophotometric determination of traces of selenium with diaminobenzidine. *Anal. Chim. Acta* **12**:158–161.
30. Jensen, E. N., L. J. Laslett, D. S. Martin, Jr., F. J. Hughes and W. W. Pratt. 1953. Radiation from Se^{75}. *Phys. Rev.* **90**:557–563.
31. Kelleher, W. J. and M. J. Johnson. 1961. Determination of traces of selenium in organic matter. Combined spectrophotometric and isotope dilution method. *Anal. Chem.* **33**:1429–1432.
32. Klein, A. K. 1943. Report on selenium. *J. Assoc. Offic. Agr. Chem.* **26**:346–352.
33. Klosterman, H. J. and E. P. Painter. 1947. An improved synthesis of the selenium analogs of methionine and homocystine. *J. Am. Chem. Soc.* **69**:2009–2010.
34. Klug, H. L. and D. F. Petersen. 1949. The reaction of selenous acid with cysteine, *Proc. South Dakota Acad. Sci.* **28**:87–91.
35. Kolthoff, I. M. and P. J. Elving. 1961. Treatise on analytical chemistry. Part II. Analytical chemistry of the elements S.Se-Te.F.Halogens.Mn.Re. **7**:137–205. Interscience Pub., a Div. of John Wiley & Sons, New York.

36. Lambert, J. L., P. Arthur and T. E. Moore. 1951. Determination of trace amounts of selenium in water. *Anal. Chem.* **23**:1101–1106.
37. Leddicotte, G. W. 1961. The radiochemistry of selenium. NAS-NS 3030, Nuclear Sci. Ser.
38. Matson, E. J. 1956. Selenium sulfide as an antidandruff agent. *J. Soc. Cosmetic Chem.* **7**:459–466.
39. Mautner, H. G. 1956. The synthesis and properties of some selenopurines and selenopyrimidines. *J. Am. Chem. Soc.* **78**:5292–5294.
40. Mautner, H. G. and W. D. Kumler. 1956. 2-Phenyl-selenosemicarbazide and related compounds. Dipole moment and spectroscopic measurements on analogous ureides, thioureides and selenoureides. *J. Am. Chem. Soc.* **78**:97–101.
41. Mautner, H. G. and E. M. Clayton. 1959. 2-Selenobarbiturates. Studies of some analogous oxygen, sulfur and selenium compounds. *J. Am. Chem. Soc.* **81**:6270–6273.
42. Mautner, H. G., S. H. Chu and C. M. Lee. 1962. Studies of 2-selenopyridine and related compounds. *J. Org. Chem.* **27**:3671–3673.
43. Mautner, H. G., S. H. Chu, J. J. Jaffe and A. C. Sartorelli. 1963. The synthesis and antineoplastic properties of selenoguanine, selenocytosine and related compounds. *J. Med. Chem.* **6**:36–39.
43a. Medotopes from Squibb. 1963. Se^{75}-selenomethionine. A new agent for radioisotope scanning of the pancreas. *Nuclear Notes* **5**: No. 1.
43b. Meschan, I., J. L. Quinn, R. L. Witcofski, and T. A. Hosick. 1959. The utilization of radioactive zinc and manganese in an effort to visualize the pancreas. *Radiology* **73**:62–70.
44. Moeller, T. 1952. Inorganic chemistry. Wiley, New York.
45. Moxon, A. L. and A. E. Schaefer, 1940. Decomposition of selenium-cystine in electrodialysis and acid hydrolysis. *Proc. South Dakota Acad. Sci.* **20**:28–33.
46. Norlander, B., U. S. Patent No. 1,711,742 1929; U. S. Patent No. 1,860,336 1932; U. S. Patent No. 1,860,320 1932.
47. Norris, J. F. and H. Fay. 1896. Iodometric determination of selenious and selenic acids. *Am. Chem. J.* **18**:703–706.
48. Okada, M. 1960. Non-destructive analysis of selenium by neutron activation followed by gamma-ray spectrometry. *Nature* **187**:594–595.
49. Painter, E. P., K. W. Franke and R. A. Gortner. 1940. Organic selenium compounds. Their decomposition in alkaline solutions and other properties related to the behavior of selenium compounds in cereals. *J. Org. Chem.* **5**:579–589.
50. Painter, E. P. 1941. The chemistry and toxicity of selenium compounds, with special reference to the selenium problem. *Chem. Rev.* **28**:179–213.
51. Painter, E. P. 1947. New syntheses of the selenium analogs of *dl*-cystine and cysteine derivatives. *J. Am. Chem. Soc.* **69**:229–232.
52. Painter, E. P. 1947. A synthesis of selenium analogs of *dl*-methionine and *dl*-homocystine. *J. Am. Chem. Soc.* **69**:232–234.
53. Parker, C. A. and L. G. Harvey. 1961. Fluorometric determination of submicrogram amounts of selenium. *Analyst* **86**:54–62.
54. Petersen, D. F. 1951. The reaction of selenious acid with glutathione. *Proc. South Dakota Acad. Sci.* **30**:53–56.
55. Peterson, P. J. and G. W. Butler, 1962. Paper chromatographic and electrophoretic systems for the identification of sulphur and selenium amino acids. *J. Chromatog.* **8**:70–74.
56a. Pichot, L., M. Herbert and M. Thiers. 1961. Etudes sur les methodes de preparation de la selenocystamine, selenohypotaurine et selenotaurine. *Tetrahedron* **12**:1–6.

56b. Pihl, A. and L. Eldjarn. 1958. Pharmacological aspects of ionizing radiation and of chemical protection in mammals. *Pharm. Rev.* **10**:437–467.

57. Pirie, N. W. 1932. Sulfur metabolism of the dog. XI. The metabolism of methionine and related sulfides. *Biochem. J.* **26**:2041–2045.

58. Plieninger, H. 1950. Die Aufspaltung des γ-Butyrolactons und α-Amino-γ-Butyrolactons mit Natriummethylmercaptid bzw.-selenid. Eine Synthese des Methionins. *Chem. Ber.* **83**:265–268.

59. Rosenfeld, I. 1961. Biosynthesis of seleno-compounds from inorganic selenium by sheep. *Federation Proc.* **20**:10.

60. Rosenfeld, I. and H. F. Eppson. 1964. Metabolic effects and metabolism of selenium in animals. Pt. V. Metabolism of selenium in sheep. *Wyoming Agr. Expt. Sta. Bull. No.* **414**:53–64.

61. Rothman, S. 1955. "Physiology and Biochemistry of the Skin," 644 pp. Univ. of Chicago Press, Chicago, Illinois.

62. Sanderson, R. T. 1961. "Chemical Periodicity," 330 pp. Reinhold, New York.

63. Sawicki, E. 1957. New color test for selenium. *Anal. Chem.* **29**:1376–1377.

64. Sawicki, E. and A. Carr. 1957. Structure of 2,1,3-benzoselenadiazole and its derivatives. I. Ultraviolet-visible absorption spectra. *J. Org. Chem.* **22**:503–506.

65. Schardt, A. W. and J. P. Welker. 1953. Decay scheme of Se^{75} and Ge^{75}. *Am. Phys. Soc. Bull.* **28**:12.

66. Shapiro, E. M., C. M. Pomerat and J. F. Mullins. 1955. Toxicity studies on selenium disulfide suspension. *J. Invest. Dermatol.* **24**:423–428.

67. Smith, M. I., B. B. Westfall and E. F. Stohlman. 1938. Studies on the fate of selenium in the organism. *Public Health Rept.* (*U.S.*) **53**:1199–1216.

68. Stekol, J. A. 1942. Selenium tetracystine. *J. Am. Chem. Soc.* **64**:1742.

69. Throop, L. J. 1960. Spectrophotometric determination of selenium in steroids. *Anal. Chem.* **32**:1807–1809.

70. Tobias, C. A., R. Wolfe, R. Dunn and I. Rosenfeld. 1952. The abundance and rate of turnover of trace elements in laboratory mice with neoplastic disease. *Extrait de Acta Unio Intern. Contre Cancer* **7**:874–881.

71. Trelease, S. F., A. A. Di Somma and A. L. Jacobs. 1960. Seleno-amino acid found in *Astragalus bisulcatus*. *Science* **132**:3427.

72. Tsen, C. C. and A. L. Tappel. 1958. Catalytic oxidation of glutathione and other sulfhydryl compounds by selenite. *J. Biol. Chem.* **233**:1230–1232.

73. Tuve, T. W. and H. H. Williams. 1957. Identification of selenomethionine in the proteins of *Escherichia coli* employing the chromatographic "fingerprint" method. *J. Am. Chem. Soc.* **79**:5830–5831.

74a. Watkinson, J. H. 1960. Fluorometric determination of traces of selenium. *Anal. Chem.* **32**:981–983.

74b. Wheeler, J. E., F. D. W. Lukens and P. György. 1949. Studies on the localization of tagged methionine within the pancreas. *Proc. Soc. Exptl. Biol. Med.* **70**:187–189.

75. Williams, L. R. and A. Ravve. 1948. Benzyl chloromethyl selenide. *J. Am. Chem. Soc.* **70**:3524.

76. Williams, L. R. and A. Ravve. 1948. Syntheses of selenium analog of *dl*-cystine. *J. Am. Chem. Soc.* **70**:1244–1245.

CHAPTER X

BIOCHEMISTRY OF SELENIUM

The studies reviewed in this chapter deal with the effects of selenium compounds on biological systems in tissue homogenates and of unicellular organisms in contrast to the observed biochemical changes produced by selenium in intact animals.

The biological effects of selenium compounds may be produced by an excess or deficiency of the element in animals and plants. There is considerable experimental evidence to indicate that selenium inhibits a number of enzyme systems in bacteria, yeast cells, tissue brei or extracts, tissue slices or in purified enzymes. Some correlation between the toxic effects of selenium in intact animals and inhibition of liver succinic dehydrogenase has been reported (52). This correlation between an enzyme system and *in vivo* effects may not reflect the true physiological events in intact animals.

The large number of sulfur compounds in the living system suggests that it would be fallacious to postulate that the toxic or nutritional effect of selenium is due to the inhibition or stimulation of one enzyme or to some aberration or change in a sulfur compound. A multitude of metabolic functions may be altered to some degree in intact animals and the response to selenium may be the manifestation of the total effects of selenium on metabolic activities of the animals. Although studies in isolated systems do not explain the mechanism of action of selenium in selenosis or in deficiency diseases at the present time, future studies may fill the existing gap.

In this chapter the discussion will be limited to biological systems dealing with (a) selenium and sulfur antagonisms, (b) effects of selenium compounds on cell growth and cell division, (c) reduction of selenium compounds, (d) biological selenium activation and transmethylation, (e) effects of selenium on enzymes, and (f) biosynthesis of selenocompounds. The above divisions are artificial since many of the processes may occur simultaneously in the same biological system, but some division was necessary in order to discuss the biochemistry of selenium in a unified manner.

METABOLIC ANTAGONISTS OF SELENIUM COMPOUNDS

Selenium and Sulfur Antagonism

The modern concept of competitive inhibition by structural analogs arose as the result of studies on the inhibition of succinic dehydrogenase by malonic acid (*87, 88*). These studies suggested that the active center of an enzyme is so constituted that molecules possessing the same type of chemical structure may compete with each other for attachment to the reactive sites.

In recent years, intensive and fruitful studies on biological antagonisms or competitions between structurally similar substances have been reported. Woolley (*125*) reviewed the theories as well as the application of antimetabolites in research and medicine. The studies dealing with sulfur and selenium antagonism will be presented in a sequence that indicates the step-by-step development of the present knowledge.

Selenate and sulfate antagonism was demonstrated by Hurd-Karrer (*47*) when selenate growth inhibition of wheat plants was reduced by sulfate. The growth inhibition by selenate depended on the amount of sulfate present.

Fels and Cheldelin (*33*) reported that growth inhibition of *Saccharomyces cerevisiae* by selenate was partially reversed by the addition of methionine. Within limits, the growth of yeast in the presence of selenate was directly proportional to the amount of methionine present. Neither cysteine, glutathione, cystine nor a number of amino acids were able to reverse the growth inhibition of the yeast by selenate. The reversal of selenate growth inhibition by sulfur compounds differs in different organisms. This was indicated by the studies with *Escherichia coli* (*34*). Cysteine and to some extent glutathione reversed selenate growth inhibition of *E. coli*, but methionine was ineffective.

Fels and Cheldelin (*35*) demonstrated selenium and sulfur antagonism in yeast cultures. The toxicity of selenate to *S. cerevisiae* was reversed by sulfate. The sulfate concentration that restored growth to half maximum in the presence of varying concentrations of selenate was in about one molar ratio. That the toxic action of selenate in yeast cultures may be the blocking of methionine synthesis from sulfate has been suggested by earlier studies. The role of L-methionine in reversing selenate toxicity in yeast culture does not involve the oxidation of methionine to sulfate or the methylation of selenate by methionine, since neither sulfate nor dimethyl selenide could be detected in the culture (*36*). Thiamine and cysteine enhanced the effect of methionine, suggesting that one action of selenate may be to block the synthesis of cysteine and thiamine from methionine although thiamine biosynthesis by yeast from methionine has not been confirmed up to the present time. D-Methionine and DL-methionine sulfone are utilized by the yeast as a sulfur source but they were ineffective in reversing the selenate effect. These studies indicate that the over-all toxic effect of selenate in yeast is one in which more than one system is involved. Two of these are probably methionine and thiamine.

The selenate ion is a competitive antagonist in the reduction of sulfate by sulfate-reducing bacteria. According to Postgate (*81*), *Desulfovibrio desulfuricans* reduces sulfate with an uptake of 4 molecules of hydrogen per ion of sulfate at a pH of 6.3. Similar reduction of sulfite and thiosulfate at the proper pH by the use of the above organism has been observed (*82*). Selenate itself is not reduced, but it competitively inhibits the sulfate reduction by this bacterium. Selenate inhibition was prevented in a noncompetitive manner by sulfite but methionine, cysteine, and glutathione had no anti-selenate effect in the inhibited cells of *D. desulfuricans* (*83*).

These results are at variance with the findings of studies by Fels and Cheldelin (*36*) in which L-methionine reversed selenate toxicity to yeast but was ineffective against selenate toxicity to *E. coli*. Reversal of selenate toxicity to *E. coli* was obtained by cysteine and to some extent by glutathione (*34*). This difference may be attributed to the fact that sulfate reduction is quantitatively most important as an energy-yielding reaction for *D. desulfuricans* (*83*). The sulfate reduction and oxygen utilization by this bacterium are dependent upon a thermostable cytochrome which is temporarily antagonized by structural analogs of sulfate (*84*).

Mycelial growth and selenium accumulation by *Aspergillus niger* were found to be a function of the sulfur:selenium ratio when sulfur was supplied as sulfate and selenium as selenate. By increasing the sulfate there was a corresponding increase in growth and decrease in accumulation of selenium in the mycelia. When sulfate:selenate ratios were designed to give half-maximum growth, sodium caseinate increased the inhibition, but casein hydrolyzate, glutathione, cystine, cysteine, homocystine, and methionine partially or wholly counteracted selenate inhibition. Isomers of methionine, D and L, reversed selenate inhibition in the absence of sulfate. Selenate in the presence of methionine remained as inorganic selenate suggesting that the sulfur amino acids may have prevented the conversion of the inorganic compound to organic form(s) by the organism (*120*).

The growth responses of *Chlorella vulgaris* obtained with sulfate and selenate conform to the criteria established for competitive antagonism (*101*). Selenate decreased the rate of growth. Sulfate reversed this action. D- and L-Methionine partially reduced selenate toxicity in a noncompetitive manner.

The toxic effect of selenate on the growth of *Neurospora crassa* was not reduced by equivalent amounts of sulfur or sulfate, α-hydroxy-γ-methylmercapto butyric acid, homocystine, or choline. Methionine, homocysteine, homocystine, or adenosine and formate in some degree reversed the toxic effects (*121*). The failure of sulfate to prevent the toxicity of selenate suggests that in *Neurospora crassa* the biochemical synthesis of organic sulfur compounds probably is blocked by high concentrations of selenate which could not be reversed by sulfate.

Organoselenium and Sulfur Analog Antagonism

The competitive nature of sulfate-selenate antagonism suggested that organic seleno-analogs may act in a similar manner. Competitive antagonism in *Chlorella vulgaris* cultures of L-methionine and selenomethionine was demonstrated by Shrift (*102*). Analyses of the *Chlorella* cells indicated that the sulfur metabolite prevented the absorption of its selenium analog. The amount of selenium that entered the cell depended on the external S:Se ratio, not the amount of selenium supplied to the organisms. Sulfates did not antagonize the action of selenomethionine.

The results suggest that selenate toxicity involves more than just the prevention of sulfate utilization. The narrower range of selenomethionine toxicity suggests that the toxicity of selenate may be due to the formation of seleno-analogs of the sulfur amino acids which are more toxic than selenate.

In an attempt to produce variations in the composition of bacterial proteins by changes in the amino acid composition of culture media, Cohen and Cowie (*22, 26*) found that the methionine-requiring mutant of *E. coli* utilized selenomethionine for growth. Selenomethionine antagonized the incorporation of S^{35}-methionine into the cell proteins of the organisms and competed with S^{35}-methionine for protein synthesis in the methionine-requiring *E. coli* cultures (Fig. 45) (*26*).

The application of antagonism between seleno- and sulfur-amino acids as a possible therapeutic agent has been studied by a few investigators. L-Cysteine and L-cystine have an important role in the metabolism of leucocytes. In nitrogen mustard leucopenia, L-cysteine or L-cystine has a distinct protective effect on depressed leucocytosis (*116*). The observations that leukemic leucocytes had a more rapid turnover of radioactive-L-cystine than normal leucocytes and that cultures of human bone marrow deficient in either L-cysteine or L-cystine degenerated rapidly suggested the use of selenium analogs of cystine for studies on malignant cells (*119*). A highly specific structural configuration is required to inhibit the incorporation of S^{35}-cysteine in leukemic leucocytes. Any loss of the sulfhydryl, amino, or carboxyl groups resulted in complete loss of activity. Pre-incubation of leukemic leucocytes with L-selenocystine or phenylselenocysteine prevented the influx of S^{35}-cysteine, while selenium oxide selenic acid, and diphenyl diselenide were ineffective. Benzylselenocysteine *in vitro* was effective in decreasing the influx of S^{35}-L-cysteine in human leukemic leucocytes but was ineffective in rat Murphy lymphosarcoma cells (*117, 118*).

The deficiencies of pantothenic acid and coenzyme A in rat tumor suggested that tumor tissues may be vulnerable to the action of pantetheine antagonists. Selenopantethine was tested in *Lactobacillus helveticus*, an organism which requires preformed pantethine (*66*). This organism cannot convert pantothenic acid to pantetheine efficiently and is able to reduce pantethine (PSSP) to pantetheine (PSH) which is the active growth factor for the organism (*109*). Selenopantethine, on a mole for

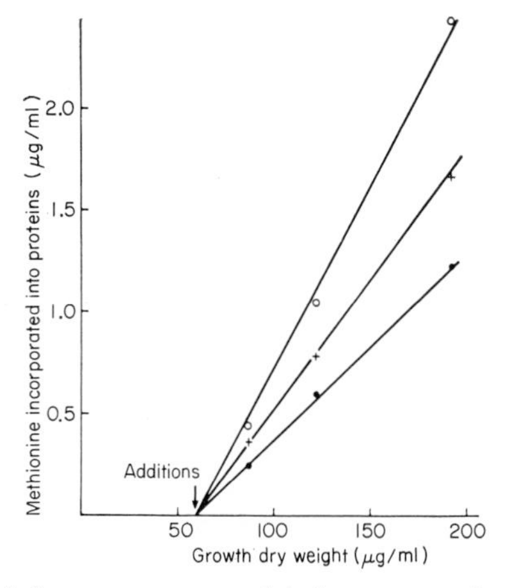

FIG. 45. Reduction of the incorporation of radioactive methionine by selenomethionine. Mutant (ML 304d) in *E. coli*. o: control culture; DL-methionine ($5 \times 10^{-5}M$). +: same as control plus DL-selenomethionine ($5 \times 10^{-5}M$). •: same as control plus DL-selenomethionine ($10^{-4}M$). From Cowie and Cohen (*26*).

mole basis, completely replaced the normal metabolite and supported optimal growth. No growth occurred when pantethine or selenopantethine was replaced by pantothenic acid and cystamine, pantothenic acid and cysteine, or pantothenic acid and selenocystamine. Thus, selenopantethine appears to be a metabolically functional analog of pantethine. Since sulfur in the form of sulfhydryl is the key atom through which pantetheine and coenzyme A exert their action (*109*), it was suggested that selenopantetheine may be converted to seleno-coenzyme A, which then is formed into selenoacyl compounds similar to the thioacyl intermediates. The above postulate suggests a number of interesting studies in relation to biological antagonism between selenium and sulfur. Not only can selenopantethine replace pantethine as a growth factor for *L. helveticus* but it also acts as an antagonist of pantethine in pigeon liver system (*68*).

Arsenic and Other Selenium Antagonists

Studies of selenium and arsenic antagonism with microorganisms were unsuccessful (*8, 76, 78*). Sodium selenite or potassium arsenite inhibited the absorption of glucose from intestinal loops (*80*). Selenite inhibition was reversed by washing while arsenite inhibition of glucose absorption was irreversible.

Bonhorst (*12*) reversed selenite-inhibited yeast respiration with arsenite or arsenate as well as with phosphate. The action of selenate on yeast metabolism differs from the action of selenite as indicated by the inability of arsenate to reverse selenate inhibition, but a combination of phosphate and arsenate was effective.

The beneficial effects of arsenic on selenium toxicity in experimental animals were discussed in Chapter V. The failure to demonstrate antagonism between arsenic and selenium compounds in test systems requires further studies before the significance of these conflicting results can be evaluated.

Competition between tetrazolium and tellurite or selenite in growing cells of a parent strain and a filamentous mutant strain of *Candida albicans* was studied by Nickerson (*72*). It is known that tetrazolium dyes are reduced *in vitro* by coenzyme I-linked flavoprotein catalysis of the so-called "diaphorase" type (*17*). The reduction of selenite or tellurite was confined to the flavoprotein locus oxidation site in the parent and mutant cells without impairment of growth. This is the site at which a reaction essential for cell division is coupled via an oxidation-reduction to cellular metabolism.

Transport mechanism. Simultaneous transport of Se^{75}-selenomethionine and S^{35}-methionine in everted hamster intestinal sacs was studied, and the results suggested that the permeation mechanism of these compounds was practically identical. The transport values were based on the ratio of serosal concentration of the compounds to mucosal concentration as indicated in Table 65. A Lineweaver-Burk type plot of the transport data indicated that the apparent K_m calculated from the line was $0.8 \times 10^{-3} M$ for Se^{75} and S^{35}. Chromatographic studies of the mucosal and serosal solution indicated that Se^{75}-selenomethionine was not degraded during the transmural transport (*110*).

EFFECTS OF SELENIUM COMPOUNDS ON CELL GROWTH AND CELL DIVISION

The events of cell division and the function of a particular enzyme or enzyme system(s) are not fully understood at the present time. It may be stated that certain stages in mitosis vary in susceptibility to a number of inhibitors. The relation between glutathione and cell division was formulated by Rapkine (89). The mechanism of action of –SH groups in cell division and cell growth is unknown. Rapkine postulated that cell growth and cell division were accompanied by configurational changes of the cell proteins resulting in an increase of protein –SH groups. There is some agreement that a definite relationship exists between cell division and thiols. The thiol content of cells is at a maximum level just before the division stage. Although there is no direct evidence that the thiol content of cells at cellular division is affected by selenium, inhibition of growth, cellular division, and morphological changes were observed by exposure of cells to selenium compounds.

TABLE 65

In Vitro Intestinal Concentration of L-Methionine Measured by S^{35}-L-Methionine and Se^{75}-Selenomethionine[a]

Original concentration of L-methionine	Serosal concentration/mucosal concentration (at 1 hr)		Concentration ratio by β / Concentration ratio by γ
	By β activity	By γ activity	
$8 \times 10^{-3} M$	2.11	2.20	0.96
$4 \times 10^{-3} M$	3.86	3.70	1.04
$2 \times 10^{-3} M$	4.51	4.33	1.04
$1 \times 10^{-3} M$	7.60	8.20	0.93
Mean			0.99

NOTE: Initial serosal and mucosal fluids were of identical composition. Stock solution: Krebs-bicarbonate buffer pH 7.4 (without calcium, magnesium, or glucose); L-methionine ($8 \times 10^{-3} M$, diluted as indicated); S^{35}-methionine (0.05 μc/ml); Se^{75}-selenomethionine (0.02 μc/ml). Incubation, 1 hour; oscillating water bath, 37° C. Gas phase, 95% O_2 and 5% CO_2.

[a] From Spencer and Blau (*110*).

Cell Growth

Growth inhibition by selenium compounds was reported by a number of investigators. The growth inhibitory effects of selenourea (0.001–0.1%), colloidal selenium (0.01%), and SeO_2 (0.0033%) solutions on tissue cultures of chicken myocardium and articular cartilage explants were observed (95). Selenite and fluoride ions inhibited both deoxyribonuclease and mitosis in tissue cultures (45). There were differences between the action of sulfhydryl reactants and selenite on cell division in tissue cultures. Iodoacetamide and chloroacetophenone at low concentrations arrested movement within the cell, blocked nuclear reconstruction, and inhibited mitosis at metaphase. Iodoacetate was an effective inhibitor of preprophase but selenite at sublethal doses only partially inhibited metaphase and nuclear reconstruction. Higher doses of selenite (10 mmole) caused death of the cells (*46*).

The affinity of selenium and tellurium for the nuclear structure of *Corynebacterium diphtheriae, C. fascians,* and *Bacillus cereus* was indicated by phase-contrast microscopic studies (*41, 42*). In *C. diphtheriae* the deposition of the elements appeared in defined localities in the cells and there were replications of these deposits in each bacterial cell segment. The site of the nuclear structures of the cells and the refractile spots were similar to the pairs of chromatinic structures in spores. *Bacillus cereus* grown in the presence of selenite developed some filamentous forms. These forms contained cross-septa and refractile patches which may represent nuclear structures. Levine (*58*) described the deposition of selenium in *C. diphtheriae* cells and regarded it as an intracellular phenomenon. The reduction of selenium occurred in growing cultures through the metabolic activity of the cells. It is possible that the sites of reduction of selenite and tellurite may be regions of intense metabolic activity or there may be a specific affinity of these ions for nuclear material.

Modifications of developmental patterns of newly fertilized eggs and early larvae of *Dandraster excentricus* (sand dollar) by sodium selenite were observed by Rulon (*96*). The continuous exposure of the one-cell stage to various concentrations of selenite caused the development of a high percentage of radially elongated larvae, with structural abnormalities such as inhibition of skeletal formation and exogastrulation. Developmental defects varied with age of the embryo, dose, and the duration of exposure to selenite (*96*). Some of these developmental defects resembled malformations observed in chicks (discussed in Chapter V).

Growth inhibition of organisms and the simultaneous interference with glucose utilization have been observed (*76*). Bacterial growth and glucose consumption by *E. coli* were inhibited when $10^{-4}M$ selenite was added to the culture medium. Selenite, azide, cyanide, and arsenite were powerful growth inhibitors of *Paramecium caudatum* (*44*). Selenite and azide not only inhibited the growth of the organism but inhibited the oxidation of glucose substrate, whereas cyanide, fluoride, and malonate gave only moderate inhibition.

The effects of sodium salts of selenate, selenite, arsenate (dibasic), and arsenite on the growth of *Saccharomyces cerevisiae* indicate that selenate and arsenite at 60 ppm completely inhibited growth while selenite and arsenate had no inhibitory effect (*78*). The growth of yeast cultures in the presence of selenate was neither enhanced nor further depressed by the addition of arsenate. In the same manner, selenite neither increased nor reversed the growth inhibitory effect of arsenite.

The selective growth inhibition by selenite in different strains of

Salmonella, E. coli, Proteus vulgaris, and *Citrobacter freundii* indicates that removal of peptone from the broth culture depressed the growth and increased the toxic effects of selenious acid to some species (*108*). The ability of *Salmonella* species to grow in peptone-selenite broth appeared to be due to the binding of selenite by peptides. Organisms differed in their ability to use different sulfur sources.

Considerable evidence was presented that cystine and polythionates were highly preferred sulfur sources for a number of bacterial species. This may be of special significance in studying the inhibitory effects of selenite on bacterial growth. Selenite enters into the chemical reactions with substances which are present in the medium. Selenopentathionate (formed by a reaction between selenite and thiosulfate) may act as an inhibitory analog of pentathionate in a species of bacteria which requires preformed pentathionate. Since sodium selenite reacts with inorganic sulfur compounds to form selenopolythionates or other seleno-sulfur compounds, the rational explanation for the selective action of selenite in some species of bacteria may be due not only to the direct effect of selenite but also to the formation of inhibitory analogs of essential sulfur compounds.

Selenate-induced growth inhibition of *S. cerevisiae* was reversed by L-methionine (*33*). In *E. coli,* cysteine, and to some extent glutathione, reversed the effect of selenate but methionine was ineffective (*34*).

The above studies indicated that methionine neither enhanced nor reversed the toxicity of selenate to *E. coli.* Scala and Williams (*97*) reported that the toxicity of $SeO_3^{=}$ to wild type *E. coli* was enhanced by exogenous L-methionine in the growth medium. Exogenous D-methionine was not utilized by the organism and exerted no effect on growth in the presence of selenite. L-Homocystine enhanced selenite toxicity similar to methionine (*98*). Exogenous L-cystine and taurine had no effect on selenite toxicity but increased the toxicity of tellurite. Ethionine, djenkolic acid, thiourea, or 2,4-thiazolidinedione added to the medium containing various concentrations of selenite (24×10^{-6} to $80 \times 10^{-6} M$) had no inhibitory effect on the growth of *E. coli,* while tellurite inhibition was enhanced by these compounds.

The enhanced toxicity of selenite to microorganisms in the presence of exogenous methionine was suggested to be the suppression of the biosynthesis of selenomethionine as well as methionine. Roberts *et al.* (*90*) have shown that exogenous methionine was incorporated directly by the organism into the protein, and biosynthesis of methionine ceased.

The growth response of *Chlorella vulgaris* to DL-selenomethionine in the presence of sulfur metabolites was studied by Shrift (*102*). The cells were grown under the conditions that the synthesis of L-methionine from the sulfur metabolities had to be carried out by the organisms. Under these conditions the selenomethionine inhibited cell division but not growth (in cell size) or dry weight. The effect of selenomethionine may have prevented the utilization of methionine in an enzymatic reaction essential for cell division. Other reactions were not blocked and the cells were able to increase in volume and dry weight.

The form of selenium compounds utilized by *E. coli* for growth was studied by Cowie and Cohen (*26*). A methionine-requiring mutant of *E. coli* was subcultured in liquid media with selenomethionine to more than 100 generations without any detectable change in morphology (*26*). The growth was exponential but slightly depressed in the presence of $10^{-4}M$ selenomethionine. Wild-type *E. coli* upon transfer to sulfur-deficient medium has a two-phase growth curve. During the first phase the cells utilize their internal store of glutathione as well as the sulfur in the medium; during the second, slower growth phase the addition of sulfate initiated the normal exponential growth (*90*). The growth rate of *E. coli* cells was unaffected by the presence of selenite. In the presence of endogenous glutathione-sulfur, the typical diphasic growth curve was observed and Se^{75}-selenite was incorporated in the cellular proteins at a rate proportional to new cell growth.

The growth inhibitory effect of selenium compounds appeared to be mainly interference of normal metabolism of sulfur compounds or substitution for sulfur. The selenium and sulfur analogs discussed up to the present time have essentially the same steric configurations and they produce biological effects by antagonism of normal metabolites.

That many organic selenium compounds inhibit growth more than organic sulfur compounds was suggested by Mautner and co-workers to be due to differences in the electron distribution, the greater electronegativity of the selenium atom, higher polarity of the carbon-selenium double bond than the carbon-sulfur double bonds, and the higher acidity of selenium compounds than their sulfur analogs (*62–65*).

The antifungal and antibacterial properties of 2-phenylselenosemicarbazide, its selenosemicarbazine derivatives, phenylselenourea, and their sulfur and oxygen analogs were compared by Mautner *et al.* (*62*) against pathogenic and saprophytic organisms. The selenium compounds were 10 to 1000 times more active on molar basis than the sulfur compounds, while the oxygen analogs showed slight activity. The possibility that the released selenium was the active agent was proved to be of little importance.

A large number of sulfur-substituted purines and pyrimidines have been tested experimentally for their antitumor activity. The most useful of the purines up to the present time is 6-mercaptopurine in various types of leukemias (*38*).

6-Mercaptopurine differs in structure from 6-selenopurine only by the substitution of selenium at C-6 for sulfur. The comparative effectiveness of 6-selenopurine and 6-mercaptopurine with respect to ability to inhibit growth of a wide range of microorganisms and *Lactobacillus casei* (an organism used in assaying "antipurines") was studied by Mautner (*63*). Selenopurine inhibited the growth of *L. casei* in the presence of optimal amounts of folic acid, adenine, hypoxanthine, or guanine. Reversal of the inhibition caused by selenopurine or mercaptopurine was obtained with hypoxanthine, guanine, or xanthine and partial reversal with glutathione, cysteamine, or cystine. Selenopurine inhibited a mercaptopurine-resistant strain of *L. casei* as efficiently as the wild strain in contrast to the finding with a mercaptopurine-resistant strain of mouse leukemia (L-1210) which showed full cross resistance to selenopurine (*48*). 6-Selenopurine also inhibited the growth of a fairly wide range of microorganisms being more active than the corresponding sulfur compound. Studies on the mechanism of action of selenopurine and mercaptopurine in an Ehrlich ascites tumor system indicated that these compounds or their metabolic derivatives interfere to a greater extent with the synthesis of the purine ring than with the utilization of adenine or its derivatives.

In tissue culture, selenopurine was more active than mercaptopurine in inhibiting the growth of mouse leukemia cells (L-5178) (*64*). In some tumor systems, 6-selenopurine had lower antitumor activity and greater host toxicity than equimolar quantities of 6-mercaptopurine (*49*). 6-Selenopurine is unstable at body temperature of the animal with a half life of about 6 hours. Methylation decreased the activity of both compounds. The possibility that the decomposition products may be active was not supported by subsequent studies (*50*).

6-Thioguanine, a neoplasm inhibitor in animals and to some extent an anti-leukemia agent in man, has been studied extensively. This compound has antimitotic activity (*9*) and it has been shown to be incorporated into deoxyribonucleic acid (DNA) by LePage (*57*). Although the mechanism of action of 6-thioguanine is unknown, it was suggested by Mautner and Jaffe (*67*) that charge separation might lead to stronger hydrogen-bonding with the amino group of cytosine facing thioguanine in the double helix of DNA. Such intra-helical interaction could be expected to interfere with the replication of DNA. Similar charge separation has been found from thiocarbamyl to selenocarbamyl compounds (*61, 65*) with increased antimicrobial activity of the seleno-compounds.

Studies with 6-selenoguanine indicate that growth of *L. casei* (ATCC-7469) was inhibited with one tenth the concentration required for thioguanine (*67*). The effects of selenoguanine and thioguanine on the growth of several experimental murine neoplasms indicate that antitumor activities of these 2 compounds were comparable, while the therapeutic index of selenoguanine was higher than its sulfur analog.

Cell Morphogenesis

The concept that morphogenesis can be controlled experimentally in microorganisms has long been accepted and recorded in literature. That growth in the absence of cellular division results from uncoupling cellular growth from cellular division has been achieved by a variety of methods, thereby providing means for independent study of growth and cellular division (*43, 115*).

Earlier studies indicated that an important aspect of glucose metabolism was the maintenance of normal strains of *Candida albicans* in a yeast state and the prevention of filamentation due to the metabolic synthesis of intracellular reducing substances which force the disulfide equilibrium to sulfhydryl (–S-S ⇌ –SH) (*73*). The maintenance of the yeast state in *Candida albicans* and prevention of filamentation were accomplished by the addition of small amounts of cysteine or glutathione to a polysaccharide medium (*71*). These observations suggested that after depletion of rapidly metabolized nutrients in *C. albicans*, the cellular division was blocked and the filamentous mutant was obtained. These filamentous cells reduced tetrazolium dyes. The addition of a metal-chelating agent increased the dye reduction in cells. Further studies indicated that uncoupling growth from cellular division (by genetic block) in the mutant or in the parent resulted in impairment of an enzymatic mechanism(s) which was essential to the process of cellular division in yeast (*73*).

The selective action of selenite and tellurite in promoting cellular division in the filament-producing cells was indicated by the transformation of the filamentous form to the yeast phase in the presence of these ions. Similar transformations of the filamentous strain of *C. albicans* and other filamentous fungi with the addition of $SeO_3^{=}$ and $TeO_3^{=}$ were observed but $SO_3^{=}$ had no effect on cellular division. These morphological changes produced by selenite and tellurite were not due to the selection of back mutants to the yeast type. On transfer to medium free of selenite, the cells reverted to the filamentous form. Selenite appeared to function by permitting cellular division in the genetically blocked, divisionless strain of *C. albicans* (*72, 74*).

This unique effect of selenite, a growth-inhibitor substance, in stimulating cellular division of yeast cells is contrary to the observations of Shrift (*102*) who reported the inhibition of cellular division in *Chlorella vulgaris* by selenomethionine. Selenomethionine blocked cellular division in *C. vulgaris* with subsequent increase of giant cells containing autospores as indicated in Fig. 46 (*102, 105*). These experiments suggest that one function of methionine in the alga is related to cellular division. Selenomethionine, a competitive structural analog, cannot be substituted for methionine in these metabolic processes. The addition of L-methionine during lag phase restored cell division.

The specificity of selenomethionine in uncoupling growth from division in *C. vulgaris* cultures was suggested when 6 other methionine analogs were ineffective in uncoupling growth from division. Selenomethionine failed to uncouple growth from division in *Chlamydomonas reinhardi*, *Chlorella pyrenoidosa*, *E. coli*, and *Torulopsis utilis* (*104*). The growth uncoupled from cell division in *C. vulgaris* was accompanied by the production of altered proteins. It was suggested that 2 classes of cellular proteins exist: one involved in growth in which methionine may replace selenomethionine, and the other involved directly with cellular division mechanism. (In this protein the selenomethionine cannot sub-

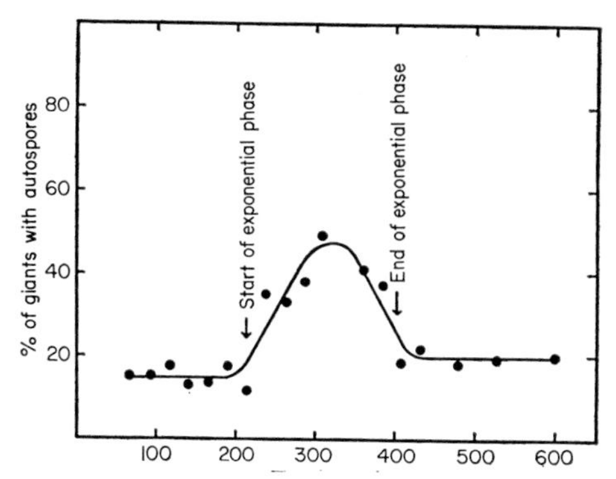

FIG. 46. Change in proportion of giant *Chlorella vulgaris* cells containing autospores during culture in $3.0 \times 10^{-5}M$ selenomethionine. From Shrift (*105*).

stitute for methionine.) This would suggest that the integrity of proteins involved in cellular division must be maintained and sulfur atoms cannot be substituted by selenium (*103, 104*) in *C. vulgaris* without interference with cellular division. The inhibition by selenomethionine of cellular division in *C. vulgaris* appears to be temporary and the cells adapt and resume division.

The progenies after adaptation are morphologically identical with normal cells and their proteins once more contain methionine. In liquid media, two passages or 20 generations of the organisms in selenomethionine were sufficient to give a population marked by the absence of an uncoupled growth phase. The adaptation to the growth-uncoupling effect of selenomethionine appears to involve all cells rather than the selection of mutants (*102, 105*).

Stability studies of the selenomethionine-adapted *C. vulgaris* population in liquid media indicated that even after 220 generations, the transformation was stable after withdrawal of selenomethionine. This suggested that exposure to selenomethionine had produced a stable, heritable change in the cells. The adapted *C. vulgaris* population was resistant to the growth-uncoupling effect of selenomethionine and the cells were able to divide when subcultured in the presence of the analog (*106*).

One form of adaptation in microorganisms involves induction of adaptive enzymes in response to new constituents of the medium so that the cellular requirements for growth and cell division are met. Such adaptive enzymes disappear after withdrawal of the analog which induced their formation. The adaptability of *C. vulgaris* to selenomethionine without reversion suggested the possibility that the mechanism of adaptation involved increased methionine incorporation by the cells in the presence of selenomethionine. The following mechanism for the increased methionine synthesis was suggested by Shrift *et al.* (*105*): Selenomethionine, by blocking the incorporation of methionine into proteins, may produce an accumulation of the various intermediates between sulfate and methionine. The intermediates act as inducers for the increased synthesis of the enzymes responsible for their further metabolism. The inducing agent in the increased methionine synthesis was not selenomethionine but the sulfate or its metabolic products.

Evidence of the above-suggested mechanism was indicated by exposure to sulfur starvation of *C. vulgaris* and subsequent exposure of the organism to selenomethionine. The subcultures of sulfur-starved, adapted organisms reverted to their original state of sensitivity to selenomethionine. Partial reversal to selenomethionine sensitivity could be achieved with D- or L-methionine as the only source of sulfur (*106*).

Shrift and Kelly (*107*) reported on the adaptation of *E. coli* (K12) to selenate in a culture medium containing a minimum concentration of sulfate with increased concentrations of potassium selenate (2, 4, 6, or $8 \times 10^{-4} M$). At 4 and $6 \times 10^{-4} M$ selenate levels, almost complete growth inhibition was observed up to 24 and 48 hours, but growth consistently resumed after this lag and eventually attained the maximum growth of the control. Complete inhibition was observed with the $8 \times 10^{-4} M$ selenate. The adapted cells when re-exposed to selenate after 9 transfers to selenium-free medium were able to grow exponentially at a rate almost equal to the control. This suggests that the adaptation of *E. coli* to selenate was stable. Adaptation of the alga to selenate was not observed (*101*) presumably due to the differences in the experimental procedure.

REDUCTION OF SELENIUM COMPOUNDS

Competitive antagonism is often pictured as a process in which there is no change in the inhibitor and it merely displaces the metabolite from its enzyme or reactive site. However, studies in biological systems indicate that the reduction of selenium compounds does occur and this reduction does not interfere with the competitive nature of selenium compounds. The deposition of selenium occurs at levels which produce some inhibition of growth or interference with metabolism. In completely inhibited cells, no reduction of selenium was observed (*58, 108, 129*). Whether the normal sulfate-utilizing enzymes are involved in the reduction of selenium compounds cannot be resolved at the present time. However, there is considerable evidence to indicate that the reduction of selenium compounds is enzymatic in nature.

That bacteria are capable of reducing selenium salts to elemental selenium has been known for over a century. A review of literature was made by Levine (*58*), who also studied the effects of various selenium compounds upon growth and ability of a number of bacteria to reduce selenium. The compounds could be arranged in a series of decreasing toxicity, i.e., selenium dioxide (selenious acid), selenic acid, sodium selenite, sodium selenate, and potassium selenocyanide. Reduction occurred only in liquid medium and the degree of reduction paralleled growth. The selenium deposited within the cells was regarded as an intracellular phenomenon. Smith (*108*) discussed and summarized some of the factors involved in the reduction of selenite by different genera and species of bacteria. He suggested that the selectivity of selenite broth may be due to the formation of selenopolythionates and other selenosulfur compounds in the medium which act as growth-inhibitor analogs of highly preferred sulfur sources by some bacteria. The reduction of selenite is a late manifestation of the growth and is due to the activity of the growing organisms. The intensity of reduction is related to the profuseness of growth.

In vitro studies indicate that mammalian tissues are able to reduce selenite to elemental selenium. Fresh tissue homogenates reduced selenite or selenate to elemental selenium (*91, 93*). The amount of selenate or selenite which was reduced to elemental form varied from tissue to tissue (Table 66). Selenite was more readily reduced than selenate by all tissue homogenates. Spleen homogenate reduced 19.5 per cent of the added selenite to elemental form but only 0.8 per cent of selenate selenium was reduced by the same tissue homogenate. That the reduction of selenate or selenite was enzymatic was suggested by the fact that autoclaving of the tissues destroyed the substances which brought about the decomposition of the compounds (Table 67) (*91*).

There is no evidence at the present time that in intact animals reduction to elemental selenium does take place. If reduction of selenate or selenite does occur in the intact animal, it is not the predominant feature of detoxification. Before selenate or selenite could be reduced to elemental form, the reactive seleno-intermediates would enter into the meta-

TABLE 66

Chemical Decomposition of Sodium Selenate and Selenite in Contact with Fresh Beef Liver for 2 Hours at Room Temperature[a]

Form of Se added	Se recovered from	Form of Se recovered from various fractions: Selenite (%)	Selenate (%)	Elemental (%)	Total (%)	Combined Se[b] (%)	Volatile Se recovered (%)
Sodium selenate	Supernatant liquid	26.0	23.4	0	49.8	0.4	
	Centrifuged sediment from supernatant liquid			0	3.6		
	Macerated liver			0	28.9		5.0
Sodium selenite	Supernatant liquid	4.0			33.7	29.7	
	Centrifuged sediment from supernatant liquid			3.6	9.7		
	Macerated liver			4.9	26.3		15.0

[a] Rosenfeld and Beath (*91*).

[b] Combined selenium = total Se — (selenate + selenite).

Reaction mixture: 20 gm liver, 5 gm sodium selenate or selenite suspended in isotonic NaCl and shaken 2 hours at room temperature.

bolic pool and react with a number of biological systems to form seleno-compounds or -complexes or would be eliminated by respiration as volatile selenium (*91*) (Table 66).

Intracellular large, reddish granules were observed in *Saccharomyces cerevisiae* cultures in the absence of any nutrient after the addition of selenate to a washed suspension in phosphate buffer (*36*). The density of the granules gradually increased and after 10 days the cells were opaque. These insoluble and nondiffusible deposits may produce physical interference (in contrast to chemical effects) with the normal metabolism of the yeast cell and finally lead to cellular destruction.

The deposition of red droplets of selenium inside the mycelia of wild-type *Neurospora crassa* cultures containing selenite was described (*129*). Methionine-less mutants of *Neurospora* in which the biosynthesis of methionine was blocked after homocysteine reduced selenite only in proportion to the amount of methionine added. Methionine-less mutants blocked before homocysteine were able to reduce selenite in excess of the amount of methionine added. They reduced selenite either in the presence or absence of necessary growth factors. The role of methionine in the reduction of selenite was to provide labile methyl groups presumably for transmethylation, but no methylated selenium compounds were found. The reduction of selenite and the appearance of selenium inside the mycelia were observed only in living organisms. The effect of respiratory enzyme inhibitors indicated that an intact oxidation-reduction enzyme system was essential to sustain this reduction. A genetic factor appears to function in preventing or inhibiting the reduction of selenite without any effect on the mycelia.

Selenite-reducing yeast cells were isolated from a mutant of *Candida albicans* (*74*). The selenite-reducing ability of these yeast cells and their

TABLE 67

Effect of Autoclaved Liver on Sodium Selenate and Selenite[a]

Form of Se added	Se recovered from	Form of Se recovered[b] from various fractions: Selenite (%)	Selenate (%)	Total (%)
Sodium selenate	Supernatant liquid	0	85.7	85.0
	Centrifuged sediment from supernatant liquid			11.5
	Macerated liver			2.5
Sodium selenite	Supernatant liquid	20	0	20.2
	Centrifuged sediment from supernatant liquid			33.6
	Macerated liver			46.3

[a] Rosenfeld and Beath (*91*).

[b] Elemental, none; volatile, none. Reaction mixture: same as in Table 66.

ability to grow in a high concentration of selenite were not directly related. The red material produced by the strains of *C. albicans* grown in media containing selenite appeared as small particles in the liquid medium and in or on the cells (*31*). Studies by phase-contrast microscope indicated that the red material inside the cells was localized as granules suspended in the cytoplasm while on the external surface of the cells they appeared as small particles (less than 1 μ in diameter). Studies of the red material based on differential centrifugation, ion exchange resins, and solubility in sodium sulfite suggested that these particles and granules were red amorphous selenium.

The effect of heavy metals on the reduction of selenite and/or sulfite by *C. albicans* indicates that without the addition of suitable heavy metals the enzymatic reducing systems of the cells cannot achieve reduction of selenite (or sulfite) to the Se^{-1} (S^{-1}) stage, and only metallic selenium (Se^0) accumulates in these cultures (*31*).

The reduction of selenite by wild type *Neurospora crassa* was inhibited by potassium cyanide, mercuric chloride, iodoacetate, carbon monoxide, and copper sulfate (*129*). Dinitrophenol (DNP) completely suppressed selenite reduction by growing cells of *C. albicans* (*31*). DNP inhibition of selenite reduction was reversed by addition of riboflavin phosphate to the culture. The reduction of selenite by *C. albicans* (strain RM-806) was inhibited not only by DNP but by methionine and formate as well as by fluoride and sulfhydryl inhibitors (*32*).

Cell-free preparations from *C. albicans* and Baker's yeast are capable of reducing selenite (*32*). The enzymatic system has optimal activity at pH 7 with $10^{-2}M$ selenite and the activity of the enzyme is lost by dialysis. The addition of dialyzate or of boiled or undialyzed extract to the dialyzed enzyme restored activity. The addition of G-6-P (glucose-6-phosphate), TPN (triphosphopyridine nucleotide), GSSG (oxidized glutathione), and menadione also restored the ability of dialyzed enzymes to reduce selenite. Menadione and glutathione could be replaced in the dialyzed enzyme system by thiodione (2-methyl-3-glutathionyl-1,4-naphthoquinone).

BIOLOGICAL SELENIUM ACTIVATION AND TRANSMETHYLATION

In the living organism there are large numbers of metabolically formed sulfurylated compounds mostly in ester linkages (*59*) and it was postulated that there may be a common metabolic carrier which would serve as a general sulfur donor in the enzymatic make-up of the cells. This was confirmed when DeMeio *et al.* (*27*) demonstrated that in cell-free systems adenosine triphosphate (ATP) could serve as the source of energy for sulfate activation. The mechanism of sulfate activation was clarified by Bernstein and McGilvery (*7*). Lipmann (*59*) summarized the literature dealing with studies on the mechanism of biological sulfate activation and sulfate transfer.

The observations that sulfate and selenate utilize the same enzyme system for the formation of "active sulfate" and "active selenate," respectively, have given further evidence of the substitution of selenium for sulfur in metabolic pathways (*2, 122*). The addition of selenate or sulfate to a crude yeast enzyme fraction liberated orthophosphate. The liberation of orthophosphate by sulfate or selenate was dependent upon the enzyme concentration and Mg^{++}. The reaction was inhibited by Be^{++}. The addition of selenate to a S^{35}-sulfate activation reaction mixture reduced the amount of radioactive sulfate bound, demonstrating that selenium and sulfur in the substrate may compete with each other for attachment to the enzymes.

Studies with sulfurylase and adenosine-5-phosphosulfate(APS)-kinase in the presence of S^{35}-sulfate or Se^{75}-selenate indicated that the reactivity of selenate in the reaction was similar to that of sulfur (*123*). The formation of adenosine-5′-phosphoselenate (APSe) was detected by electrophoretic studies. The component had approximately the same mobility as APS. There was a marked contrast between the amount of phosphate liberated and the small amounts of APSe recovered. Investigations of the factors responsible for low recoveries suggested that the compound was unstable. The half life of APSe at pH 4.5, 30° C, was approximately 30 minutes and if the reaction was stopped with alcohol the nucleotide-bound anion was stable for 90 minutes at pH 7.5 and 30°. When either selenate or sulfate was present as a substrate, the addition of APS-kinase to the incubation mixtures containing sulfurylase produced increases both in the liberation of phosphate and in the synthesis of nucleotide-bound selenate or sulfate (Table 68).

TABLE 68
Formation of Phosphate and Nucleotide-Bound Sulfate and Selenate by Sulfurylase and Sulfurylase plus APS-Kinase[a]

Addition	Phosphate liberated μmoles	Nucleotide-bound anions μmoles	Ratio of phosphate liberated to nucleotide-bound anion
Sulfate	0.55	0.016	3.5
Selenate	0.223	0.002	111.0
Sulfate + kinase	0.250	0.107	2.5
Selenate + kinase	0.285	0.005	57.0

NOTE: Reaction mixture in μmoles/tube: ATP 5; $MgCl_2$ 1; EDTA 0.3; Tris-HCl, pH 7.5, 50; $Na_2S^{35}O_4$ (0.1 μc/μmole) or $K_2Se^{75}O_4$ (0.2 μc/μmole), 5; sulfurylase 3.4 μg; pyrophosphatase 1.8 μg; crude APS-kinase 780 μg where indicated; total volume 0.50 ml; incubation 2 hours at 30° C.

[a] Wilson and Bandurski (*123*).

Reaction (1) catalyzed by ATP-sulfurylase in the presence of selenate anion was proposed (*123*).

$$\mathrm{ATP} + \mathrm{SeO_4^{=}} \rightleftharpoons \mathrm{APSe} + \mathrm{PP} \xrightarrow{\mathrm{HOH}} \mathrm{AMP} + \mathrm{SeO_4^{=}} \qquad (1)$$

Electrophoretic analysis showed neither 3′-phosphoadenosine-5′-phosphoselenate (the selenate analog of PAPS) nor 3′, 5′-diphosphoadenosine (the expected decomposition product) accumulation. This would suggest that there are differences between adenyl sulfates and adenyl selenates which cannot be accounted for by chemical instability of the selenate anhydride.

Enzymatic transmethylations from N to S, S to S, S to N, N to N, and O to N have been well substantiated in the literature. Present investigations indicate that the ATP-dependent enzymatic activation initiating methyl transfer by the formation of S-adenosylmethionine can also act on a selenium substrate.

ATP-dependent enzymatic activation is a prerequisite for the transfer of the methyl group of methionine in the formation of S-adenosylmethionine. S-Adenosylmethionine can act as a methyl donor in the presence of specific methylpherases and a suitable methyl acceptor (*18*). The essential feature in the activation reaction is the conversion of sulfur atom from a thioether to a sulfonium configuration. The importance of selenium in many biological systems prompted investigation of selenomethionine's ability to replace methionine in this reaction in which the sulfur atom of the amino acid is functionally involved (*70*). Selenomethionine, incubated with a methionine-activating yeast enzyme, was a better substrate than methionine as indicated in Fig. 47. Se-Adenosylselenomethionine was isolated and tested with guanidoacetic acid and creatine methylpherase from pig liver to determine the ability of the seleno-

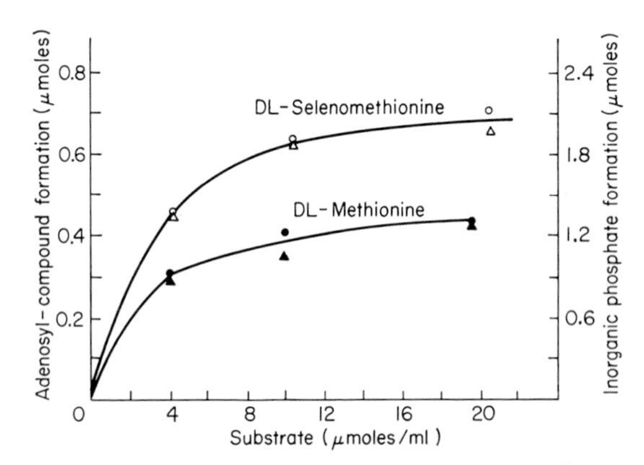

FIG. 47. Comparison of methionine and selenomethionine substrates for the yeast methionine-activating enzyme. Each vessel contained in a final volume of 0.5 ml.: tris (hydroxymethyl) aminomethane, pH 7.6, 75 μmoles; potassium chloride, 150 μmoles; magnesium chloride, 150 μmoles; adenosine triphosphate, neutralized with potassium hydroxide, 12 μmoles; reduced glutathione, neutralized with potassium hydroxide, 5 μmoles; substrate as indicated; an excess of yeast inorganic pyrophosphatase; 90 μg of methionine-activating enzyme purified 250-fold from an extract of baker's yeast. Incubation was for 30 minutes at 37°. The reaction was terminated by addition of perchloric acid and aliquots of the protein-free supernatant were used for determination of the inorganic phosphate (triangles) and adenosyl compound (circles). A control was run without added substrate and the control value subtracted from the experimental. The stoichiometry of the reaction requires the mineralization of 3 moles of phosphate for each mole of adenosyl compound formed. From Mudd and Cantoni (*70*).

compound to serve as a methyl donor in this system. The methylation of guanidoacetic acid to creatine takes place as in Eq. (2).

$$\text{Guanidoacetic acid} + \text{Se-adenosylselenomethionine} \xrightarrow[\text{methylpherase}]{\text{enzyme}} \text{Se-adenosylselenohomocysteine} + \text{creatine} + H^{+} \quad (2)$$

Se-Adenosylselenomethionine at 0.28 μmole supported the formation of 0.21 μmole of creatine by transmethylation while 0.32 μmole of S-adenosylmethionine was needed to give a quantitative yield of creatine.

These studies emphasize the ability of seleno-compounds to substitute for their sulfur analogs as substrates in 2 enzymatic reactions involved in biological transmethylation.

Bremer and Greenberg (*15*) have described a system for choline biosynthesis in which $C^{14}H_3$-S-adenosylmethionine was incubated with rat liver microsomes. Se-Adenosylselenomethionine was found to be as efficient a methyl donor in choline synthesis as S-adenosylmethione. Se-Adenosylselenomethionine was tested as a methyl donor in the methylation of a sulfhydryl compound, 2-methoxyethanethiol. The selenium compound again was found to be an effective methyl donor as estimated by the formation of a volatile radioactive, toluene-soluble product, presumably *O*, S-dimethylmercaptoethanol. Further studies on the ability of other selenium compounds to act as methyl acceptors in enzymatic transmethylations indicated that H_2Se and methyl selenol served as methyl acceptors in microsomal systems. Some methylation occurred when boiled microsomes were used suggesting that a nonenzymatic transmethylation from S-adenosylmethionine to sulfhydryl compounds may take place (*16*).

Experimental evidence indicated that in liver homogenate, transmethylation was depressed by selenate and selenite when the methyl acceptors were homocystine or homocysteine and the methyl donor, choline or betaine (*93*). Both selenium compounds interfered with transmethylation, but selenite was a more effective inhibitor than selenate. The interference with transmethylation was indicated by decreased methionine formation. The decrease in methionine may have been due to (1) oxidation of sulfhydryl groups, or (2) the methyl capture by "active" seleno-compound(s). There was some evidence to indicate that both processes occurred simultaneously.

The biological methylation of arsenate, selenate, selenite, tellurate, tellurite, and arsenious acid by fungi has been investigated since the early 1930's by Challenger and co-workers. *Scopulariopsis brevicaulis*, *Aspergillus niger*, and *Penicillium notatum* are able to convert selenate or selenite to dimethyl selenide. Biological methylation was reviewed by Challenger (*19, 21*).

The methylation of inorganic selenium by fungi as suggested by Challenger and co-workers proceeds as in Eq. (3).

The postulated intermediate selenium compounds were not detected but S. *brevicaulis* and certain *Penicillia* convert methane-, ethane-, and propane-1-seleninic acids to dimethyl-, methyl-ethyl-, and methyl-*n*-propyl selenides (*10*).

The mechanism of biological methylation may be by transfer of an intact methyl group or the transfer of a one-carbon fragment followed by reduction or a combination of these 2 mechanisms.

$$H_2SeO_3 \longrightarrow H^+ + :\overset{\overline{O}\,/}{\underset{\downarrow \atop O}{Se}}-OH \xrightarrow{CH_3^+} CH_3\cdot\overset{O \atop \uparrow}{\underset{\downarrow \atop O}{Se}}-OH \xrightarrow[\text{and reduction}]{\text{ionization}}$$

Ion — Methaneselenonic acid

$$CH_3\cdot\overset{\overline{O}\,/}{\underset{\downarrow \atop O}{Se}}: \xrightarrow{CH_3^+} (CH_3)_2\overset{O \atop \uparrow}{\underset{\downarrow \atop O}{Se}} \xrightarrow{\text{reduction}} (CH_3)_2SeO \xrightarrow{\text{reduction}} (CH_3)_2\ddot{Se}:$$

Ion of methane-seleninic acid — Dimethyl selenone — Dimethyl selenoxide — Dimethyl selenide

The potential sources of methyl groups in the formation of dimethyl selenide from inorganic selenate or selenite by S. *brevicaulis* or A. *niger* were investigated with C^{14}-labeled methyl donors such as formate, DL-methionine, and one C^{14}-methyl group in choline and betaine (*20*, *28*). Methylation with choline, betaine, or formate was very low, but the $C^{14}H_3$ of D- or L-methionine was transferred intact to selenium by the fungi. Only a small percentage of methionine methyl groups was converted to CO_2 when compared with other methyl donors in the experiment. It appears that mycological methylation is analogous to other biological methylations; that is, methionine appears to be the most important methyl donor. The addition of homocystine to betaine-selenate and formate-selenate cultures of A. *niger* increased transmethylation 2 to 5 times. This increased methylation suggests that the mechanism of methylation by fungi involves a true transmethylation from methionine. Dimethylthetins cannot serve as direct methyl donors to selenate in cultures of A. *niger*. Thetins as effective methyl donors *in vivo* in rats were discussed by du Vigneaud (*30*) and in rat tissue homogenates by Dubnoff and Borsook (*29*).

That S-adenosylmethionine may be the principal methyl donor in certain molds grown in cultures containing inorganic selenate, selenite, or arsenic has been inferred by Challenger (*21*).

It is apparent from these reviews that numerous enzymatic systems which utilize sulfur can also utilize selenium analogs in various metabolic pathways. The statement by Challenger (*21*) that selenium replaced sulfur in biologically important compounds without serious alteration in their functions is valid under his experimental conditions.

THE EFFECT OF SELENIUM COMPOUNDS ON ENZYME SYSTEMS

There is considerable evidence that most of the enzyme systems which require –SH groups for their function are effectively inhibited by selenium compounds. Selenium compounds inhibit a number of glycolytic enzymes as well as many respiratory enzymes.

The effect of selenium on fermentation and glycolysis will be discussed in a general sense as related to a reaction sequence which involves sugars. The term fermentation will be restricted to reactions which occur in cells or enzymes and consume no oxygen. There is only limited information on glycolysis, the series of reactions elucidated by Embden, Meyerhof, and Parnas, in relation to the inhibitory effects of selenium compounds. The term respiration will refer to the uptake of oxygen.

The inhibition by selenium compounds of fermentation and respiration of yeast, tissue slices, or tissue homogenates was reported by various investigators (*5, 8, 12, 13, 31, 37, 40, 56, 69, 85, 124, 126, 127*).

Yeast cells apparently are as sensitive to traces of certain elements as are higher organisms. The effect of equivalent moles of sodium salts of selenite, selenide, selenate, metavanadate, orthoarsenite, tellurite, sulfide, sulfite, and sulfate as well as elemental selenium and sulfur was studied on yeast fermentation of glucose by Moxon and Franke (*69*). The production of CO_2 by yeast during the fermentation of glucose was depressed by the addition of selenium, vanadium, arsenic, or tellurium. Selenate and selenide were less effective inhibitors than selenite. The addition of sulfide increased CO_2 output, probably in direct relation to the hydrogen sulfide concentration. Sulfide reduced the inhibitory effects of selenite but sulfite, sulfate, thiosulfate, and elemental sulfur were not effective. The effect of selenite on the respiration of living yeast was investigated by Potter and Elvehjem (*85*). The oxygen uptake was depressed about 80 per cent in glucose, mannose, and fructose substrates in the presence of selenite. The inhibition of yeast respiration by selenite in lactate and pyruvate substrates was negligible (4–9%). That selenite inhibited not only the glycolytic system of yeast but also the respiration was indicated by its inhibitory effect on the oxidation of acetic acid and alcohol. Parallel experiments using the various substrates with sodium arsenite indicated that this salt was considerably more toxic to the respiratory system than selenite. The minimum effective concentrations for inhibition were approximately 0.003 *M* for selenite and 0.001 *M* for arsenite. The mechanism of inhibition of glycolysis by selenite has been suggested as an interference with rupture of the glycosidic linkage (*1*).

The effect of arsenic and selenium compounds on glucose fermentation by Baker's yeast indicates that selenate and selenite reduced the CO_2 output (*56*). Arsenate or arsenite enhanced selenate inhibition while arsenite reduced the inhibitory effect of selenite. In *E. coli* cultures, glucose utilization was reduced by selenite and selenite inhibition was not reversed by arsenic. Cysteine and histidine reversed the inhibitory effect of selenite on glucose utilization; however, they had no effect on the depressed growth rate (*76*).

The effect of selenium and arsenic compounds on the O_2 uptake of resting *Saccharomyces cerevisiae* was investigated (*8*). These studies indicated that in the absence of phosphate, arsenite was as effective an inhibitor of respiration as was selenite. The addition of arsenite to the substrate increased the toxicity of selenite to the yeast cells and reduced the O_2 uptake to a greater extent than when either compound was used separately. In the presence of phosphate, arsenite was a less effective inhibitor of respiration of yeast cells than selenite.

The effect of various ions on the inhibition of respiration by selenate and selenite was studied in some detail (*12*). Yeast respiration was strongly inhibited by selenite in glucose substrate but was not affected by selenite when lactate, pyruvate, or acetate were used as substrates. Arsenite, arsenate, or phosphate reduced the inhibitory effect of selenite on yeast respiration. A combination of phosphate and arsenate reversed the inhibitory effect of selenite. Selenate inhibition was not influenced by phosphate or the combination of phosphate and arsenate. Glucose breakdown proceeded at a more rapid rate in the presence of selenite, probably due to the less efficient metabolism of the organisms.

The mechanism whereby arsenate or arsenite can act as selenite antagonists is difficult to interpret. Both arsenate and arsenite uncouple oxidative phosphorylation. Arsenate, by replacing phosphate in triose phosphate, interferes with ATP synthesis by forming an unstable compound, 1-arseno-3-phosphoglyceric acid, which is rapidly decomposed in water. Arsenite is a potent inhibitor of decarboxylases of α-keto acids. Further studies will be needed to clarify interesting biochemical reactions.

Studies of metabolic interactions of selenate and sulfate in yeast culture indicate that both selenate and sulfate depressed O_2 uptake of washed and aerated yeast cells (*13*). The combined effect of selenate and sulfate on yeast respiration was less inhibitory than the individual compounds. The reversal of selenate inhibition of O_2 uptake by sulfate probably was due to competition between these ions for a transport mechanism. Phosphate had no effect on sulfate metabolism, but selenite-phosphate antagonism on respiration of S. *cerevisiae* (*8, 12*) and *Candida albicans* (*31*) has been observed.

Studies with selenium-resistant and nonresistant mutants of *C. albicans* indicate that these strains showed differences in their metabolism of glucose (*31*). In the Se-resistant mutant, respiration and fermentation of glucose were insensitive to selenite. In the nonresistant mutant, selenite inhibited glucose oxidation at the same time CO_2 was produced in excess of the oxygen consumed. This indicates that the selenium-resistant strain was able to utilize glucose in the presence of selenite, while in the nonresistant strain the fermentation of internal glucose was stimulated but the absorption of glucose was blocked by selenite.

Only a few enzymes in the glycolytic pathway were studied as to their susceptibility to selenite; these investigations indicated that they are susceptible to the ion. Triose phosphate and isocitrate dehydrogenases were susceptible to selenite poisoning (*4, 5*). The addition of an aqueous extract of boiled yeast counteracted the inhibition by the selenite ion (*4*). The removal of codehydrogenase (TPN) by charcoal from enzyme preparations increased the enzyme sensitivity to selenite. It is postulated that the removal of codehydrogenase from triose phosphate dehydrogenase exposed the thiol groups and allowed selenite to act on the enzyme. The enzyme sensitivity to selenite was reduced by the addition of codehydrogenase.

The sensitivity of glycolytic enzymes to selenite was studied on tissue slices from Walker tumor (*126, 127*). There was no evidence in these studies that glycolysis in liver, kidney, and tumor slices was affected by selenite and diselenodiacetic acid. The effect of selenite on the glycolytic pathway in mammalian tissue slices appeared to differ from that on yeast cells. There was some evidence to indicate that cellular permeability of the tissues may have been responsible for the lack of inhibition by selenite.

Glycolysis in rat liver homogenate (in a nitrogen atmosphere) was inhibited by sodium selenite, and the inhibition was proportional to the molarity of the inhibitor (*40*). The apparent discrepancies on the effect of selenite on the glycolytic pathway in tissue slices and homogenates may be due to the inherent differences in the experiments.

Embryonic cartilage, unlike adult cartilage, has a high respiratory rate. Chick embryonic cartilage respiration as well as chondroitin sulfate synthesis was inhibited by the addition of selenate, malonate, methylene blue, or dinitrophenol but was not affected by ammonium molybdate. The rate of respiration as well as the synthesis of chondroitin sulfate was stimulated by glucose (*14*).

Studies indicate that the major portion of the tricarboxylic acid cycle functions in the mantle of the oyster (*51*). Selenite appeared to have a dual effect on respiration. A lower concentration ($10^{-5}M$) produced a slight inhibition. As the concentration was increased ($10^{-3}M$), a mean increase of 49 per cent was observed. A control with sea water and selenite indicated that the increased respiration was not due to the autoxidation of selenite.

The inhibitory effect of selenium compounds on succinic dehydrogenase (or oxidase) was studied most extensively among the enzymes which require sulfhydryl groups for their activity (*1, 3, 6, 23–25, 40, 53–55, 76, 86, 99, 100, 111, 126, 128*).

Labes and Krebs (*55*) demonstrated that the cytochrome-indophenol-oxidase system in muscle powder remained active in the presence of selenite and that the inhibition by selenite was limited to succinic dehydrogenase. Studies on tissue slices also indicate that cytochrome oxidase and arginase, which contain no –SH groups, were not affected by selenite (*127, 128*).

The inhibition of succinoxidase by selenite differs from that of heavy metals in that selenite inhibition was not reversed by all dithiols. 1,3-Dimercaptopropanol and propane-1,3-dithiol, at a ratio of Se:dithiol of 1:7, produced about half reactivation, while BAL and 5 other dithiols had no effect. The irreversibility of selenite inhibition by dithiols may be due to the large amounts of dithiols required for reactivation. In high concentrations, dithiols inhibit succinoxidase activity (*3*).

The effect of reduced glutathione and selenite on tissue respiration indicated that glutathione reversed either completely or partially the inhibitory effect of selenite. If the glutathione was added 30 to 60 minutes after the selenite, the inhibition was not reversed (*126*).

Inhibition of some enzyme systems does not occur immediately with addition of selenate or selenite. This latent period in most studies was not due to the delayed penetration of selenite or selenate into the cells (*6, 12, 85*). It may be related to the time required for the conversion of selenate or selenite to a "form" which can react with the enzyme.

All tissues have a long induction period (30–60 minutes) during which selenate has no effect on oxygen consumption. The difference between selenite and selenate is that higher concentrations of selenate and longer induction periods are required for equivalent enzyme inhibition. Several specific dehydrogenases were investigated for their relative sensitivity to selenite (*6*). The action of selenium on "*l*-proline oxidase" was studied in greater detail. There was a latent period before an inhibition was observed in the oxidations of all the substrates except *l*-proline. The oxidation of this substrate was inhibited immediately by low concentrations of selenite. On the basis of these studies the various enzymes were divided into 3 classes: (a) those relatively insusceptible to selenite, including the glucose, lactate, pyruvate oxidases of brain and probably *l*-tyrosinase, xanthine, and alcohol oxidases of liver; (b) those in which selenium catalyzes the destruction of an active group, including succinoxidase, choline oxidase, *d*-proline oxidase, and tyramine oxidase; and (c) "*l*-proline oxidase," which is inactivated immediately, suggesting that selenium combines with an active group in the enzyme.

Lactate, pyruvate, citrate, and succinate did not increase O_2 uptake in the selenite-inhibited respiration of tissue slices (*127, 128*). The preincubation of muscle preparation with malonate, fumarate, or succinate prevented the inhibitory effects of selenite, and cysteine reversed selenite inhibition of the enzyme system (*5*).

The mechanism of selenite inhibition of succinic dehydrogenase in rat liver homogenates indicated that the order of addition of succinate affects the extent of inhibition, and studies with malonate and selenite indicated that they are mutually exclusive inhibitors. The inhibition of the enzyme by selenite was an irreversible type. The sulfhydryl concentration of the inhibited system as well as the selenium content in the supernatant decreased. The addition of reduced glutathione did not prevent inhibition or restore the activity of the inhibited systems. Studies also indicated that liver malic dehydrogenase, fumarase and APTase were not sensitive to selenite, but oxalacetic acid oxidase and choline oxidase were sensitive to the inhibitory effect of selenite (*53*).

The effect of a number of seleno-compounds on succinic dehydrogenase activity of rat liver homogenate was investigated (*54*). Of a series of seleno-compounds, selenocystine was the most toxic and selenomethionine the least toxic. Replacement of the amino group of selenocystine by hydrogen resulted in a less toxic compound. This was also true for the larger molecule of selenohomocystine. "Selenium tetraglutathione," a mixture of compounds, was a fairly potent inhibitor of the enzyme. The order of inhibition of succinic dehydrogenase by the seleno-compounds was as follows: selenocystine, selenohomocystine, β,β'-diselenodipropionic acid, "selenium tetraglutathione," selenocystathionine, colloidal selenium, sodium selenite, methyl isoselenourea sulfate, and selenomethionine. Red and black elemental selenium did not affect the enzyme activity. There was no correlation between the degree of enzyme inhibition *in vitro* and the toxicity of seleno-compounds in intact animals.

The comparative inhibition of a number of purified sulfhydryl enzymes by selenite, cupric chloride, and *p*-chloromercuribenzoate was investigated by Tsen and Collier (*112*). The enzymes were incubated at room temperature for at least 30 minutes with the inhibitor before activity was determined. The inhibition of sulfhydryl enzymes with cupric chloride (0.001 *M*) and *p*-chloromercuribenzoate (0.001 *M*) was from 89 to 100 per cent. Selenite (0.001 *M*) inhibited 3 enzymes—D-amino acid oxidase, β-amylase, and urease—62, 49, and 60 per cent, respectively. The other enzymes—lactic and alcohol dehydrogenases and aldolases—were not affected. The relatively weak inhibition by selenite suggests that, compared with mercaptide-forming agents, selenite does not react with all thiols in a similar manner.

The enzymatic degradation of DNA and deoxyribonucleohistone by pancreatic DNase was strongly inhibited by selenite, arsenate, fluoride, and several other inhibitors. The degradation by the enzyme involves depolymerization and hydrolysis of DNA. Selenite and arsenate inhibited the depolymerization of DNA. It was suggested that the inhibitory action of selenite and arsenate may be due to the ability of these ions to combine with the Mg^{++} and form sparingly soluble magnesium salts. The enzymatic activity was not affected by pretreatment of the substrate with —SH reactants, therefore, the selenite inhibitory effect may not have involved the inactivation of essential sulfhydryl groups but the binding of the essential Mg^{++} ions (*39*).

Requirement of Selenium Compounds for Synthesis of Enzymes

The metabolic requirement for selenium by a number of selenium indicator plants and the need for selenium in avian and mammalian disease syndromes have been presented in preceding chapters.

In enzymatic studies, selenium is usually used as an inhibitor. The recognition of the function of trace amounts of selenium in various biological systems suggests that it is of considerable importance in enzymatic studies to ascertain that selenium as an impurity is absent in the reagents.

The need for selenite, molybdate, and iron in the production of formic dehydrogenase by *Escherichia coli-Aerobacter aerogenes* group was described by Pinsent (*79*). Sufficient precautions were taken to purify the salts and to avoid contamination of the chemicals and media. These studies established that selenite and molybdate have essential functions in the biosynthesis of formic dehydrogenase. In the absence of selenite and molybdate, growth was normal but no enzyme activity could be detected.

As far as could be determined from these experiments, the need for selenite and molybdate was highly specific for the induction of formic dehydrogenase. Selenate had slight activity, but this may have been due to some reduction of selenate to selenite during autoclaving; it is also possible that the organism may have the capacity to reduce some selenate to selenite. Similar reduction with tissue homogenates and microorganisms has been discussed in this chapter. Tellurite and tellurate could not replace selenite, and molybdate could not be replaced by tungstate, vanadate, uranyl, or chromate ions either in the presence or absence of the essential ions. Neither selenite alone nor molybdate alone increased the formic dehydrogenase activity of the cells.

The concentrations of selenite and molybdate which stimulated *E. coli* cells to maximum formic dehydrogenase synthesis were $3 \times 10^{-8} M$ and $1 \times 10^{-8} M$, respectively, in nitrate-free medium. Based on the weight of a single *E. coli* cell, it was calculated that full enzyme activity was obtained when the medium contained 5000 to 10,000 selenite and 5000 molybdate molecules per cell.

At the present time it is difficult to state how these ions stimulated biosynthesis of the enzyme. It may be that each ion acts independently in the presence of the other; or they undergo some combination and eventually are incorporated into the enzyme molecule; or they are involved more remotely in the enzyme synthesis. Further studies on this and other enzyme systems may furnish clues to this complex and interesting ionic interrelation on the biosynthesis of enzymes.

Another enzyme, fumarase, may be activated by inorganic selenium (selenate). These studies were carried out on recrystallized pig heart fumarase which was well dialyzed in order to remove impurities (*60*). Several anions affected the activity of the enzymes. Sodium selenate (0.025 *M*) and sodium sulfate (0.025 *M*) were identical in increasing the fumarase activity, suggesting that in this enzyme the activation site that accepted the sulfate ion also accepted the selenate ion. Arsenite, citrate, borate, phosphate, and arsenate, in increasing order of effectiveness, activated salt-free fumarase and altered the pH of optimal activity. They were more effective activators than selenate or sulfate. Chloride, bromide, thiocyanate, and iodide, in increasing order of effectiveness, inhibited the action of fumarase either in the presence or absence of activating anions.

Selenium Compounds in Biosynthesis of Enzymes

The differential rates of synthesis of β-galactosidase by a methionine-requiring mutant of *E. coli* grown in the presence of methionine, selenomethionine, and various mixtures of both compounds were investigated (*26*). In the presence of methionine, and with gradual increase of selenomethionine, synthesis of the enzyme was correspondingly depressed. In the presence of selenomethionine the synthesis of the enzyme was about one third of the amount of enzyme synthesized in the presence of methionine (Fig. 48). The differential rate of enzyme activity was postulated to be due to (a) the synthesis of an enzyme with modified affinity for the substrate, (b) a decrease in the total enzyme synthesized, or (c) the synthesis of an enzyme of lower specific activity. Only further studies will indicate which mechanism was involved in the reduced synthesis of an enzymatically active protein, probably seleno-β-galactosidase.

The incorporation of seleno-amino acids into protein may be mediated in a manner similar to the incorporation of normal amino acids into proteins. The requirements for the incorporation of amino acids in a cell-free system are a microsome-rich fraction, a soluble, nondialyzable fraction of the cytoplasm and an ATP generating system (*130*). This is an accepted mechanism whereby amino acids are built into proteins. An enzyme system prepared from disrupted *E. coli* incorporated both

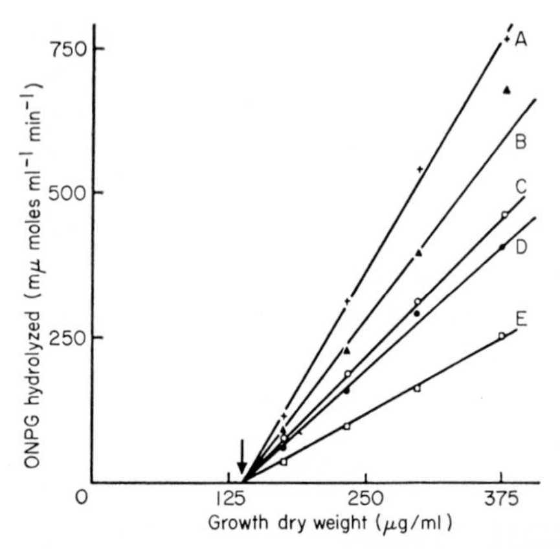

FIG. 48. Synthesis of β-galactosidase by *E. coli* mutant (ML 304d) in presence of methionine, selenomethionine, and various mixtures of the two metabolites. The arrow indicates the addition of TMG ($10^{-3}M$). A: DL-methionine ($5 \times 10^{-5}M$). B: same as A plus DL-selenomethionine ($5 \times 10^{-5}M$). C: same as A plus DL-selenomethionine ($2.5 \times 10^{-4}M$). D: same as A plus DL-selenomethionine ($5 \times 10^{-4}M$). E: DL-selenomethionine ($10^{-4}M$). From Cowie and Cohen (*26*).

methionine and selenomethionine into protein (*75*). Although no further studies on the incorporation of other seleno-amino acids in cell-free systems were carried out, this investigation suggests one mechanism whereby seleno-amino acids may be incorporated into proteins.

The formation of β-galactosidase in the presence of selenite (Se^{75}) differed from that of selenomethionine. The normal rate of enzyme synthesis occurred only during the first part of the utilization of the internal glutathione-sulfur (*26*). In the latter part of glutathione-sulfur utilization, no β-galactosidase was formed. During the first period the alcohol-soluble proteins incorporated radioactive selenium in proportion to new cell mass, but ceased to incorporate selenium at about the same time that enzyme synthesis ceased.

BIOSYNTHESIS OF ORGANIC SELENIUM COMPOUNDS

The chemical synthesis of organoselenium compounds was discussed in Chapter IX. The use of organoselenium compounds for biological studies is hindered by the lack of availability of these compounds. The use of radioactive Se^{75} for the chemical synthesis of organic selenium compounds adds the problem of gamma radiation to the existing hazard of selenium toxicity. If suitable microorganism(s) or plant(s) could be found for the biosyntheses of stable seleno-compounds from inorganic radioactive selenium compounds, it would greatly assist in the production of organoselenium compounds for metabolic studies. A few attempts were made with plants and microorganisms to isolate seleno-compounds from biological material. Only small amounts (or less than μg quantities) of organic selenium compounds were isolated from these sources. The compounds so obtained were always mixtures of sulfur and selenium analogs (*11, 92*).

The bacterial flora of the rumen in ruminants utilize inorganic sulfur compounds for the syntheses of essential organic sulfur compounds. Selenate or selenite probably is utilized by the same mechanism for the syntheses of seleno-amino acids (*94*) and bile salts (*92*). In animals, plants, or microorganisms which are susceptible to the toxic effects of selenium, the selenium level cannot be increased to that of sulfur. Therefore, the biosynthesis of sulfur compounds always exceeds that of selenium analogs. Before a "steady state" of sulfur-selenium could be established in most biological systems, not only would the normal metabolic functions be depressed but selenium toxicity would inhibit the systems. By use of Se^{75}, the concentration of selenium in biological systems can be reduced below toxic levels and selenium in the chemically purified compounds can be detected by their radioactivity.

A methionine-requiring mutant of *E. coli* was able to utilize both selenomethionine and Se^{75}-selenite for the synthesis of proteins (*22, 26*). However, Se^{75}-selenite was utilized only in the presence of reserve cellular glutathione- or sulfate-sulfur for protein synthesis. The residual protein fractions contained a radioactive material with chromatographic properties similar to those of cysteine. The incorporation of sulfur and selenium compounds in proteins is indicated in Fig. 49. These results also indicate that the incorporation of sulfur exceeded that of selenium in the proteins. The synthesis of seleno-amino acid required reserve sulfur or the addition of sulfate which was an essential for the incorporation of selenite into the proteins of *E. coli*.

The incorporation of Se^{75}-selenite into the protein by wild-type *E. coli* strain B increased after sulfur depletion (*114*). The selenium compounds from seleniferous *E. coli* protein hydrolyzates were isolated by ion exchange resin chromatography. There were 2 amphoteric selenium compounds in the enzymatic and acid hydrolyzates. Identification of the compounds was made by paper chromatography. Only selenomethionine was identified as a component of *E. coli* proteins, and selenocystine was not detected by the methods used.

Incubation of Baker's yeast in medium containing Se^{75}-selenite indicated that about 93 per cent of the radioactivity was firmly bound to TCA-insoluble material (*113*). Enzymatic and acid hydrolyzates of the TCA-insoluble fraction contained no selenomethionine or selenocystine. The major components of these hydrolyzates moved with the solvent fronts. The TCA-soluble fraction contained at least 2 radioselenium components. One component had R_f values similar to selenotetraglutathione.

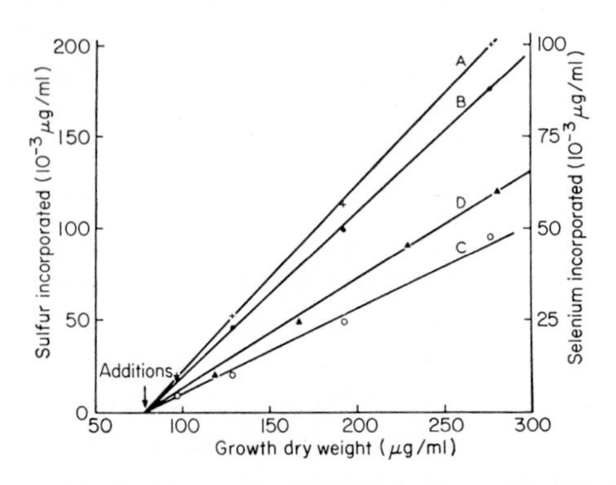

FIG. 49. Sulfur and selenium incorporation into the residual proteins of wild-type (ML 30) *E. coli*. DL-Methionine ($10^{-4}M$) was present in all flasks. Culture A: radiosulfate (2 µg S/ml). Culture B: same as A plus selenite (3.9 µg Se/ml). Culture C: radioselenite (3.9 µg Se/ml) plus sulfate (2 µg S/ml). Culture D: radioselenite (3.9 µg Se/ml), S^{35} (37,500 counts/min/µg S), Se^{75} (7440 counts/min/µg Se). From Cowie and Cohen (*26*).

Isolation of seleno-amino acids in small quantities from the yeast, *Saccharomyces cerevisiae*, was described by Blau (*11*). The procedure was revised, thereby improving the biosynthesis of Se^{75}-methionine and also separation of the compound (Blau, personal communication). The modifications of procedures gave better growth yield and less loss by oxidation of Se^{75}-selenomethionine. The volume of growth medium for the yeast was reduced to 500 ml. The hydrolysis of the yeast proteins was carried out in the absence of oxygen and air to prevent loss by oxidation. Methionine and cystine (in a ratio of 1:10) were added to the 6 *N* HCl used for hydrolysis of the dehydrated and extracted yeast proteins. The yeast protein was hydrolyzed at 105° C under vacuum overnight. The protein hydrolyzate after filtration was placed on resin and separated as described previously (*11*). The separated Se^{75}-selenomethionine was stored at low temperature and cystine was added to prevent oxidation (1 mg cystine/ml of Se^{75}-methionine).

Aspergillus niger and *Scopulariopsis brevicaulis* grown with selenate or selenite in the presence of C^{14}-labeled D-, L- or DL-methyl-methionine synthesized dimethyl selenide. The 2 stereoisomers appeared to be equally available as methyl donors (*28*). However, no quantitative yield of dimethyl selenide by this biosynthetic method was obtained.

Other unknown selenium compounds were synthesized by bacteria and yeast which were not identical to known sulfur compounds.

An unknown reducing compound in cultures of *E. coli* was detected when some enzyme inhibitors were added to the medium (*76*). The reducing compound obtained from *E. coli* cultures when selenite was added to the medium had the same R_f value as the compound detected in cultures of *E. coli* inhibited by iodoacetate. It was not identical with any compound known to occur in glucose metabolism of *E. coli*. The compound was not utilized by *E. coli* as a source of carbon (*77*). Unknown seleno-protein(s) were isolated from cell walls of a strain of *Candida albicans* grown in the presence of selenite (*74*). No further attempt was made to identify the components of this seleno-protein.

The isolation of seleno-compounds from biological sources is still in the embryonic stage. The increased importance of selenium metabolism should stimulate investigation of biological systems for the biosyntheses of organic seleno-compounds. Methods for the hydrolysis of proteins whereby labile seleno-compounds are not decomposed must also be devised. The resolution of seleno from sulfur organic compounds by resins, paper chromatography, and proper solvent systems is still a problem which in the future requires and deserves attention.

References

1. Abe, T. and R. Nakaya. 1951. The mechanism of the effectiveness of the selenite medium (for *Salmonella*). *Japan J. Bacteriol.* **6**:463–465.
2. Bandurski, R. S. and L. G. Wilson. 1957. A comparison of sulfate and selenate as substrates for adenosine triphosphate sulfurylase. *Plant Physiol. Suppl.* **32**:xli.
3. Barron, E. S. G. and G. Kalnitsky. 1947. The inhibition of succinoxidase by heavy metals and its reactivation with dithiols. *Biochem. J.* **41**:346–351.
4. Bergstermann, H. 1948. Increased susceptibility of thiol-containing enzymes to poisons during substrate and vitamin deficiencies. *Klin. Wochschr.* **26**:435–436.
5. Bergstermann, H. 1949. Fermentschutz durch Codehydrase bei Vergiftung der Triosephosphatdehydrase durch Selenit. (Ein Beitrag zur Frage der Bedeutung von Thiolgruppen für Fermente.) *Biochem. Z.* **319**:439–443.
6. Bernheim, F. and J. R. Klein. 1941. Action of sodium selenite on the oxidation of *l*-proline. *J. Biol. Chem.* **139**:827–833.
7. Bernstein, S. and R. W. McGilvery. 1952. Substrate activation in the synthesis of phenyl sulfate. *J. Biol. Chem.* **199**:745–748.

8. Berry, E. C. and R. Pengra. 1954. Respiration of *Saccharomyces cerevisiae* in the presence of selenium and arsenic. *Proc. South Dakota Acad. Sci.* **33**:67–70.
9. Biesele, J. J. 1958. Chemically induced imitations of mitotic anomalies common to cancer cells. *Ann. New York Acad. Sci.* **71**:1054–1067.
10. Bird, M. L. and F. Challenger. 1942. Studies in biological methylation. Part IX. The action of *Scopulariopsis brevicaulis* and certain Penicillia on salts of aliphatic seleninic and selenonic acids. *J. Chem. Soc.* pp. 574–577.
11. Blau, M. 1961. Biosynthesis of (^{75}Se) selenomethionine and (^{75}Se) selenocystine. *Biochim. et Biophys. Acta* **49**:389–390.
12. Bonhorst, C. W. 1955. Selenium poisoning. Anion antagonisms in yeast as indicators of the mechanism of selenium toxicity. *J. Agr. and Food Chem.* **3**: 700–703.
13. Bonhorst, C. W. and I. S. Palmer. 1957. Selenium poisoning. Metabolic interactions of selenate, sulfate and phosphate. *J. Agr. and Food Chem.* **5**:931–933.
14. Boyd, E. S. and W. F. Newman. 1954. Chondroitin sulfate synthesis and respiration in chick embryonic cartilage. *Arch. Biochem. Biophys.* **51**:475–486.
15. Bremer, J. and D. M. Greenberg. 1960. Biosynthesis of choline *in vitro*. *Biochim. et Biophys. Acta* **37**:173–175.
16. Bremer, J. and Y. Natori. 1960. Behavior of some selenium compounds in transmethylation. *Biochim. et. Biophys. Acta* **44**:367–370.
17. Brodie, A. F. and J. S. Gots. 1952. The reduction of tetrazolium salts by an isolated bacterial flavoprotein. *Science* **116**:588–589.
18. Cantoni, G. L. and J. Durell. 1957. Activation of methionine for transmethylation. II. The methionine-activating enzyme: studies on the mechanism of the reaction. *J. Biol. Chem.* **225**:1033–1048.
19. Challenger, F. 1951. Biological methylation. *Advan. in Enzymol.* **12**:429–491.
20. Challenger, F., D. B. Lisle and P. B. Dransfield. 1954. Studies on biological methylation. Part XIV. The formation of trimethylarsine and dimethyl selenide in mould cultures from methyl sources containing C^{14}. *J. Chem. Soc.* pp. 1760–1771.
21. Challenger, F. 1959. "Aspects of the Organic Chemistry of Sulphur," Chapter V, pp. 162–206. Butterworths, London.
22. Cohen, G. N. and D. B. Cowie. 1957. Remplacement total de la méthionine par la sélénométhionine dans les protéines d'*Escherichia coli*. *Compt. Rend. Acad. Sci.* **244**:680–683.
23. Collett, M. E. 1924. The specificity of the intracellular hydrogenases in frog's muscle. *J. Biol. Chem.* **58**:793–797.
24. Collett, M. E. and M. F. Clark. 1929. On the question of the specificity of the intracellular dehydrogenases. II. The effect of poisons upon the dehydrogenase systems of frog and of fish muscle. *J. Biol. Chem.* **82**:429–433.
25. Collett, M. E., M. Rheinberger and E. G. Little. 1933. On the question of the specificity of the intracellular dehydrogenases. V. Toxicity of arsenic, selenium and tellurium compounds to the dehydrogenase systems of frog and fish muscle. *J. Biol. Chem.* **100**:271–275.
26. Cowie, D. B. and G. N. Cohen. 1957. Biosynthesis by *Escherichia coli* of active altered proteins containing selenium instead of sulfur. *Biochim. et Biophys. Acta* **26**:252–261.
27. DeMeio, R. H., M. Wizerkaniuk and E. Fabiani. 1953. Role of adenosinetriphosphate in the enzymatic synthesis of phenyl sulfate. *J. Biol. Chem.* **203**: 257–263.

28. Dransfield, P. B. and F. Challenger. 1955. Studies on biological methylation. Part XV. The formation of dimethyl selenide in mould cultures in presence of D- and L-methionine, or of thetins, all containing the $^{14}CH_3$ group. *J. Chem. Soc.*, pp. 1153–1160.
29. Dubnoff, J. W. and H. Borsook. 1948. Dimethylthetin and dimethyl-β-propiothetin in methionine synthesis. *J. Biol. Chem.* **176**:789–796.
30. Du Vigneaud, V. 1952. "A Trail of Research in Sulfur Chemistry and Metabolism." Chapter IV, pp. 91–125. Cornell Univ. Press, Ithaca, New York.
31. Falcone, G. and W. J. Nickerson. 1960. Metabolism of selenite and mechanism of inhibitory action of selenite on yeasts. *Giorn. Microbiol.* **8**:129–150.
32. Falcone, G. and W. J. Nickerson. 1960. Enzymatic reduction of selenite. *Bacteriol. Proc.* p. 152.
33. Fels, I. G. and V. H. Cheldelin. 1948. Methionine in selenium poisoning. *J. Biol. Chem.* **176**:819–828.
34. Fels, I. G. and V. H. Cheldelin. 1949. Selenate inhibition studies. II. The reversal of selenate inhibition in *E. coli*. *Arch. Biochem. Biophys.* **22**:323–324.
35. Fels, I. G. and V. H. Cheldelin. 1949. Selenate inhibition studies. III. The role of sulfate in selenate toxicity in yeast. *Arch. Biochem. Biophys.* **22**:402–405.
36. Fels, I. G. and V. H. Cheldelin. 1950. Selenate inhibition studies. IV. Biochemical basis of selenate toxicity in yeast. *J. Biol. Chem.* **185**:803–811.
37. Franke, K. W. and A. L. Moxon. 1934. A new toxicant occurring naturally in certain samples of plant foodstuffs. IV. Effects of proteins on yeast fermentation. *J. Nutrition* **8**:625–632.
38. Galton, D. A. G. 1957. The use of 6-mercaptopurine in the treatment of leukemia. *In* "The Chemistry and Biology of Purines," Ciba Foundation Symposium, Little, Brown, Boston, Massachusetts.
39. Gilbert, L. M., W. G. Overend and M. Webb. 1951. The inhibition of pancreas deoxyribonuclease. *Exptl. Cell Res.* **2**:349–365.
40. Harshfield, R. D. and H. L. Klug. 1950. The effect of selenium on anaerobic glycolysis of rat liver homogenate. *Proc. South Dakota Acad. Sci.* **29**:94–98.
41. Hewitt, L. F. 1951. Cell structure of *Corynebacterium diphtheriae*. *J. Gen. Microbiol.* **5**:287–292.
42. Hewitt, L. F. 1951. Effect of cultural conditions on bacterial cytology. *J. Gen. Microbiol.* **5**:293–297.
43. Hinshelwood, C. N. and R. M. Lodge. 1944. A physiochemical study of some induced changes in morphology of *Bacterium lactis aerogenes*. *Proc. Roy. Soc.* **132**:47–67.
44. Holland, J. and G. F. Humphrey. 1953. The metabolism of *Paramecium caudatum*. II. The effect of respiratory inhibitors. *Australian J. Exptl. Biol. Med. Sci.* **31**:299–310.
45. Hughes, A. F. W. 1949. The effect of iodoacetamide upon cell division in tissue cultures of the chick embryo. *J. Roy. Microscop. Soc.* **69**:215–224.
46. Hughes, A. F. W. 1950. The effect of inhibitory substances on cell division. A study on living cells in tissue cultures. *Quart. J. Microscop. Sci.* **91**:251–275.
47. Hurd-Karrer, A. M. 1938. Relation of sulfate to selenium absorption by plants. *Am. J. Botany* **25**:666–675.
48. Jaffe, J. J. and H. G. Mautner. 1958. A comparison of the biological properties of 6-mercaptopurine and 6-selenopurine in mice. *Proc. Am. Assoc. Cancer Res.* **2**:311.
49. Jaffe, J. J. and H. G. Mautner. 1958. The activity of 6-selenopurine and related compounds against some experimental mouse tumors. *Cancer Res.* **18**:294–298.

50. Jaffe, J. J. and H. G. Mautner. 1960. A comparison of the biological properties of 6-selenopurine, 6-selenopurine ribonucleoside and 6-mercaptopurine in mice. *Cancer Res.* **20**:381–386.
51. Jodrey, L. H. and K. M. Wilbur. 1955. Studies on shell formation. IV. The respiratory metabolism of the oyster mantle. *Biol. Bull.* **108**:346–358.
52. Klug, H. L., A. L. Moxon, D. F. Petersen and V. R. Potter. 1950. The *in vivo* inhibition of succinic dehydrogenase by selenium and its release by arsenic. *Arch. Biochem.* **28**:253–259.
53. Klug, H. L., D. F. Petersen and A. L. Moxon. 1951. Effect of selenium on activity of certain enzymes in homogenates of rat tissues. *Federation Proc.* **10**:209.
54. Klug, H. L., A. L. Moxon, D. F. Petersen and E. P. Painter. 1953. Inhibition of rat liver succinic dehydrogenase by selenium compounds. *J. Pharmacol. and Exptl. Therap.* **108**:437–441.
55. Labes, R. and H. Krebs. 1935. Die verschiedene Angriffsart von Tellurit, Selenit, Arsenit und anderen Giften auf die Dehydridase-und Oxydaseatmung des Muskelgewebes. *Fermentforschung* **14**:430–442.
56. Lardy, H. A. and A. L. Moxon. 1939. The effect of selenium and arsenic at various ratios on the fermentation of glucose by baker's yeast. *Proc. South Dakota Acad. Sci.* **19**:109–111.
57. LePage, G.A. 1960. Incorporation of 6-thioguanine into nuclei acids. *Cancer Res.* **20**:403–408.
58. Levine, V. E. 1925. The reducing properties of microorganisms with special reference to selenium compounds. *J. Bacteriol.* **10**:217–262.
59. Lipmann, F. 1958. Biological sulfate activation and transfer. Studies on a mechanism of group activation and its role in biosynthesis are described. *Science* **128**:575–580.
60. Massey, V. 1953. Studies on fumarase. 2. The effects of inorganic anions on fumarase activity. *Biochem. J.* **53**:67–71.
61. Mautner, H. G. 1956. The synthesis and properties of some selenopurines and selenopyrimidines. *J. Am. Chem. Soc.* **78**:5292–5294.
62. Mautner, H. G., W. D. Kumler, Y. Okano and R. Pratt. 1956. Antifungal activity of some substituted selenosemicarbazones and related compounds. *Antibiotics & Chemotherapy* **6**:51–55.
63. Mautner, H. G. 1958. A comparative study of 6-selenopurine and 6-mercaptopurine in the *Lactobacillus casei* and Ehrlich ascites tumour systems. *Biochem. Pharmacol.* **1**:169–173.
64. Mautner, H. G. and J. J. Jaffe. 1958. The activity of 6-selenopurine and related compounds against some experimental mouse tumors. *Cancer Res.* **18**:294–298.
65. Mautner, H. G. and E. M. Clayton. 1959. 2-Selenobarbiturates. Studies of some analogous oxygen, sulfur, and selenium compounds. *J. Am. Chem. Soc.* **81**:6270–6273.
66. Mautner, H. G. and W. H. Gunther. 1959. Selenopantethine, a functional analog of pantethine in the *Lactobacillus helveticus* system. *Biochim. et Biophys. Acta* **36**:561–562.
67. Mautner, H. G. and J. J. Jaffe. 1961. 6-Selenoguanine (2-amino-6-selenopurine). Synthesis and biological studies. *Biochem. Pharmacol.* **5**:343–344.
68. Mautner, H. G. and W. H. Gunther, 1962. Unpublished data quoted from K. P. McConnell, H. G. Mautner and G. W. Leddicotte. Radioactivation as a method for preparing ^{75}Se-labelled selenium compounds. *Biochim. et Biophys. Acta* **59**:217–218.

69. Moxon, A. L. and K. W. Franke. 1935. Effect of certain salts on enzyme activity. *Ind. Eng. Chem.* **27**:77–81.

70. Mudd, S. H. and G. L. Cantoni. 1957. Selenomethionine in enzymatic transmethylations. *Nature* **180**:1052–1054.

71. Nickerson, W. J. and Z. Mankowski. 1953. Role of nutrition in the maintenance of the yeast shape in *Candida*. *Am. J. Botany* **40**:584–592.

72. Nickerson, W. J. 1954. An enzymatic locus participating in cellular division of a yeast. *J. Gen. Physiol.* **37**:483–494.

73. Nickerson, W. J. 1954. Experimental control of morphogenesis in microorganisms. *Ann. New York Acad. Sci.* **60**:50–57.

74. Nickerson, W. J., W. A. Tabor and G. Falcone. 1956. Physiological bases of morphogenesis in fungi. 5. Effect of selenite and tellurite on cellular division of yeastlike fungi. *Can. J. Microbiol.* **2**:575–584.

75. Nisman, B. and M. L. Hirsch. 1958. Étude de l'activation et de l'incorporation des acids aminés par des fractions enzymatiques d'*E. coli*. *Ann. Inst. Past[illegible]r* **95**:615–636.

76. Opienska-Blauth, J., and H. Iwanowski. 1952. The effect of selenite on the growth and glucose metabolism in liquid cultures of *Escherichia coli*. (In Polish with English summary.) *Acta Microbiol. Polon.* **1**:273–290.

77. Opienska-Blauth, J., T. Borkowshi and I. Madecka-Borkowska. 1953. The substance giving positive Voges-Proskauer test in fluid cultures of *Escherichia coli* in the presence of some enzyme inhibitors. (In Polish with English summary.) *Acta Microbiol. Polon.* **2**:263-276.

78. Pengra, R. M. and E. C. Berry. 1953. Growth of *Saccharomyces cerevisiae* in the presence of selenium, arsenic and selenium-arsenic mixtures. *Proc. South Dakota Acad. Sci.* **32**:120–124.

79. Pinsent, J. 1954. The need for selenite and molybdate in the formation of formic dehydrogenase by members of the *Escherichia coli-Aerobacter aerogenes* group of bacteria. *Biochem. J.* **57**:10–16.

80. Ponz, F. 1952. Efecto del arsenito y del selenito sobre la absorcion intestinal de glucose. *Rev. Espan. Fisiol.* **8**:261–267.

81. Postgate, J. R. 1949. Competitive inhibition of sulfate reduction by selenate. *Nature* **164**:670–671.

82. Postgate, J. R. 1951. The reduction of various sulfur compounds by *Desulphovibrio desulphuricans*. *J. Gen. Microbiol.* **5**:725–738.

83. Postgate, J. R. 1952. Competitive and non-competitive inhibitors of bacterial sulphate reduction. *J. Gen. Microbiol.* **6**:128–142.

84. Postgate, J. R. 1954. Dependence of sulphate reduction and oxygen utilization on a cytochrome in *Desulphovibrio*. *Biochem. J.* **58**:ix.

85. Potter, V. R. and C. A. Elvehjem. 1936. The effect of selenium on cellular metabolism. The rate of oxygen uptake by living yeast in the presence of sodium selenite. *Biochem. J.* **30**:189–196.

86. Potter, V. R. and C. A. Elvehjem. 1937. The effect of inhibitors on succinoxidase. *J. Biol. Chem.* **117**:341–349.

87. Quastel, J. H. and W. R. Wooldridge. 1927. Experiments on bacteria in relation to the mechanism of enzyme action. *Biochem. J.* **21**:1224–1251.

88. Quastel, J. H. and W. R. Wooldridge. 1928. Some properties of the dehydrogenating enzymes of bacteria. *Biochem. J.* **22**:689–702.

89. Rapkine, L. 1938. Sulphydryl groups and enzymic oxido-reduction. *Biochem. J.* **32**:1729–1939.

90. Roberts, R. B., P. H. Abelson, D. B. Cowie, E. T. Bolton, and R. J. Britten. 1955. Studies of biosynthesis in *Escherichia coli. Carnegie Inst. Washington Publ.* **607**:318–405.
91. Rosenfeld, I. and O. A. Beath. 1948. Metabolism of sodium selenate and selenite by the tissues. *J. Biol. Chem.* **172**:333–341.
92. Rosenfeld, I. 1961. Biosynthesis of seleno-compounds from inorganic selenium by sheep. *Federation Proc.* **20**:10.
93. Rosenfeld, I. 1962. Effect of selenium on methionine formation *in vivo* and *in vitro. Proc. Soc. Exptl. Biol. Med.* **109**:624–628.
94. Rosenfeld, I. 1962. Biosynthesis of seleno-compounds from inorganic selenium by sheep. *Proc. Soc. Exptl. Biol. Med.* **111**:670–673.
95. Ruffilli, D. 1948. Action of selenium and its compounds on tissue cultures *in vitro. Studi Sassaresi* **26**:95–97.
96. Rulon, O. 1952. The modification of developmental patterns in the sand dollar by sodium selenite. *Physiol. Zool.* **25**:333–346.
97. Scala, J. and H. H. Williams. 1962. The enhancement of selenite toxicity by methionine in *Escherichia coli. Arch. Biochem. Biophys.* **99**:363–368.
98. Scala, J. and H. H. Williams. 1963. A comparison of selenite and tellurite toxicity in *Escherichia coli. Arch. Biochem. Biophys.* **101**:319–324.
99. Schneider, H. A. 1936. Selenium in nutrition. *Science* **83**:32–34.
100. Schneider, W. C. and V. R. Potter. 1943. The assay of animal tissues for respiratory enzymes. II. Succinic dehydrogenase and cytochrome oxidase. *J. Biol. Chem.* **149**:217–227.
101. Shrift, A. 1954. Sulfur-selenium antagonism. I. Antimetabolite action of selenate on the growth of *Chlorella vulgaris. Am. J. Botany* **41**:223–230.
102. Shrift, A. 1954. Sulfur-selenium antagonism. II. Antimetabolite action of selenomethionine on the growth of *Chlorella vulgaris. Am. J. Botany* **41**:345–352.
103. Shrift, A. 1959. Nitrogen and sulfur changes associated with growth uncoupled from cell division in *Chlorella vulgaris. Plant Physiol.* **34**:505–512.
104. Shrift, A. 1960. A role for methionine in division of *Chlorella vulgaris. Plant Physiol.* **35**:510–515.
105. Shrift, A., J. Nevyas and S. Turndorf. 1961. Mass adaptation to selenomethionine in populations of *Chlorella vulgaris. Plant Physiol.* **36**:502–509.
106. Shrift, A., J. Nevyas and S. Turndorf. 1961. Stability and reversibility of adaptation to selenomethionine in *Chlorella vulgaris. Plant Physiol.* **36**:509–519.
107. Shrift, A. and E. Kelly. 1962. Adaptation of *Escherichia coli* to selenate. *Nature* **195**:732–733.
108. Smith, H. G. 1959. On the nature of the selective action of selenite broth. *J. Gen. Microbiol.* **21**:61–71.
109. Snell, E. E. and G. M. Brown. 1953. Pantethine and related forms of the *Lactobacillus bulgaricus* factor (LBF). *Advan. in Enzymol.* **14**:49–71.
110. Spencer, R. P. and M. Blau. 1962. Intestinal transport of selenium-75 selenomethionine. *Science* **136**:155–156.
111. Stotz, E. and A. B. Hastings. 1937. The components of the succinate-fumarate-enzyme system. *J. Biol. Chem.* **118**:479–498.
112. Tsen, C. C. and H. B. Collier. 1959. Selenite as a relatively weak inhibitor of some sulphydryl enzymes. *Nature.* **183**:1327–1328.
113. Tuve, T. and K. Schwarz. 1961. Incorporation of radioselenite by baker's yeast. *Federation Proc.* **20**:295.
114. Tuve, T. and H. H. Williams. 1961. Metabolism of selenium by *Escherichia coli*: Biosynthesis of selenomethionine. *J. Biol. Chem.* **236**:597–601.

115. Webb, M. 1948. The influence of magnesium on cell division. I. The growth of *Clostridium welchii* in complex media deficient in magnesium. *J. Gen. Microbiol.* **2**:275–287.
116. Weisberger, A. S. and R. W. Heinle. 1950. The protective effect of cysteine on leukopenia induced by nitrogen mustard. *J. Lab. Clin. Med.* **36**:872–876.
117. Weisberger, A. S. and L. G. Suhrland. 1956. Studies on analogues of L-cysteine and L-cystine. II. The effect of selenium cystine on Murphy lymphosarcoma tumor cells in the rat. *Blood* **11**:11–18.
118. Weisberger, A. S. and L. G. Suhrland. 1956. Studies on analogues of L-cysteine and L-cystine. III. The effect of selenium cystine on leukemia. *Blood* **11**:19–30.
119. Weisberger, A. S., L. G. Suhrland and J. Seifter. 1956. Studies on analogues of L-cysteine and L-cystine. I. Some structural requirements for inhibiting the incorporation of radioactive L-cystine by leukemic leukocytes. *Blood* **11**:1–10.
120. Weissman, G. S. and S. F. Trelease. 1955. Influence of sulfur on the toxicity of selenium to *Aspergillus*. *Am. J. Botany* **42**:489–495.
121. Widstrom, V. R. 1961. Effect of selenate ions on the growth of *Neurospora crassa* in the presence of various sulfur sources. *Proc. South Dakota Acad. Sci.* **40**:208–212.
122. Wilson, L. G. and R. S. Bandurski. 1956. An enzymatic reaction involving adenosine triphosphate and selenate. *Arch. Biochem. Biophys.* **62**:503–506.
123. Wilson, L. G. and R. S. Bandurski. 1958. Enzymatic reactions involving sulfate, sulfite, selenate and molybdate. *J. Biol. Chem.* **233**:975–981.
124. Woodruff, I. O. and W. J. Gies. 1902. On the toxicology of selenium and its compounds. *Am. J. Physiol.* **6**:xxix–xxx.
125. Woolley, D. W. 1952. "A Study of Antimetabolites." Wiley, New York. Chapman and Hall, London.
126. Wright, C. I. 1938. Effect of sodium selenite and selenate on the oxygen consumption of mammalian tissues. *Public Health Rept.* (*U.S.*) **53**:1825–1836.
127. Wright, C. I. 1939. The effect of diselenodiacetic acid on the metabolism of tissue slices. *J. Pharmacol. Exptl. Therap.* **66**:40.
128. Wright, C. I. 1940. Effect of selenium on urease and arginase. *J. Pharmacol. Exptl. Therap.* **68**:220–230.
129. Zalokar, M. 1953. Reduction of selenite by *Neurospora*. *Arch. Biochem. Biophys.* **44**:330–337.
130. Zamecnik, P. C. and E. B. Keller. 1954. Relation between phosphate energy donors and incorporation of labelled amino acids into proteins. *J. Biol. Chem.* **209**:337–354.

Author Index

Numbers in parentheses are reference numbers and indicate that an author's work is referred to although his name is not mentioned in the text. Numbers in italics indicate the pages on which the complete references are given.

C

D

E

F

G

M

N

O

Y

Z

Subject Index

Selenium in the index will be indicated by the chemical symbol, Se. Isomeric forms of all compounds are entered under the appropriate single term.

B

D

E

G

Q

R

T